Algebra 2

HOLT, RINEHART AND WINSTON

A Harcourt Classroom Education Company

Austin • New York • Orlando • Atlanta • San Francisco • Boston • Dallas • Toronto • London

To the Teacher

Algebra 2 Assessment Resources contains blackline masters that provide the teacher with both traditional and alternative assessments, giving teachers a variety of choices to best suit their needs.

- **Quick Warm-Up: Assessing Prior Knowledge** and **Lesson Quiz** (one page per lesson) contains a short set of prerequisite exercises for each lesson followed by a quiz consisting of free-response questions.

- **Mid-Chapter Assessment** (one page per chapter) contains multiple-choice questions and free-response questions that assess the instruction in the first half of each chapter.

- **Chapter Assessment** (two forms per chapter)

  Form A is a two-page multiple-choice test that includes assessment questions for every lesson in the chapter.

  Form B is a two-page free-response test that includes questions for every lesson in the chapter.

- **Alternative Assessment** (two forms per chapter)

  Form A is a one-page authentic-assessment activity or performance-assessment activity that involves concepts from the first half of the chapter.

  Form B is a one-page authentic-assessment activity or performance-assessment activity that involves concepts from the second half of the chapter.

Printed in the United States of America

ISBN 0-03-054073-9

1   2   3   4   5   6   7   066   02   01   00   99

Table of Contents

Quick Warm-Up: Assessing Prior Knowledge

1.1 Tables and Graphs of Linear Equations

Graph and label each point on the same coordinate plane.

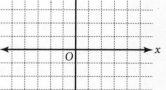

1. $A(-1, 2)$ 2. $B(4, 7)$ 3. $C(-3, 0)$ 4. $D(0, 3)$

5. Refer to Exercises 1–4. Which of the following equations gives the relationship between each pair of x- and y-coordinates?

   a. $y = 3x$ b. $y = -3x$ c. $y = x + 3$ d. $y = x - 3$

Lesson Quiz

1.1 Tables and Graphs of Linear Equations

1. Jorge wants to join a fitness club. The monthly club fee is $15 plus $3 for each time that he swims in the club's pool.

   a. Write a linear equation that represents the relationship between the number of times, x, Jorge swims in the club's pool and his monthly cost, y. _____

   b. Find Jorge's cost for a month in which he swims in the club's pool 6 times. _____

2. Graph $y = \frac{3}{2}x - 4$.

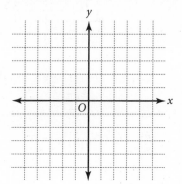

3. Determine whether the table below represents a linear relationship between x and y. If the relationship is linear, write the next ordered pair that would appear in the table.

x	-1	2	5	8
y	16	24	32	40

_____

Quick Warm-Up: Assessing Prior Knowledge

1.2 Slopes and Intercepts

In Exercises 1–3, solve for *y*.

1. $4x + y = 3$ 2. $x + 2y = 10$ 3. $-3 + 6y = 2x$

_____   _____   _____

4. Graph the points $A(2, 5)$, $B(3, 7)$, and $C(5, 11)$. Connect the points with a line. Estimate where the line crosses the *y*-axis.

_____

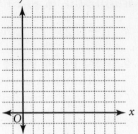

Lesson Quiz

1.2 Slopes and Intercepts

1. Find the slope of the line containing the points $(5, -3)$ and $(-2, 5)$. _____

2. Use the slope and the *y*-intercept to graph the equation $-\frac{3}{4}x + y = 1$.

3. Write an equation in slope-intercept form for the line graphed below.

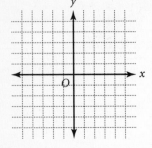

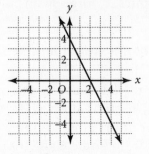

_____

4. Use intercepts to graph $3x - 5y = 15$.

5. Graph $x = 3$.

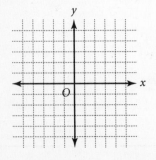

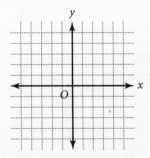

Quick Warm-Up: Assessing Prior Knowledge
1.3 *Linear Equations in Two Variables*

1. Find the slope of the line containing the points $(-1, 12)$ and $(5, -6)$.

_____

2. Identify the slope and y-intercept for the line with equation $y = -5x + 7$.

_____

3. Write the equation in slope-intercept form for the line whose
   y-intercept is 0 and whose slope is -1.

_____

Lesson Quiz
1.3 *Linear Equations in Two Variables*

1. Write an equation in slope-intercept form for the line containing
   the points $(2, 4)$ and $(5, 13)$.

_____

2. Write an equation in slope-intercept form for the line that has a slope of $-\frac{3}{5}$
   and contains the point $(10, 2)$.

_____

3. Sam leaves home and drives at a constant speed to his grandparents'
   house. On his way, he stops at a mall to buy a gift for his
   grandparents. Four hours after stopping at the mall, Sam has
   traveled 300 miles from home, and 7 hours after stopping at the
   mall, he has traveled 465 miles from home. How far is the mall from
   Sam's house?

_____

4. Write an equation in slope-intercept form for the line that contains
   the point $(0, -6)$ and is parallel to the line $-6x + 3y = 4$.

_____

5. Write an equation in slope-intercept form for the line that contains
   the point $(3, 2)$ and is perpendicular to the line $y = -\frac{3}{4}x - 8$.

_____

Quick Warm-Up: Assessing Prior Knowledge

1.4 Direct Variation and Proportion

Solve each equation.

1. $27 = c(-4)$

2. $-8 = -\frac{3}{4}z$

3. $\frac{k}{4} = -20$

_____

_____

_____

4. $\frac{n}{2} = \frac{5}{8}$

5. $2(4y + 1) = 3y$

_____

_____

Lesson Quiz

1.4 Direct Variation and Proportion

1. Find the constant of variation, k, and the direct-variation equation if y varies directly as x and $y = 50$ when $x = -20$.

_____

2. When Sally rides her exercise bike at a constant rate, she burns 300 calories in 40 minutes. At the rate that Sally rides, how many minutes will it take her to burn 1800 calories?

_____

3. A carpet company charges $450 to lay carpet on a floor whose area is 200 square feet.

   a. How much would the company charge to lay carpet on a floor whose area is 280 square feet?

   _____

   b. Write a direct-variation equation that gives the cost of laying carpet if cost varies directly as the size of a room. What does the constant of variation represent?

   _____

Solve each equation for x. Check your answers.

4. $\frac{5x + 8}{8} = \frac{2x}{3}$

5. $\frac{-5}{3x - 4} = \frac{7}{-5x}$

_____

_____

Mid-Chapter Assessment

Chapter 1 (Lessons 1.1–1.4)

Write the letter that best answers the question or completes the statement.

_____ 1. Which of the following equations is not linear?

    a. $5y = 7.5x$ **b.** $y = 12$

    c. $y = \dfrac{5}{x} + 7$ **d.** $7x = 4 + 3y$

_____ 2. Which of the following is the slope of the line containing the points $(2, 4)$ and $(6, -8)$?

    a. 3   **b.** -3 **c.** $\dfrac{1}{3}$ **d.** $-\dfrac{1}{3}$

_____ 3. What is the slope of every line that is parallel to the line $y = 5x - 3$?

    a. -5 **b.** $\dfrac{1}{5}$ **c.** -3 **d.** 5

_____ 4. If y varies directly as x and $y = 30$ when $x = 8$, what is the constant of variation?

    a. $k = \dfrac{4}{15}$ **b.** $k = \dfrac{7}{2}$ **c.** $k = 1.5$ **d.** $k = 3.75$

5. Write an equation in slope-intercept form for the line that contains the point $(5, -2)$ and is perpendicular to the line $y = -\dfrac{5}{3}x + 8$.

_____

Graph the following equations on your own graph paper:

6. $2x + 3y = 12$ 7. $y = -4$

Solve for x.

8. $\dfrac{-5}{x} = \dfrac{-3}{8}$ _____   9. $\dfrac{4x}{9} = \dfrac{2x - 5}{4}$ _____

10. A car rental company charges \$50 per week plus \$0.03 per mile driven to rent a car.

    a. Write a linear equation to represent the relationship between the weekly cost, y, to rent a car from this company and the number of miles driven in a week, x.   _____

    b. Amy paid \$53.75 to rent a car for one week. How many miles did she drive during that week?   _____

11. The manager of a computer assembly plant knows that the number of computers that the workers can assemble varies directly as time. If the workers at the plant can assemble 1260 computers in 150 hours, how long will it take them to assemble 1890 computers?   _____

Quick Warm-Up: Assessing Prior Knowledge

1.5 *Scatter Plots and Least-Squares Lines*

Graph each point on the same coordinate plane.

1. $A(1, 400)$ 2. $B(3, 300)$ 3. $C(6, 150)$ 4. $D(8, 50)$

5. Refer to Exercises 1–4. Suppose that a line were drawn to connect the four points. Would its slope be positive or negative?

_____

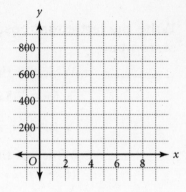

 # Lesson Quiz

1.5 *Scatter Plots and Least-Squares Lines*

Use the following table to answer Exercises 1–3.

x	-5	-2.5	-1	0	2.5	4	5
y	5	4	2.5	2	1	-1	-3

1. On the coordinate grid at right, create a scatter plot of the data in the table.

2. Describe the correlation. _____

3. Find an equation for the least-squares line.

_____

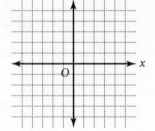

4. The table below gives the price of a hamburger at a diner for selected years.

Year	1950	1955	1963	1969	1975	1982	1995	1998
Price ($)	0.25	0.35	0.40	0.50	0.75	1.25	1.75	1.95

Let x represent years since 1900 and let y represent the cost of a hamburger in dollars. Use the least-squares line to estimate the price of a hamburger at this diner in 1990. _____

Quick Warm-Up: Assessing Prior Knowledge

1.6 *Introduction to Solving Equations*

Solve each equation.

1. $-12 + r = 3$

2. $-12b = 3$

3. $\dfrac{k}{-12} = 3$

4. $\dfrac{-12}{z} = 3$

5. $-12 - m = 3$

6. $-12 = 5x + 3$

Lesson Quiz

1.6 *Introduction to Solving Equations*

Solve each equation.

1. $40 = \frac{3}{4}x - 32$

2. $15(x + 8) = 180$

3. $4x + 12 = 30 - 6x$

4. $\frac{3}{4}x - \frac{5}{8} = \frac{3}{2} + \frac{5}{2}x$

5. Solve $3.65x - 5.26 = -2.92x + 2.62$ by graphing.

Give your answer to the nearest tenth. _____

Solve each literal equation for the indicated variable.

6. $A = wh + xh - yh$, for w

_____

7. $B = \dfrac{a(mh + t)}{P}$, for t

_____

Quick Warm-Up: Assessing Prior Knowledge

1.7 Introduction to Solving Inequalities

Graph and label the following points on the same number line.

1. $A(-1)$

2. $B(3.5)$

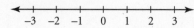

3. $C\left(-\frac{9}{4}\right)$

4. $D(0)$

Graph each inequality on a separate number line.

5. $x < 2$

6. $x \geq -3$

Lesson Quiz

1.7 Introduction to Solving Inequalities

Solve each inequality.

1. $12x - 8 < 10$

2. $15 - 5x \geq 40$

_____   _____

3. Solve $5x - 9 > 15 - 3x$ for x. Graph the solution on the number line.

_____

4. Kurt's quiz average in science class is 70. The quiz average is $\frac{1}{5}$ of the final grade, and the test average is $\frac{4}{5}$ of the final grade. What test average does Kurt need in order to have a final grade of at

least 90? _____

5. Solve $4x - 5 > 7$ *and* $5x + 4 < 34$. Graph the solution on the number line at right.

_____

6. Solve $5x + 8 \leq 3$ *or* $2x - 3 \geq 5$. Graph the solution on the number line at right.

_____

Quick Warm-Up: Assessing Prior Knowledge

1.8 Solving Absolute-Value Equations and Inequalities

Solve each equation.

1. $m + 2 = -2$

2. $m + 2 = 3m - 2$

3. $m + 2 = -(3m - 2)$

_____

_____

_____

Solve each inequality.

4. $k - 3 > 5$

5. $k - 3 > 2k + 9$

6. $k - 3 > -(2k + 9)$

_____

_____

_____

Lesson Quiz

1.8 Solving Absolute-Value Equations and Inequalities

1. Solve $|3x + 6| = 9$. Graph the solution on the number line. ←++++++++++++++++→ x

_____

2. Solve $|x + 2| = 2x - 8$. Check your solution(s). _____

3. Solve $|4x - 2| > 10$. Graph the solution on the number line. ←++++++++++++++++→ x

_____

4. Solve $|4 - 2x| \leq 6$. Graph the solution on the number line. ←++++++++++++++++→ x

_____

5. In order for a tropical plant to grow in a greenhouse, the temperature can vary no more than 2.5°F from the desired temperature of 72°F.

   a. Write an absolute-value inequality that represents the acceptable range of temperatures in the greenhouse. _____

   b. Solve your inequality.

_____

Chapter Assessment

Chapter 1, Form A, page 1

Write the letter that best answers the question or completes the statement.

_____ 1. Which of the following equations is a linear equation?

    a. $y = 3x^2 + 7$ b. $y = \frac{8}{3x} + 4$ c. $y = \frac{8}{3}x + 4$ d. $y = 2 + \sqrt{x}$

_____ 2. What is the y-intercept of the line $2x - 3y = 15$?

    a. -5 b. -3 c. 2   d. 15

_____ 3. What is the slope of the line containing the points $(5, -2)$ and $(2, 10)$?

    a. $\frac{1}{4}$ b. $-\frac{1}{4}$ c. 4   d. -4

_____ 4. What is the equation of the line whose slope is -2 and whose y-intercept is 8?

    a. $y = 8x + 2$ b. $y = 8x - 2$ c. $y = 2x - 8$ d. $y = -2x + 8$

_____ 5. The correlation coefficient for the data graphed at right is

    a. close to -1.

    b. close to 0.

    c. close to 1.

    d. close to 2.

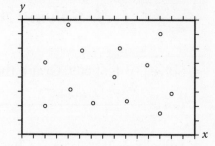

_____ 6. Find the equation for the least-squares line of the data below.

x	2	5	9	15	22	30	40
y	5	10	15	25	35	50	70

    a. $y \approx 1.7x + 0.99$ b. $y \approx 0.4x + 1.7$

    c. $y \approx 0.4x + 0.99$ d. $y \approx 1.7x + 0.4$

_____ 7. What is the equation of the line that contains the point $(6, 8)$ and is parallel to the line $y = \frac{2}{3}x + 2$?

    a. $y = \frac{3}{2}x - 1$ b. $y = -\frac{3}{2}x + 17$ c. $y = -\frac{2}{3}x + 12$ d. $y = \frac{2}{3}x + 4$

_____ 8. A tree service charges a basic fee of \$50 to make a house call plus \$20 per hour to trim trees. The equation that represents the total cost, c, of a house call and tree trimming in terms of the number of hours spent, h, is

    a. $c = 20h + 50$ b. $c = 50h + 20$ c. $c = 20h - 50$ d. $c = 20h$

_____ 9. If y varies directly as x and $y = 25$ when $x = 4$, find the constant of variation.

    a. $k = 6.25$ b. $k = -6.25$ c. $k = 0.16$ d. $k = 4$

Chapter Assessment

Chapter 1, Form A, page 2

_____ **10.** Find the solution to the equation $2x + 3(x - 7) = -2(x - 21)$.

    a. $x = 2$ **b.** $x = 9$ **c.** $x = 5$ **d.** $x = -3$

_____ **11.** Find the solution to the equation $|5x - 10| = 20$.

    a. $x = -6$ **b.** $x = -2$ **c.** $x = 6\ or\ x = -2$ **d.** $x = -6\ or\ x = 2$

_____ **12.** Find the solution to the equation $\dfrac{6x + 5}{3} = \dfrac{5 - 2x}{4}$.

    a. $x = -\dfrac{1}{3}$ **b.** $x = \dfrac{1}{3}$ **c.** $x = -\dfrac{1}{6}$ **d.** $x = \dfrac{1}{6}$

_____ **13.** Find the solution to the inequality $\dfrac{6 - 2x}{3} > -4$.

    a. $x < -15$ **b.** $x > -9$ **c.** $x < 9$ **d.** $x > 15$

_____ **14.** Find the solution to the inequality $3x - 15 < 9 + 7x$.

    a. $x > -6$ **b.** $x < -6$ **c.** $x > 6$ **d.** $x < 6$

_____ **15.** Which of the following is the graph of the solution set of the compound inequality $3x + 4 \le 13\ and\ 6 + 2x \ge -2$?

    a. 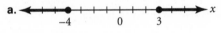   **b.**

    c.   **d.**

_____ **16.** Find the solution to the inequality $|4x - 6| > 14$.

    a. $x > 5$ **b.** $x < -2$ **c.** $x > 5\ and\ x < -2$ **d.** $x > 5\ or\ x < -2$

_____ **17.** Which property is exemplified by $9(x - 1) = 9x - 9$?

    a. Addition Property of Equality   **b.** Distributive Property

    c. Division Property of Equality   **d.** Substitution Property

_____ **18.** The cost of catering a banquet varies directly as the number of people who attend the banquet. If it costs \$3875 to cater a banquet that is attended by 250 people, how much will it cost to cater a banquet that is attended by 400 people?

    a. \$6200   **b.** \$7000   **c.** \$7750   **d.** \$8500

_____ **19.** Solve $V = \dfrac{ax + b}{r^2}$ for b.

    a. $Vr^2 + ax$ **b.** $Vax + r^2$ **c.** $Vr^2 - ax$ **d.** $Vax - r^2$

_____ **20.** Find the solution to the equation $|2x - 3| = 3x + 8$.

    a. $x = 5$ **b.** $x = -11$ **c.** $x = 5\ or\ x = -11$ **d.** $x = 5\ and\ x = -11$

Chapter Assessment

Chapter 1, Form B, page 1

1. Does the table at right represent a linear relationship between x and y? If the relationship is linear, write the next ordered pair that would appear in the table.

x	−1	4	9	14
y	15	27	39	51

_____

2. Find the slope of the line containing the points $(−3, 5)$ and $(−7, 8)$. _____

3. Graph $y = −2x + 3$.

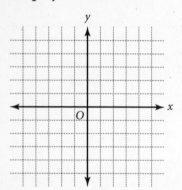

4. Graph $x = −2$.

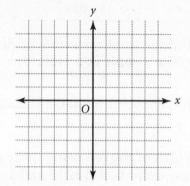

5. Write an equation in slope-intercept form for the line that has a y-intercept of 7 and a slope of $−4$.

_____

6. Write the equation of the line that passes through the point $(6, −4)$ and is perpendicular to the line $−2x + 3y = 8$.

_____

The table below contains data on the number of car accidents within a 24-hour period compared with the amount of snow, in inches, accumulated in the town of Culver.

Inches of snow, x	0	1.5	4	5	0.5	7	12	5.5
No. of accidents, y	2	9	6	5	1	10	15	7

7. Find the correlation coefficient, r, to the nearest hundredth for the data. _____

8. Find an equation for the least-squares line of the data. _____

9. Predict the number of accidents within a 24-hour period in the town of Culver if 9 inches of snow has accumulated. _____

Solve.

10. $\dfrac{3x - 2}{5} = 8$ _____

11. $\dfrac{2x - 6}{4} = \dfrac{3x + 5}{8}$ _____

Chapter Assessment

Chapter 1, Form B, page 2

Solve each equation.

12. $|8x - 12| - 4 = 14$

_____

13. $|2x - 6| = 4 - 3x$

_____

Solve each inequality.

14. $8(5 - 3x) \leq -24$

_____

15. $\frac{5}{3}x + 15 > \frac{3}{4}x - 18$

_____

Solve each inequality. Graph your solution on the number line.

16. $|x + 5| \leq 2$

_____

17. $|4x - 5| > 7$

_____

Solve each literal equation for the indicated variable.

18. $C = hr^2 + mr$, for h

_____

19. $\frac{A + B}{dt} = \frac{F}{mn}$, for t

_____

20. Find the constant of variation, k, and the direct variation equation

if y varies directly as x and $y = 20$ when $x = 80$. _____

21. The distance that Amy can drive in her car varies directly as the amount of gas that she has in her car. If Amy can drive 330 miles on 12 gallons of gas, how many gallons of gas will she need to drive 1100 miles? _____

22. Sam is a salesperson at a department store. He earns a weekly salary and a commission on his weekly sales. In one week, Sam's sales were $3500, and his income for the week was $475. The next week his sales were $5000, and his income for the week was $625.

a. Write a linear equation in slope-intercept form for Sam's weekly income, y, in terms of his weekly sales, x. _____

b. What were Sam's sales in a week in which his income was $325? _____

23. In a factory, the time to assemble a VCR should vary no more than 5 minutes from the desired time of 40 minutes. Write an absolute-value inequality to represent the acceptable time that it takes to assemble a VCR in the factory. _____

Alternative Assessment

Recognizing Linear Relationships, Chapter 1, Form A

TASK: Identify linear relationships, and write the linear equation described.

HOW YOU WILL BE SCORED: As you work through the task, your teacher will be looking for the following:

- how well you can identify a linear relationship between variables in a table
- whether you can write an equation describing a linear relationship
- how well you can identify a direct variation from a table

The junior class at Oakland High is raising funds by recycling aluminum, bi-metal, and tin cans. The class gets a $3.50 refund for 100 cans.

1. Assign variables to the number of cans recycled and the amount of the refund.

   _____

2. Make a table for the number of cans recycled and the amount of the refund. Use consecutive values.

3. Describe how you can tell if the variables are linearly related.

   _____

   _____

4. Write an equation that represents this relationship.

   _____

5. How much will the class get for 500 cans? How many cans does the class need to recycle in order to raise $525?

   _____

6. Is this linear equation a direct variation? Explain.

   _____

SELF-ASSESSMENT: Write a direct-variation equation describing a real-world proportional relationship.

Alternative Assessment

Solving Absolute-Value Equations and Inequalities, Chapter 1 Form B

TASK: Solve absolute-value equations and inequalities and use absolute-value inequalities to model real-world applications.

HOW YOU WILL BE SCORED: As you work through the task, your teacher will be looking for the following:

- how well you can solve absolute-value equations and inequalities
- whether you can write an absolute-value inequality to model a real-world application

1. a. In how many points do the graphs of $y = |2x - 6|$ and $y = 3x$ intersect? _____

   b. How many solutions are there to the equation $|2x - 6| = 3x$? _____

   c. Find the solution(s) to the equation $|2x - 6| = 3x$. _____

   d. For what values of a will $|2x - 6| = ax$ have 2 solutions? _____

2. Describe the solution to the inequality $|3x + 5| > -2$. Explain your answer. _____

   _____

3. Describe the solution to the inequality $|7x - 2| \leq -6$. Explain your answer. _____

   _____

4. a. Write a compound inequality for the absolute-value inequality $|3x + 6| \geq 9$. _____

   b. Solve your compound inequality from part **a**, and graph the solution on the number line. _____

5. A vending machine dispenses coffee into paper cups. The company that operates the machine wants the amount of coffee dispensed to differ by no more than 5 milliliters from the desired amount of 250 milliliters.

   a. Describe the acceptable amount of coffee that can be dispensed by the machine. _____

   b. Write an absolute-value inequality for the acceptable amount of coffee than can be dispensed by the machine. _____

   c. Solve your compound inequality from part **b**. _____

SELF-ASSESSMENT: What is the difference between a real-world application modeled by an equation and one modeled by an inequality?

Quick Warm-Up: Assessing Prior Knowledge
2.1 Operations With Numbers

Evaluate each expression.

1. $\frac{1}{5} - \frac{1}{3}$ _____

2. $-3 + \frac{1}{3}$ _____

3. $(-3)\left(\frac{1}{3}\right)$ _____

4. $(-3) \div \left(-\frac{1}{3}\right)$ _____

5. 25^2 _____

6. $\sqrt{25}$ _____

Lesson Quiz
2.1 Operations With Numbers

Classify each number in as many ways as possible.

1. $6.121122111222\ldots$ 2. -245 3. $124.\overline{32}$

_____   _____   _____

4. Justify each step in the simplification of $a + [b + (-a)]$.

a. $a + [b + (-a)] = a + [(-a) + b]$ _____

b. $\qquad\qquad = [a + (-a)] + b$ _____

c. $\qquad\qquad = 0 + b$ _____

d. $\qquad\qquad = b$ _____

5. You put n dollars into a bank account that pays 1.5% interest quarterly at the beginning of the quarter. When the bank puts your interest into the account at the end of the quarter, the total amount, A, in your account is given by $A = 0.015n + n$. Show that $A = 1.015n$. Justify each step.

Evaluate each expression.

6. $\dfrac{5 \cdot 8}{2^3(9 - 6)}$

7. $60 \div 4(7 + 3 - 5) - (3^{(5-2)} + 1)$

_____   _____

Quick Warm-Up: Assessing Prior Knowledge

2.2 *Properties of Exponents*

Evaluate each expression.

1. 3^3 _____

2. 7^2 _____

3. $2^5 \cdot 3^2$ _____

4. $2^3 + 2^4$ _____

5. $\dfrac{4^2}{2^3}$ _____

6. $\left(\dfrac{4}{5}\right)^2$ _____

Lesson Quiz

2.2 *Properties of Exponents*

1. The formula for centripetal acceleration for an object traveling in a circle is $a_c = 4\pi^2 r T^{-2}$, where a_c represents the centripetal acceleration in feet per second squared, r represents the radius of the circle in feet, and T represents the time for a full rotation in seconds. Find the centripetal acceleration of an object that travels around a circle with a radius of 15 feet and takes 10 seconds to complete one full rotation.

_____

Simplify each expression. Write your answers with positive exponents only.

2. $5x^{-5}y^7(4x^3y^{-2})$

3. $\left(\dfrac{-2a^2b^6}{3a^6b^3}\right)^{-3}$

_____   _____

Evaluate each expression.

4. $125^{\frac{1}{3}}$ _____

5. $4^{\frac{5}{2}}$ _____

6. The formula for finding the surface area of a person is $S = 0.007184 \times W^{0.425} \times H^{0.725}$, where S is the surface area in square meters, W is the person's weight in kilograms, and H is the person's height in centimeters. Estimate, to the nearest hundredth of a square meter, the surface area of a person that is 180 centimeters tall and weighs 75 kilograms.

_____

Quick Warm-Up: Assessing Prior Knowledge

2.3 Introduction to Functions

Evaluate each expression.

1. $x - 2$, for $x = -5$

2. $-2x$, for $x = -1.5$

3. x^2, for $x = -4$

_____

_____

_____

4. $-x^2$, for $x = -1.2$

5. x^3, for $x = -2$

6. $-x^3$, for $x = -0.1$

_____

_____

_____

Lesson Quiz

2.3 Introduction to Functions

1. Tell whether this relation represents a function. Explain.

x	5	9	13	17	21
y	7	12	7	12	7

_____

2. Tell whether the relation graphed below represents a function. Explain.

3. Find the domain and range of the function shown below.

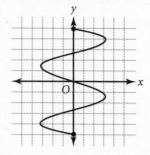

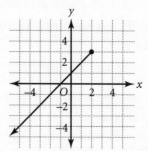

_____

_____

_____

_____

4. Evaluate $f(x) = \dfrac{3x^2 + 5}{2x}$ for $x = 5$ and $x = 2$. _____

Quick Warm-Up: Assessing Prior Knowledge
2.4 Operations With Functions

Simplify each expression.

1. $(x - 2) + (x + 5)$

2. $(3x + 4) - (2x - 6)$

3. $(x + 2)(x - 3)$

4. $\dfrac{10x^2}{-2x}$

5. $(-3x)^2 - 3x$

Lesson Quiz
2.4 Operations With Functions

Let $f(x) = x + 4$ and $g(x) = x^2 + 5$. **Write an expression for each function. State any restrictions.**

1. $(f + g)(x)$

2. $(g - f)(x)$

3. $\left(\dfrac{g}{f}\right)(x)$

4. $(fg)(x)$

5. $(g \circ f)(x)$

6. $(f \circ g)(x)$

7. An electronics store is giving away a coupon worth $10 off the price of any portable CD player. If you buy anything at the store, you must pay 5% sales tax on the purchase price of the item. Write a function, P, to represent the price of a CD player after using the coupon, and write a function, C, to represent the total amount that you would pay for the CD player including tax. Find the composites $(C \circ P)(x)$ and $(P \circ C)(x)$. Which composite gives the amount of money that you will need to buy a CD player? Explain.

Mid-Chapter Assessment

Chapter 2 (Lessons 2.1–2.4)

Write the letter that best answers the question or completes the statement.

_____ 1. The number 9.854 belongs to which set of numbers?

    a. integers   b. whole numbers

    c. rational numbers   d. irrational numbers

_____ 2. Which property of addition is illustrated by $(a + b) + c = (b + a) + c$?

    a. Commutative Property   b. Associative Property

    c. Identity Property   d. Inverse Property

_____ 3. Which of the following relations does not represent a function?

    a. $\{(1, 4), (2, 3), (3, 5), (4, 6)\}$ b. $\{(3, 5), (5, 7), (7, 7), (9, 5)\}$

    c. $\{(5, 5), (6, 5), (7, 5), (8, 5)\}$ d. $\{(1, 7), (2, 9), (1, 11), (3, 13)\}$

_____ 4. Which of the following is the range of the function $y = x^2 - 3$?

    a. $x \geq -3$ b. $x \leq -3$ c. $y \geq -3$ d. $y \leq -3$

Simplify each expression.

5. $\dfrac{5(7 - 3^2)}{8 - 5 \cdot 2}$ 6. $18 + 16 \div 4 - 3(11 - 3)^{\frac{2}{3}}$

Simplify each expression. Write your answers with positive exponents only.

7. $(6x^{-5}y^7)(-2x^4y^{-3})^3$ 8. $\left(\dfrac{23a^3b^8}{4a^9b^4}\right)^{-2}$

For Exercises 9 and 10, refer to the graph at right.

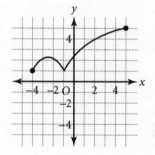

9. State the domain of the relation. _____

10. Is the relation a function? Explain.

_____

_____

Let $f(x) = x - 3$ and $g(x) = x^2 + 7$. Write an expression for each function. State any restrictions.

11. $(f + g)(x)$ 12. $\left(\dfrac{g}{f}\right)(x)$ 13. $(g \circ f)(x)$

_____   _____   _____

Quick Warm-Up: Assessing Prior Knowledge
2.5 *Inverses of Functions*

Solve each equation for y.

1. $x = -4y$

2. $x = 2y + 3$

3. $x = \dfrac{y + 3}{5}$

4. $x = -\dfrac{1}{3}(y + 1)$

5. Let $f(x) = 2x - 4$ and $g(x) = 0.5x + 2$. Find $(f \circ g)(x)$ and $(g \circ f)(x)$.

Lesson Quiz
2.5 *Inverses of Functions*

1. Solve $A = -24 + \dfrac{2}{3}(B + 18)$ for B. _____

Find the inverse of each relation. State whether the relation is a function. Tell whether the inverse is a function.

2. $\{(3, 5), (5, 7), (7, 2), (9, 0)\}$

3. $\{(7, 2), (8, 4), (9, 2), (10, 6)\}$

Find the inverse of each function.

4. $f(x) = \dfrac{3x + 9}{12}$

5. $f(x) = (x - 5)^2 + 4$

6. Show that $f(x) = \dfrac{x - 7}{5}$ and $g(x) = 5x + 7$ are inverses of each other.

Quick Warm-Up: Assessing Prior Knowledge
2.6 *Special Functions*

Find the greatest integer that is *less than* or *equal to* the given number.

1. 3.97   2. -3.97 3. 0.0051   4. -7

_____   _____   _____   _____

Evaluate.

5. $|25.1|$ _____   6. $|-0.7|$ _____

Lesson Quiz
2.6 *Special Functions*

1. On the coordinate grid at right, graph the piecewise function below.

$$f(x) = \begin{cases} x + 2 & \text{if } -3 < x \leq 1 \\ x - 3 & \text{if } 1 < x \leq 3 \end{cases}$$

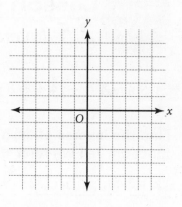

Let $f(x) = \lceil x \rceil$. Evaluate f for each value of x.

2. $x = 5.2$ _____   3. $x = 3.8$ _____   4. $x = -8.25$ _____

5. Graph $f(x) = 2.5[x]$.

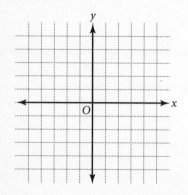

6. Graph $f(x) = 2|x| + 1$. Then graph its inverse on the same coordinate plane.

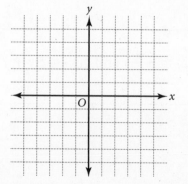

Quick Warm-Up: Assessing Prior Knowledge
2.7 A Preview of Transformations

Evaluate each expression when $x = -2$.

1. $(x - 6)^2$ 2. $x^2 - 6$ 3. $7x^2$ 4. $(7x)^2$

_____ _____ _____ _____

5. $-x^2$ 6. $(-x)^2$ 7. $-3x^2 - 1$ 8. $-(3x - 1)^2$

_____ _____ _____ _____

Lesson Quiz
2.7 A Preview of Transformations

Use a graphics calculator to graph each pair of functions. Identify the transformation(s).

1. $f(x) = x^2$ and $f(x - 6) = (x - 6)^2$

_____

2. $g(x) = |x|$ and $g(x) - 2 = |x| - 2$

_____

3. $f(x) = \sqrt{4 - x^2}$ and $4f(x) = 4\sqrt{4 - x^2}$

_____

4. $g(x) = \sqrt{36 - x^2}$ and $\frac{2}{3}g(x) = \frac{2}{3}\sqrt{36 - x^2}$

_____

5. $f(x) = \sqrt{36 - x^2}$ and $f(3x) = \sqrt{36 - (3x)^2}$

_____

6. $g(x) = \sqrt{4 - x^2}$ and $g\left(\frac{1}{5}x\right) = \sqrt{4 - \left(\frac{1}{5}x\right)^2}$

_____

7. $f(x) = x + 2$ and $-f(x) = -x - 2$

_____

8. $g(x) = \sqrt{x}$ and $g(-x) = \sqrt{-x}$

_____

9. $f(x) = x^2$ and $-3f(x + 7) = -3(x + 7)^2$

_____

10. $g(x) = |x|$ and $g(-2x) + 4 = |-2x| + 4$

_____

Chapter Assessment

Chapter 2, Form A, page 1

Write the letter that best answers the question or completes the statement.

_____ 1. Which of the following sets of numbers does not contain $3.\overline{6}$?

    a. real   b. rational   c. irrational   d. all of these

_____ 2. Which property of addition is illustrated by the statement $a + (-a) = 0$?

    a. Associative Property   b. Commutative Property
    c. Identity Property   d. Inverse Property

_____ 3. When simplified, what is the value of $\dfrac{6 + 3 \cdot 2^3}{2(5 - 3) - 2 \cdot 7} + (-3)^2$?

    a. -10 b. -6 c. 6   d. 10

_____ 4. Simplify $(-5a^{-4}b^3)(-2a^2b^{-3})^3$.

    a. $\dfrac{40a^2}{b^6}$ b. $\dfrac{-40a^2}{b^6}$ c. $30ab^3$ d. $-30ab^3$

_____ 5. Simplify $\left(\dfrac{3x^7y}{x^2y^5}\right)^{-2}$.

    a. $\dfrac{-6y^8}{x^{10}}$ b. $\dfrac{y^8}{9x^{10}}$ c. $\dfrac{-9y^{10}}{x^{10}}$ d. $\dfrac{y^{10}}{9x^{10}}$

_____ 6. What is the value of $27^{\frac{5}{3}}$?

    a. 45   b. 243   c. 643,729   d. 4,782,969

_____ 7. Which of the following relations is not a function?

    a. $\{(3, 7), (5, 8), (7, 9), (15, 10)\}$ b. $\{(7, 0), (10, 5), (13, 10), (16, 5)\}$
    c. $\{(3, 5), (5, 5), (7, 5), (9, 5)\}$ d. $\{(9, 3), (16, 4), (9, -3), (16, -4)\}$

_____ 8. What is the domain of the relation $\{(0, 1), (2, 3), (4, 5), (6, 7), (8, 9)\}$?

    a. $\{0, 2, 4, 6, 8\}$ b. $\{1, 3, 5, 7, 9\}$
    c. $\{0, 1, 2, 3, 4\}$ d. $\{0, 1, 2, 3, 4, 5, 6, 7, 8, 9\}$

_____ 9. Find the range of the function $f(x) = -x^2 + 3$.

    a. $x \leq 3$ b. $x \geq 3$ c. $y \leq 3$ d. $y \geq 3$

_____ 10. Find the value of the function $g(x) = \dfrac{x^3 + 9}{3x}$ when $x = -3$.

    a. 4   b. 2   c. -3 d. -28

_____ 11. Find the value of the function $h(x) = -10[x]$ when $x = 7.7$.

    a. 70   b. 80   c. -70 d. -80

Chapter Assessment

Chapter 2, Form A, page 2

_____ 12. The inverse of the relation shown is

   a. not a relation.
   b. not a function.
   c. a function.
   d. none of the above.

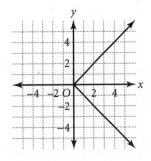

_____ 13. Find the inverse of the function $f(x) = 5(x - 6)$.

   a. $y = 5(x + 6)$ b. $y = -5(x + 6)$ c. $y = \dfrac{x + 6}{5}$ d. $y = \dfrac{x}{5} + 6$

_____ 14. If $f(x) = 6x + 3$ and $g(x) = 5x - 2$, what restrictions are on the domain of $\left(\dfrac{f}{g}\right)(x)$?

   a. $x \neq \dfrac{2}{5}$ b. $x \neq -\dfrac{2}{5}$ c. $x \neq -\dfrac{1}{2}$ d. $x \neq -2$

_____ 15. If $f(x) = x^2 + 3$ and $g(x) = x + 1$, find $(g \circ f)(x)$.

   a. $x^2 + 4$ b. $x^2 + 2x + 4$ c. $x^2 + 1$ d. $x^2 + 2x + 1$

_____ 16. Identify the transformation applied to $f(x) = x^3$ in order to obtain the function $g(x) = (-x)^3$.

   a. reflection across the x-axis   b. reflection across the y-axis
   c. vertical translation   d. horizontal translation

_____ 17. Identify the transformation applied to $f(x) = \sqrt{64 - x^2}$ in order to obtain the function $g(x) = \dfrac{3}{4}\sqrt{64 - x^2}$.

   a. horizontal stretch by a factor of $\dfrac{4}{3}$ b. horizontal compression by a factor of $\dfrac{3}{4}$

   c. vertical stretch by a factor of $\dfrac{4}{3}$ d. vertical compression by a factor of $\dfrac{3}{4}$

_____ 18. Find the function for the graph of $f(x) = \sqrt{x}$ after a translation of 4 units to the right and 3 units down.

   a. $g(x) = 3 + \sqrt{x - 4}$ b. $g(x) = 3 + \sqrt{x + 4}$

   c. $g(x) = -3 + \sqrt{x - 4}$ d. $g(x) = -3 + \sqrt{x + 4}$

_____ 19. The cost, c, to park in an airport parking lot can be modeled by the function $c(x) = 3 + \lceil x - 1 \rceil$, where x is the number of hours parked at the airport. How much will it cost to park at the airport for 2.7 hours?

   a. $6   b. $5   c. $4   d. $3

Chapter Assessment
Chapter 2, Form B, page 1

Classify each number in as many ways as possible.

1. -125

2. $5.626226222\ldots$

3. 12.345

_____   _____   _____

Evaluate each expression.

4. $16^{\frac{3}{4}} + 15 \div 5 - 3^3(5-2)^{-2}$ _____

5. $20 - \dfrac{15 + 3 \cdot 5^2}{5^2 - 4^2}$ _____

Simplify each expression. Assume that no variable has a value of zero.

6. $(-2x^{-3}x^7)^4$ _____

7. $\left(\dfrac{a^4 b^{-3}}{b^{-5}}\right)^3 \left(\dfrac{2ab^3}{a^3}\right)^{-2}$ _____

For Exercises 8–11, refer to the graph at right.

8. Is the relation a function? Explain your response.

_____

9. Write the domain and range of the relation.

_____

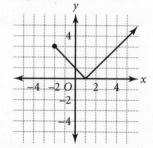

10. Is the inverse of the relation a function? Explain your response.

_____

11. Write the domain and range of the inverse.

_____

Find the value of each function for $x = -3$.

12. $f(x) = x^5 + 3x$ _____

13. $g(x) = 5[x + 5.5]$ _____

Let $f(x) = 2x + 1$ and $g(x) = x - 6$. Write an expression for each function. State any domain restrictions.

14. $(f+g)(x)$ **15.** $(fg)(x)$ **16.** $(f \circ g)(x)$ **17.** $\left(\dfrac{f}{g}\right)(x)$

_____   _____   _____   _____

18. Find the inverse of the function $f(x) = \dfrac{x}{4} + 10$. _____

Chapter Assessment

Chapter 2, Form B, page 2

19. On the coordinate grid at right, graph the piecewise function below.

$$f(x) = \begin{cases} x & \text{if } -3 < x < 2 \\ 2x - 5 & \text{if } x \geq 2 \end{cases}$$

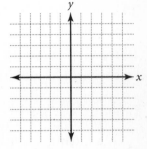

20. Identify the transformations applied to $f(x) = \sqrt{16 - x^2}$ in order to obtain the function $g(x) = \frac{3}{2}\sqrt{16 - (2x)^2}$.

_____

_____

21. Find the function for the graph of $f(x) = [x]$ after a reflection across the x-axis and a horizontal stretch by a factor of 3.

_____

22. Justify each step in the simplification of $(3a + 3b) + (-3a)$.

a. $(3a + 3b) + (-3a) = (3b + 3a) + (-3a)$ _____

b. $\qquad\qquad\quad = 3b + [3a + (-3a)]$ _____

c. $\qquad\qquad\quad = 3b + 3[a + (-a)]$ _____

d. $\qquad\qquad\quad = 3b + 3(0)$ _____

$\qquad\qquad\quad = 3b + 0$

e. $\qquad\qquad\quad = 3b$ _____

23. The monthly rent for a store in a mall is $200 plus $1.50 per square foot of area covered by the store.

a. Write a linear function to model the monthly rent, M, as a function of the number of square feet, n, that the store covers. _____

b. Find the inverse of the monthly rent function. _____

c. What is the area of the largest store that can be rented for $800 a month? _____

24. A courier service charges a basic fee of $5 to deliver packages. In addition, the company charges $0.50 per pound or fraction of a pound that the package weighs.

a. Write a function to model the cost, c, of sending a package that weighs n pounds. _____

b. Find the cost of sending a package that weighs 3.2 pounds. _____

Alternative Assessment

Exploring Rules of Exponents, Chapter 2, Form A

TASK: Identify the rules of exponents, and use these rules to perform operations with exponents.

HOW YOU WILL BE SCORED: As you work through the task, your teacher will be looking for the following:

- how well you understand the definition of an exponent
- whether you can perform operations and simplify expressions by using the rules of exponents
- how effectively you can communicate your responses in writing

1. Describe the types of numbers that you can choose to represent a base a, and its exponents, m and n.

   _____

2. Let m and n be the same two exponents from Exercise 1. Does $a^m \cdot a^n = a^{m \cdot n}$?

   Does $\dfrac{a^n}{a^m} = a^{n-m}$? If either equation is false, explain how to change it to be true.

   _____

Simplify, if possible. Then write a general rule that applies to each statement.

3. $(3xy)^{-1}$ _____

4. $(p^2 \cdot p^{-1})^0$ _____

Choose any values for a. Substitute these values in the following equations and evaluate.

5. $(1 + a)^{-1} = -1 + a^{-1}$ _____

6. $1 + a^{-1} = \dfrac{1}{1 + a}$ _____

7. $1^{-1} + a^{-1} = 1 + \dfrac{1}{a}$ _____

8. $(1 + a)^{-1} = \dfrac{1}{1 + a}$ _____

9. In Exercises 5–8, which equations are true?

   _____

10. Write a general rule that would apply to $(1 + a)^{-1}$, where a

   represents any real number. _____

SELF-ASSESSMENT: Explain how you could use your graphics calculator to find a general rule that would apply to $(1 + a)^{-1}$, where a represents any real number.

Alternative Assessment

Applications of Step Functions, Chapter 2, Form B

TASK: Solve a real-world problem by using functions.

HOW YOU WILL BE SCORED: As you work through the task, your teacher will be looking for the following:

- whether you can determine the function represented by a real-world problem
- how well you solve the problem

1. A taxi company bases its fares on the number of miles a passenger travels, as shown in the table below. Graph the data in the table.

Miles traveled	Taxi fare (in $)
$0 < m \leq 1$	0.75
$1 < m \leq 2$	1.50
$2 < m \leq 3$	2.25
$3 < m \leq 4$	3.00
$4 < m \leq 5$	3.75
$5 < m \leq 6$	4.50
$6 < m \leq 7$	5.25

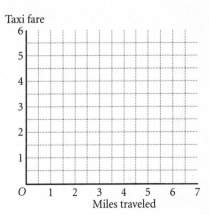

2. Discuss why a step function models this data. _____

_____

3. Is the step function for taxi fare a greatest-integer function or a rounding-up function?

Explain. _____

_____

4. Write a step function that could be used to find the taxi fare based on the miles traveled.

_____

5. What transformation of the parent step function is represented in the graph

of the taxi fare? _____

_____

SELF-ASSESSMENT: Suppose that the relation between miles traveled and taxi fares were not a function. Discuss the effect that this would have on the cost of a taxi ride.

Quick Warm-Up: Assessing Prior Knowledge

3.1 Solving Systems by Graphing or Substitution

Write each equation in slope-intercept form.

1. $x - y = 9$ _____

2. $2x = 5y$ _____

3. $4x + 7y = 14$ _____

4. $3x - \frac{1}{5}y = 6$ _____

5. $2.5y + 8.1 = 7.5x$ _____

Lesson Quiz

3.1 Solving Systems by Graphing or Substitution

Graph each system. Classify each system as inconsistent, dependent, or independent. Then find the solution from the graph.

1. $\begin{cases} y = 2x + 3 \\ 4x - 2y = 4 \end{cases}$

2. $\begin{cases} 2x + 4y = 16 \\ y + 2 = x \end{cases}$

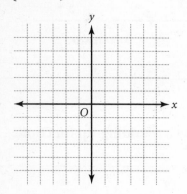

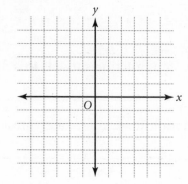

_____

_____

Use substitution to solve each system.

3. $\begin{cases} y = 5x + 12 \\ y = -3x + 4 \end{cases}$

4. $\begin{cases} x + y + 3z = 2 \\ 2y + 1 = 7 \\ 2x + 3y + 6z = 7 \end{cases}$

_____

_____

Quick Warm-Up: Assessing Prior Knowledge

3.2 Solving Systems by Elimination

Simplify.

1. $(5x + 9y) + (-5x + 6y)$ _____

2. $(11y + 7x) + (4x - 11y)$ _____

3. $4y - (4x - y)$ _____

4. $(8x + 2y) - (9x - 2y)$ _____

5. $(21x - 5y) - (15y + 4x)$ _____

Lesson Quiz

3.2 Solving Systems by Elimination

Use elimination to solve each system.

1. $\begin{cases} 3x - 2y = 11 \\ 2x + 6y = 22 \end{cases}$

2. $\begin{cases} 5x + 3y = 3 \\ 4x + 5y = 18 \end{cases}$

_____   _____

3. The Jones family and the Smith family went to a diner. The Jones family had 7 hamburgers and 4 drinks, and the Smith family had 9 hamburgers and 5 drinks. The Jones family spent $20, and the Smith family spent $25.50.

   a. Write a system of equations to find the cost of a hamburger and the cost of a drink.   _____

   b. Solve your system by using elimination.   _____

Use elimination to decide whether each system is dependent or inconsistent.

4. $\begin{cases} 8x - 12y = 28 \\ -6x + 9y = -21 \end{cases}$

5. $\begin{cases} -2x - 6y = -8 \\ 5x + 15y = -12 \end{cases}$

_____   _____

6. $\begin{cases} 2x + y = 5 \\ 4x + 2y = 6 \end{cases}$

7. $\begin{cases} -x + 2y = 3 \\ 2x - 4y = -6 \end{cases}$

_____   _____

Quick Warm-Up: Assessing Prior Knowledge
3.3 *Linear Inequalities in Two Variables*

Solve each equation or inequality. Graph the solution on a number line.

1. $2c + 7 = 1$ _____

2. $-12 \leq -6r$ _____

3. $3m + 8 > 5$ _____

Lesson Quiz
3.3 *Linear Inequalities in Two Variables*

Graph each linear inequality.

1. $y > x - 1$

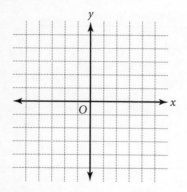

2. $3x + 2y \leq 6$

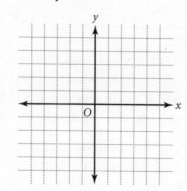

3. $y \leq -4$

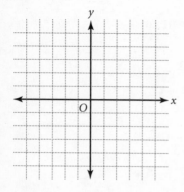

4. $x > 3$

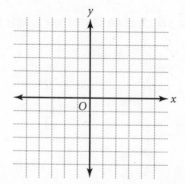

Mid-Chapter Assessment

Chapter 3 (Lessons 3.1–3.3)

Write the letter that best answers the question or completes the statement.

_____ 1. Which of the following is a solution to $\begin{cases} 3x - 6y = 15 \\ 5x - 10y = 25 \end{cases}$?

     a. $(3, -1)$ b. $(-7, -6)$ c. $(11, 3)$ d. all of these

_____ 2. The system of equations $\begin{cases} y = 3x + 2 \\ 6x + 2y = 9 \end{cases}$ is

     a. inconsistent.   b. consistent and independent.
     c. consistent and dependent.   d. none of these.

_____ 3. The system of equations $\begin{cases} -2x + 3y = 1 \\ 8x - 12y = -3 \end{cases}$ is

     a. inconsistent.   b. consistent and independent.
     c. consistent and dependent.   d. none of these.

4. Solve $\begin{cases} -2x + y = -9 \\ 12x + 3y = 9 \end{cases}$ by substitution.

5. Solve $\begin{cases} 3x + 4y = 15 \\ 7x - 3y = -39 \end{cases}$ by elimination.

_____   _____

Graph each inequality on the coordinate plane.

6. $y \geq 1$

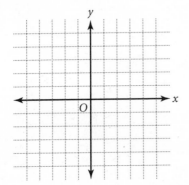

7. $-2x + 3y < -6$

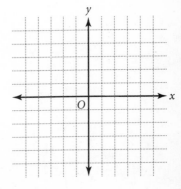

8. A chemist has a 10% acid solution and a 60% acid solution. Write and solve a system of equations to find how much of each solution the chemist must use in order to get 200 milliliters of a solution that is 45% acid. _____

9. Pat wants to burn at least 500 calories during her workout. She is able to burn 12 calories per minute on a treadmill and 9 calories per minute on an exercise bike. Write an inequality to represent how many minutes Pat must spend on each machine in order to reach her goal. _____

Quick Warm-Up: Assessing Prior Knowledge
3.4 *Systems of Linear Inequalities*

1. Graph $y < -x + 1$.

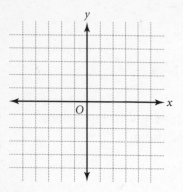

2. Graph the system. $\begin{cases} y = x + 2 \\ y = -2x - 1 \end{cases}$

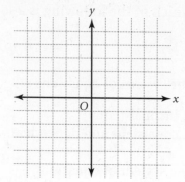

Lesson Quiz
3.4 *Systems of Linear Inequalities*

1. Graph $\begin{cases} x \geq 0 \\ y \leq -x + 4 \\ y \geq 2x - 4 \end{cases}$.

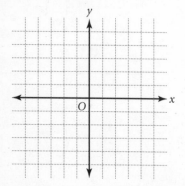

2. Graph $-2 \leq y < 3$.

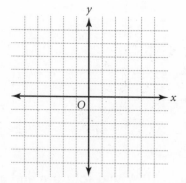

3. Write the system of inequalities whose solution is graphed at right.

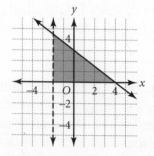

Quick Warm-Up: Assessing Prior Knowledge

3.5 Linear Programming

1. Solve the system. $\begin{cases} x + y = 7 \\ 2x - y = 8 \end{cases}$

_____

2. Graph the solution. $\begin{cases} y < 2x + 3 \\ y + x < 5 \\ x \geq 0 \\ y \geq 1 \end{cases}$

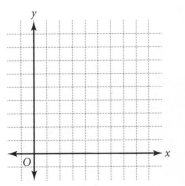

Lesson Quiz

3.5 Linear Programming

1. Ann has decided to buy no more than 50 dining-room tables to sell at her furniture store. She has also decided to restrict herself to buying only oak and mahogany tables. Ann wants to buy at least 10 oak tables and at least 15 but no more than 25 mahogany tables.

   a. Write a system of linear inequalities to represent the constraints

   Ann has set. _____

   b. Ann earns a profit of $250 on each oak table that she sells and a profit of $175 on each mahogany table that she sells. Write the objective function that Ann would use to maximize her profit

   from the tables. _____

2. a. Graph the set of constraints below, and find the corner points of the feasible region.
   $\begin{cases} y \geq -2 \\ y \leq -x + 3 \\ y \leq x + 3 \end{cases}$

   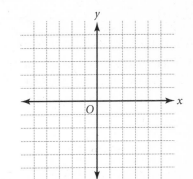

   _____

   b. Find the maximum and minimum values of $C = 80x + 75y$ on the feasible region. _____

Quick Warm-Up: Assessing Prior Knowledge
3.6 Parametric Equations

Complete the table by evaluating each expression for the given values of *x*.

	x	$4x + 3$	$-6x - 5$
1.	-2		
2.	-1		
3.	0		
4.	1		
5.	2		

Lesson Quiz
3.6 Parametric Equations

1. Graph the parametric equations for the given interval of t .

$$\begin{cases} x(t) = \frac{t}{2} + 1 \\ y(t) = t - 1 \end{cases} \text{ for } -4 \le t \le 4$$

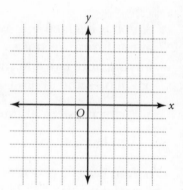

Write each pair of parametric equations as a single equation in *x* and *y*.

2. $\begin{cases} x(t) = 4t \\ y(t) = t + 2 \end{cases}$ _____

3. $\begin{cases} x(t) = 3t - 6 \\ y(t) = 9 - 6t \end{cases}$ _____

4. A model rocket is fired from a point 5 feet above the ground with a horizontal speed of 20 feet per second and a vertical speed of 128 feet per second. Parametric equations that model the path of the rocket are shown at right.

$$\begin{cases} x(t) = 20t \\ y(t) = 5 + 128t - 16t^2 \end{cases}$$

a. What is the maximum altitude that the rocket reaches? _____

b. There is a pond that is 160 feet from the point where the rocket is fired. If the rocket is aimed in the direction of the pond,

will it reach the pond? Explain your response. _____

Chapter Assessment

Chapter 3, Form A, page 1

Write the letter that best answers the question or completes the statement.

_____ 1. How many solutions does the system $\begin{cases} 8x = 12y - 9 \\ 27y + 18x = 21 \end{cases}$ have?

     a. 0   b. 1   c. 2   d. infinitely many

_____ 2. The system $\begin{cases} 45x - 30y = -90 \\ -12x + 8y = 24 \end{cases}$ is

     a. inconsistent.   b. consistent and independent.
     c. consistent and dependent.   d. none of these.

_____ 3. Which of the following is a solution to the system $\begin{cases} 3x + 2y - 3z = 15 \\ -2x + 4y + 2z = 6? \\ 4z + 12 = -8 \end{cases}$

     a. $(2, -3, 5)$ b. $(2, 3, -1)$ c. $(-2, 3, -5)$ d. all of these

_____ 4. Which inequality is graphed here?

     a. $y > -2x - 2$
     b. $y < -2x + 2$
     c. $y \geq -2x + 2$
     d. $y > -2x + 2$

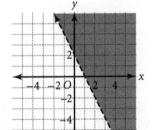

_____ 5. A vehicle manufacturer operates a plant that assembles and finishes both cars and trucks. It takes 5 person-days to assemble and 2 person-days to finish a truck. It takes 4 person-days to assemble and 3 person-days to finish a car. Assembly can take no more than 180 person-days per week, and finishing can take no more than 135 person-days per week. If x represents the number of trucks and y represents the number of cars, which of the following systems represent the weekly constraints on assembly and finishing?

     a. $\begin{cases} 5x + 2y \leq 180 \\ 4x + 3y \leq 135 \end{cases}$ b. $\begin{cases} 5x + 4y \leq 180 \\ 3x + 2y \leq 135 \end{cases}$

     c. $\begin{cases} 5x + 4y \leq 180 \\ 2x + 3y \leq 135 \end{cases}$ d. $\begin{cases} 4x + 5y \leq 180 \\ 2x + 3y \leq 135 \end{cases}$

_____ 6. Which of the following is a point on the line defined by $\begin{cases} x(t) = 3t + 4 \\ y(t) = -5t + 6 \end{cases}$?

     a. $(3, -5)$ b. $(10, 16)$ c. $(-5, -9)$ d. $(13, -9)$

Chapter Assessment

Chapter 3, Form A, page 2

_____ 7. Which system is graphed at right?

a. $\begin{cases} x > -2 \\ y \le -\frac{1}{2}x - 1 \end{cases}$

b. $\begin{cases} x < -2 \\ y \ge -\frac{1}{2}x - 1 \end{cases}$

c. $\begin{cases} x > -2 \\ y < -\frac{1}{2}x - 1 \end{cases}$

d. $\begin{cases} x \le -2 \\ y > -\frac{1}{2}x - 1 \end{cases}$

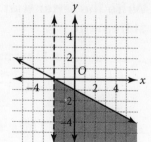

_____ 8. Find the minimum value of the objective function $C = 12x + 20y$ on the feasible region shown at right.

a. -20

b. -44

c. -72

d. -104

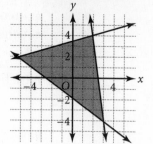

_____ 9. Which of the following is equivalent to $\begin{cases} x(t) = 4t + 8 \\ y(t) = 6t - 1 \end{cases}$?

a. $y = -\frac{3}{2}x + 13$ b. $y = \frac{3}{2}x - 13$ c. $y = -\frac{2}{3}x - 13$ d. $y = \frac{3}{2}x + 13$

_____ 10. A chemist needs to create a 38% saline solution by using a 20% saline solution and a 50% saline solution. If x is the amount of 20% solution and y is the amount of 50% solution, which system of equations must the chemist solve in order to find how much of each solution is needed to make 300 milliliters of a 38% solution?

a. $\begin{cases} x + y = 300 \\ 20x + 50y = 3800 \end{cases}$

b. $\begin{cases} x + y = 300 \\ 0.20x + 0.50y = 38 \end{cases}$

c. $\begin{cases} x + y = 38 \\ 0.20x + 0.50y = 300 \end{cases}$

d. $\begin{cases} x + y = 300 \\ 0.20x + 0.50y = 114 \end{cases}$

_____ 11. A quarterback throws a football towards a receiver from a point 5 feet above the ground with a horizontal speed of 60 feet per second and a vertical speed of 33 feet per second. $\begin{cases} x(t) = 60t \\ y(t) = 5 + 33t - 16t^2 \end{cases}$

Parametric equations that describe the flight of the football are shown. If the receiver is 120 feet away from the quarterback, what is the height of the football when it reaches the receiver?

a. 3 feet   b. 5 feet   c. 7 feet   d. 9 feet

Chapter Assessment

Chapter 3, Form B, page 1

1. a. Classify the system $\begin{cases} 24y - 8x = 40 \\ 3x = 9y - 21 \end{cases}$. _____

b. How many solutions does the system have? _____

2. Solve $\begin{cases} 5x + 3y = 5 \\ 3x + y = -1 \end{cases}$ by substitution. _____

3. Solve $\begin{cases} 2x - 3y = 24 \\ 6x + 2y = 6 \end{cases}$ by elimination. _____

4. Solve $\begin{cases} 5x - 3 = 7 \\ 3x + 5y - 4z = -13 \\ x - 3y + 5z = 16 \end{cases}$ by any method. _____

5. Graph $2x + 3y \geq 9$ on the coordinate grid below.

6. Graph the system $\begin{cases} -2x + y \leq -4 \\ x \leq 4 \\ y > -3 \end{cases}$ 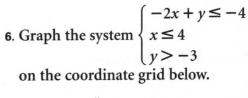 on the coordinate grid below.

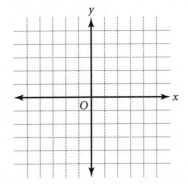

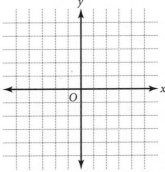

7. Some students want to start a business that cleans and polishes cars. It takes 1.5 hours of labor and costs $2.25 in supplies to clean a car. It takes 2 hours of labor and costs $4.50 in supplies to polish a car. The students can work a total of 120 hours in one week. They also decide that they want to spend no more than $160 per week on supplies. The students expect to make a profit of $7.75 for each car that they clean and a profit of $8.50 for each car that they polish.

a. Write a system of inequalities to represent the

constraints the students have set. _____

b. Write an objective function for the profit. _____

Chapter Assessment

Chapter 3, Form B, page 2

8. Find the maximum value of the objective function

$P = 300x + 450y$ on the feasible area shown at right.

_____

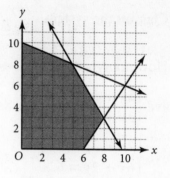

9. Consider the parametric equations $\begin{cases} x(t) = 3 - t \\ y(t) = 2t + 1 \end{cases}$.

   a. Graph the parametric equations for $-2 \le t \le 2$.

   b. Find a single equation in x and y that is equivalent

   to the parametric equations. _____

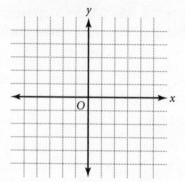

10. There are 120 seats on an airplane. If a passenger reserved a
    seat at least two weeks early, the passenger paid $150 for the
    flight. Other passengers paid $200. If all 120 seats were sold
    and the total amount paid by the passengers was $22,550,
    write and solve a system of equations to find how many

    many passengers paid the lower fare. _____

11. A juice company wants to make a drink that is 60% fruit juice. The
    company already makes a drink that is 90% fruit juice and a drink
    that is 40% fruit juice. How much of each drink should they use to

    make 2 liters of a drink that is 60% fruit juice? _____

12. An arrow is shot from a point 20 feet above the ground with an
    initial horizontal velocity of 45 feet per second and an initial
    vertical velocity of 80 feet per second. The parametric equations
    that describe the arrow's path are shown at right.
    $\begin{cases} x(t) = 45t \\ y(t) = 20 + 80t - 16t^2 \end{cases}$

   a. The arrow is aimed at a target that is a horizontal distance of
      90 feet from the point where the arrow is shot. If the arrow hits

      the target, how high is the target? _____

   b. How far does the arrow travel before it hits the ground? _____

Alternative Assessment

Solving Inequalities, Chapter 3, Form A

TASK: Solve inequalities that model real-world applications.

HOW YOU WILL BE SCORED: As you work through the task, your teacher will be looking for the following:

- how well you can write an inequality describing a real-world application
- whether you can graph an inequality in one variable

Adventure games cost $15 each, and sports games cost $10 each. If Demane has $120 to spend, what combinations of adventure games and sports games can Demane choose?

1. Assign variables to adventure games and sports games. Then write an inequality that describes the situation.

   _____

   _____

2. Solve the inequality from Exercise 1 for one of the variables.

   _____

3. Describe the *x*- and *y*-values that are possible for this situation.

   _____

4. Sketch a graph that shows how many of each game Demane could buy.

5. What will be the cost of 6 adventure games and 4 sports games?

   _____

6. What combinations of adventure and sports games can Demane purchase if he wants to spend as much as possible of the $120?

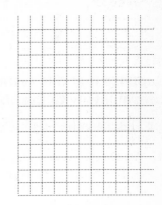

   _____

SELF-ASSESSMENT: What is the difference between real-world applications modeled by an equality and those modeled by an inequality?

Alternative Assessment

Exploring Systems of Linear Inequalities, Chapter 3, Form B

TASK: Solve a real-world problem by using matrices.

HOW YOU WILL BE SCORED: As you work through the task, your teacher will be looking for the following:

- how well you can identify solutions to a system of linear inequalities
- whether you can identify the feasible region corresponding to a set of constraints
- how well you can find minimum and maximum values for an objective function

The graph at right represents a system of linear inequalities.

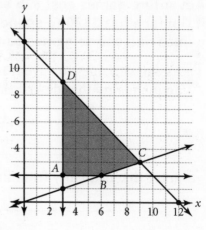

1. Describe the shape of the shaded region.

   _____

2. Does this system of inequalities have solutions in a bounded or unbounded region? Explain.

   _____

   _____

3. Find any 4 points that are solutions to this system of inequalities. Describe how you know that your 4 points are solution points.

   _____

   _____

Suppose that this system of inequalities corresponded to a set of constraints with the objective function $P = 6x + 3y$.

4. Describe the feasible region.

   _____

5. What are the coordinates of points A, B, C, and D? Explain what the coordinates represent.

   _____

6. Find the maximum value of the objective function that satisfies the contraints.

   _____

SELF-ASSESSMENT: What does it mean when an objective function intersects the feasible region?

_____

NAME _____ CLASS _____ DATE _____

Quick Warm-Up: Assessing Prior Knowledge
4.1 *Using Matrices to Represent Data*

Evaluate each expression for $a = -5$, $b = 1.3$, **and** $c = -7$.

1. $a + b$ _____

2. $b - c$ _____

3. $a - b + c$ _____

4. $-4b$ _____

Solve each equation.

5. $16 = 2x - 5$ _____

6. $3y + 8 = -y - 15$ _____

Lesson Quiz
4.1 *Using Matrices to Represent Data*

1. The table shows the results of three high schools in a track meet. Represent the data in a matrix, T. Interpret t_{31}.

	Central	North	South
First place	7	5	3
Second place	3	5	7
Third place	4	6	5

_____

2. Solve $\begin{bmatrix} 2x + 3 & 5x - 2 \\ 17 & 5y + 8 \end{bmatrix} = \begin{bmatrix} 15 & 28 \\ 17 & 3y - 6 \end{bmatrix}$ for x and y. _____

Let $A = \begin{bmatrix} 3 & -5 \\ 7 & 6 \end{bmatrix}$, $B = \begin{bmatrix} -8 & 10 \\ 2 & 0 \end{bmatrix}$, and $C = \begin{bmatrix} 1 & 7 \\ -5 & 7 \end{bmatrix}$. **Find the following.**

3. $A + B$

4. $C - B - A$

5. $2.5B$

_____   _____   _____

6. Represent quadrilateral $ABCD$ by using a matrix.

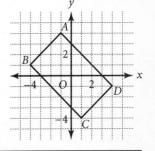

_____

Quick Warm-Up: Assessing Prior Knowledge
4.2 Matrix Multiplication

Give the dimensions of each matrix.

1. $\begin{bmatrix} -5 & 0 & 7 & -11 \\ 0 & 3 & 7 & -19 \end{bmatrix}$ _____

2. $\begin{bmatrix} -15 & 7 \\ 10 & 9 \\ 6 & 6 \end{bmatrix}$ _____

Identify the entry at each location of matrix $B = \begin{bmatrix} -7 & 0 & 13 \\ -2 & 4 & -2 \\ 12 & 1 & 10 \end{bmatrix}$.

3. b_{12} _____

4. b_{21} _____

5. b_{32} _____

Lesson Quiz
4.2 Matrix Multiplication

Let $A = \begin{bmatrix} 2 & 3 \\ 5 & 1 \end{bmatrix}$, $B = \begin{bmatrix} 1 & 4 \\ 0 & 2 \end{bmatrix}$, **and** $C = \begin{bmatrix} 1 & 4 \\ 2 & 1 \\ 3 & 0 \end{bmatrix}$. **Find each product, if it exists.**

1. BA

2. BC

3. CB

_____   _____   _____

4. Matrix T shows the results of three teams in a track meet. Suppose that a first-place finish earns a team 5 points, a second-place finish earns a team 3 points, and a third-place finish earns a team 1 point.

$$\begin{array}{c} \\ \text{First} \\ \text{Second} \\ \text{Third} \end{array} \begin{array}{ccc} \text{Central} & \text{North} & \text{South} \\ \left[\begin{array}{ccc} 7 & 5 & 3 \\ 3 & 5 & 7 \\ 4 & 6 & 5 \end{array}\right] \end{array} = T$$

a. Use a 1 × 3 matrix, N, to represent the point values for finishing first, second, and third. _____

b. Find NT. _____

c. What do the entries in matrix NT represent? Who won the track meet? _____

Use the network at right.

5. a. Represent this network in an adjacency matrix.

b. Find the matrix that gives the number of 2-stage paths in this network.

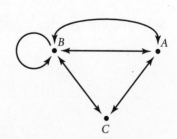

_____   _____

Quick Warm-Up: Assessing Prior Knowledge
4.3 *The Inverse of a Matrix*

Find the multiplicative inverse of each number.

1. -3 _____

2. 2.5 _____

3. $-\frac{1}{7}$ _____

4. $1\frac{1}{5}$ _____

Find each product.

5. $(-5)(-0.2)$ _____

6. $\left(\frac{2}{3}\right)\left(1\frac{1}{2}\right)$ _____

Lesson Quiz
4.3 *The Inverse of a Matrix*

1. Show that $\begin{bmatrix} 3 & 2 \\ 7 & 5 \end{bmatrix}$ and $\begin{bmatrix} 5 & -2 \\ -7 & 3 \end{bmatrix}$ are inverses of each other.

_____

Find the inverse of each matrix.

2. $\begin{bmatrix} -4 & 6 \\ -5 & 8 \end{bmatrix}$ _____

3. $\begin{bmatrix} 4 & 0 & -2 \\ 0 & 16 & 6 \\ 2 & 2 & 1 \end{bmatrix}$ _____

Find the determinant of each matrix. Tell whether each matrix has an inverse.

4. $\begin{bmatrix} 7 & 5 \\ 6 & 4 \end{bmatrix}$

5. $\begin{bmatrix} 1 & 2 & 3 \\ 4 & 5 & 6 \\ 7 & 8 & 9 \end{bmatrix}$

_____   _____

6. Find x so that $\begin{bmatrix} 5 & 10 \\ x & 4 \end{bmatrix}$ has no inverse. _____

Mid-Chapter Assessment
Chapter 4 (Lessons 4.1–4.3)

Write the letter that best answers the question or completes the statement.

_____ 1. Which of the following is not true for all 2 × 2 matrices A, B, and C?

    a. $A + B = B + A$ b. $(A + B) + C = A + (B + C)$

    c. $AB = BA$ d. all are true

_____ 2. If matrix A is 2 × 3 and matrix B is 3 × 4, what are the dimensions of matrix AB?

    a. 3 × 3   b. 2 × 3   c. 3 × 4   d. 2 × 4

_____ 3. Which of the following does not have an inverse?

    a. $\begin{bmatrix} 5 & 9 \\ 3 & 4 \end{bmatrix}$ b. $\begin{bmatrix} 4 & -8 \\ 2 & 4 \end{bmatrix}$ c. $\begin{bmatrix} 9 & 6 \\ 18 & 12 \end{bmatrix}$ d. $\begin{bmatrix} 11 & -14 \\ -15 & 18 \end{bmatrix}$

Let $A = \begin{bmatrix} 2 & 5 \\ 0 & 1 \end{bmatrix}$, $B = \begin{bmatrix} 4 & -3 \\ 1 & 2 \end{bmatrix}$, $C = \begin{bmatrix} 1 & 3 & 5 \\ 0 & -2 & 4 \end{bmatrix}$, and $D = \begin{bmatrix} 1 & 3 & 0 \\ 2 & 0 & -3 \\ 1 & 4 & 0 \end{bmatrix}$.

Calculate the following, if possible.

4. $A - 3B$ _____

5. $4C + D$ _____

6. CD _____

7. CA _____

8. B^2 _____

9. A^{-1} _____

Solve for x.

10. $\begin{bmatrix} 8 & 9 \\ 3x + 7 & 5x - 4 \end{bmatrix} = \begin{bmatrix} 8 & 9 \\ 6x + 13 & 7x \end{bmatrix}$

11. $\begin{bmatrix} 5 & 3 & 1 \\ x & 3 & 0 \end{bmatrix} \begin{bmatrix} 2 & 0 \\ 4 & 2 \\ 5 & 8 \end{bmatrix} = \begin{bmatrix} 27 & 14 \\ 20 & 6 \end{bmatrix}$

_____   _____

12. a. At a refreshment stand, cups of frozen yogurt are available in three sizes: small for $0.50, medium for $0.75, and large for $1.25. On Saturday, 65 small cups, 120 medium cups, and 45 large cups were sold. On Sunday, 95 small cups, 150 medium cups, and 80 large cups were sold. Use a 2 × 3 matrix, S, to represent yogurt sales and a 3 × 1 matrix, P, to represent yogurt prices. _____

    b. Find SP. What does SP represent? _____

Quick Warm-Up: Assessing Prior Knowledge

4.4 Solving Systems With Matrix Equations

Find each product.

1. $\begin{bmatrix} 4 & 1 \\ -6 & 9 \end{bmatrix} \begin{bmatrix} 0 & 12 \\ -6 & -5 \end{bmatrix}$ _____

2. $\begin{bmatrix} 0 & -4 \\ 2 & -2 \end{bmatrix}^{-1} \begin{bmatrix} 8 & 16 \\ 36 & -20 \end{bmatrix}$ _____

Lesson Quiz

4.4 Solving Systems With Matrix Equations

1. Bob won $25,000 in the lottery. He wants to invest some in an account that pays 15% per year and put the rest into an account that pays 7% per year. Bob wants to earn $3000 in interest per year. Write and solve a system of equations to find how much he should invest at each interest rate.

_____

Write each system as a matrix equation.

2. $\begin{cases} y = 3x - 8 \\ 5x - y = 4 \end{cases}$

3. $\begin{cases} 2y - 3z = 12 \\ 3x + 5y - 4z = 9 \\ 5x = 2y \end{cases}$

_____   _____

Solve each system of equations by using a matrix inverse.

4. $\begin{cases} 5x + 8y = 11 \\ -4x - 9y = -1 \end{cases}$

5. $\begin{cases} 3x + 7y + 4z = 29 \\ -5x - 3y - 5z = 16 \\ 4x + 3y - 9z = 31 \end{cases}$

_____   _____

Quick Warm-Up: Assessing Prior Knowledge

4.5 Using Matrix Row Operations

Write each system as a matrix equation. Then solve the system, if possible, by using the matrix equation.

1. $\begin{cases} x + 7y = 5 \\ -3x + 2y = 8 \end{cases}$ _____

2. $\begin{cases} 3x - 6y = -3 \\ -4x + 8y = -4 \end{cases}$ _____

Lesson Quiz

4.5 Using Matrix Row Operations

Write an augmented matrix for each system of equations.

1. $\begin{cases} y = 6 - 7x \\ y = 4x \end{cases}$ _____

2. $\begin{cases} 2x + 5y = 9 \\ x + 6y + z = 0 \\ 5x = 8 \end{cases}$ _____

3. Use row operations to transform $\begin{bmatrix} 2 & 4 & 0 & \vdots & 6 \\ 0 & 1 & 0 & \vdots & 1 \\ 3 & 4 & 2 & \vdots & 1 \end{bmatrix}$ to reduced row-echelon form.

_____

Use the row-reduction method to solve each system. Then classify the system as independent, dependent, or inconsistent.

4. $\begin{cases} x + z = 1 \\ -2x + y = 2 \\ 3y + 6z = 4 \end{cases}$

5. $\begin{cases} 3x + 9y = 6 \\ 2y - 2z = 4 \\ x + 2y + z = 0 \end{cases}$

_____   _____

Chapter Assessment

Chapter 4, Form A, page 1

Write the letter that best answers the question or completes the statement.

_____ 1. Let $M = \begin{bmatrix} 2 & 15 & 1 & 9 & 0 \\ 12 & 6 & 5 & 4 & 3 \\ 7 & 10 & 11 & 8 & 14 \end{bmatrix}$. What is the entry in location m_{31}?

    a. 1   **b.** 3   **c.** 4   **d.** 7

_____ 2. Which value of x makes $3\begin{bmatrix} 6 & 2 \\ 0 & x \end{bmatrix} - 5\begin{bmatrix} 1 & 0 \\ 2 & x \end{bmatrix} = \begin{bmatrix} 13 & 12 \\ -10 & 6 \end{bmatrix}$ true?

    a. 3   **b.** −3   **c.** 5   **d.** −5

_____ 3. If $AB = \begin{bmatrix} 3 & 2 & 9 & 7 \\ 5 & 1 & 0 & 6 \end{bmatrix}$ and A is a 2 × 3 matrix, what are the dimensions of B?

    a. 2 × 4   **b.** 4 × 2   **c.** 3 × 4   **d.** 4 × 3

_____ 4. Which value of x makes $\begin{bmatrix} 2 & 1 & 0 \\ 5 & x & 2 \end{bmatrix}\begin{bmatrix} 3 & 3 \\ 0 & 4 \\ 4 & x \end{bmatrix} = \begin{bmatrix} 6 & 10 \\ 23 & -9 \end{bmatrix}$ true?

    a. 6   **b.** 1   **c.** −4   **d.** −9

_____ 5. Let $A = \begin{bmatrix} 6 & 7 \\ 1 & 2 \end{bmatrix}$. Which of the following is A^{-1}?

    a. $\begin{bmatrix} -6 & -7 \\ -1 & -2 \end{bmatrix}$ **b.** $\begin{bmatrix} 1 & 2 \\ 6 & 7 \end{bmatrix}$ **c.** $\begin{bmatrix} -1.2 & 0.2 \\ 1.4 & -0.4 \end{bmatrix}$ **d.** $\begin{bmatrix} 0.4 & -1.4 \\ -0.2 & 1.2 \end{bmatrix}$

_____ 6. If the reduced row-echelon form of the augmented matrix for

a system of equations is $\begin{bmatrix} 1 & 0 & 2 & : & 0 \\ 0 & 1 & 1 & : & 0 \\ 0 & 0 & 0 & : & 1 \end{bmatrix}$, then the system is

    a. inconsistent.   **b.** consistent and independent.

    c. consistent and dependent.   **d.** none of these.

_____ 7. Find the matrix form of the system $\begin{cases} 3x + 2y = 8 \\ 4x - y = -5 \end{cases}$.

    a. $\begin{bmatrix} 3 & 2 \\ 4 & -1 \end{bmatrix}\begin{bmatrix} 8 \\ -5 \end{bmatrix} = \begin{bmatrix} x \\ y \end{bmatrix}$ **b.** $\begin{bmatrix} 3 & 2 \\ 4 & -1 \end{bmatrix}\begin{bmatrix} x \\ y \end{bmatrix} = \begin{bmatrix} 8 \\ -5 \end{bmatrix}$

    c. $\begin{bmatrix} 3 & 4 \\ 2 & -1 \end{bmatrix}\begin{bmatrix} x \\ y \end{bmatrix} = \begin{bmatrix} 8 \\ -5 \end{bmatrix}$ **d.** $\begin{bmatrix} 3 & 4 \\ 2 & -1 \end{bmatrix}\begin{bmatrix} 8 \\ -5 \end{bmatrix} = \begin{bmatrix} x \\ y \end{bmatrix}$

Chapter Assessment

Chapter 4, Form A, page 2

Write the letter that best answers the question or completes the statement.

_____ 8. Let $A = \begin{bmatrix} 2 & 3 \\ 4 & -2 \end{bmatrix}$. Find A^2.

     a. $\begin{bmatrix} 4 & 9 \\ 16 & 4 \end{bmatrix}$
     b. $\begin{bmatrix} 4 & 9 \\ 16 & -4 \end{bmatrix}$
     c. $\begin{bmatrix} 4 & 6 \\ 8 & -4 \end{bmatrix}$
     d. $\begin{bmatrix} 16 & 0 \\ 0 & 16 \end{bmatrix}$

_____ 9. Find the determinant of $\begin{bmatrix} 3 & x \\ x & y \end{bmatrix}$.

     a. $3y - x^2$
     b. $3y + x^2$
     c. $3x - xy$
     d. $3x + xy$

_____ 10. Find the determinant of $\begin{bmatrix} 2 & 1 & 0 \\ 3 & 0 & 2 \\ 4 & 5 & 1 \end{bmatrix}$.

     a. 0
     b. –2
     c. 10
     d. –15

_____ 11. Let $A = \begin{bmatrix} 2 & 1 & \vdots & 4 \\ 4 & 5 & \vdots & 2 \end{bmatrix}$. Which of the following is matrix A after the row operation $-2R_1 + R_2 \rightarrow R_2$?

     a. $\begin{bmatrix} -4 & -2 & \vdots & -8 \\ 0 & 3 & \vdots & -6 \end{bmatrix}$
     b. $\begin{bmatrix} 2 & 1 & \vdots & 4 \\ 0 & 5 & \vdots & 2 \end{bmatrix}$

     c. $\begin{bmatrix} 2 & 1 & \vdots & 4 \\ 0 & 3 & \vdots & 2 \end{bmatrix}$
     d. $\begin{bmatrix} 2 & 1 & \vdots & 4 \\ 0 & 3 & \vdots & -6 \end{bmatrix}$

_____ 12. Find the reduced row-echelon form of the system $\begin{cases} x + z = 4 \\ y - 2z = -8. \\ 2x - y = 4 \end{cases}$

     a. $\begin{bmatrix} 1 & 0 & 0 & \vdots & 1 \\ 0 & 1 & 0 & \vdots & -2 \\ 0 & 0 & 1 & \vdots & 3 \end{bmatrix}$
     b. $\begin{bmatrix} 1 & 0 & 0 & \vdots & -1 \\ 0 & 1 & 0 & \vdots & 2 \\ 0 & 0 & 1 & \vdots & -3 \end{bmatrix}$

     c. $\begin{bmatrix} 1 & 0 & 1 & \vdots & 1 \\ 0 & 1 & 0 & \vdots & -2 \\ 1 & 0 & 1 & \vdots & -3 \end{bmatrix}$
     d. $\begin{bmatrix} 0 & 0 & 1 & \vdots & 1 \\ 0 & 1 & 0 & \vdots & -2 \\ 1 & 0 & 0 & \vdots & 3 \end{bmatrix}$

_____ 13. Solve the equation $\begin{bmatrix} 2 & 3 & 4 \\ 5 & -2 & 3 \\ -3 & 5 & -2 \end{bmatrix} \begin{bmatrix} x \\ y \\ z \end{bmatrix} = \begin{bmatrix} -6 \\ 1 \\ 8 \end{bmatrix}$.

     a. $(2, -4, -5)$
     b. $(4, 2, -5)$
     c. $(-5, 2, 4)$
     d. $(4, -2, 5)$

Chapter Assessment

Chapter 4, Form B, page 1

Perform each operation for the given matrices, if possible.

$$A = \begin{bmatrix} 5 & 2 \\ 9 & 4 \end{bmatrix} \qquad B = \begin{bmatrix} -4 & -1 \\ 0 & -2 \end{bmatrix} \qquad C = \begin{bmatrix} 3 & 1 \\ 2 & 4 \\ 0 & 1 \end{bmatrix} \qquad D = \begin{bmatrix} 1 & 2 & 0 \\ 5 & 3 & 1 \\ 0 & 6 & 2 \end{bmatrix}$$

1. $-2B + 3A$ _____

2. C^2 _____

3. DC _____

4. A^{-1} _____

Find x in each equation.

5. $\begin{bmatrix} 4 - 2x & 7 \\ 9 & 3 \end{bmatrix} = \begin{bmatrix} 2x + 16 & 7 \\ 9 & 3 \end{bmatrix}$

6. $\begin{bmatrix} 1 & 3x & 2 \\ 3 & 0 & 5 \end{bmatrix} \begin{bmatrix} 4 & 1 \\ 2 & 0 \\ 0 & 1 \end{bmatrix} - \begin{bmatrix} 16 & 3 \\ 6 & 2 \end{bmatrix} = 3 \begin{bmatrix} x - 2 & 0 \\ 2 & 2 \end{bmatrix}$

_____ _____

7. a. Find the determinant of the matrix $B = \begin{bmatrix} 7 & 8 & 9 \\ 5 & 10 & 15 \\ 8 & 10 & 12 \end{bmatrix}$. _____

b. Find B^{-1}, if it exists. _____

8. a. Write the system as a matrix equation. $\begin{cases} 2x + 3y + z = 12 \\ 3x + y - 4z = -5 \\ -4x - y + 3z = 6 \end{cases}$

_____

b. Solve the system by using a matrix inverse.

_____

9. Find x and y in the equation $\begin{bmatrix} x & y \\ 0 & 4 \end{bmatrix} \begin{bmatrix} 3 & 5 \\ 2 & 3 \end{bmatrix} = \begin{bmatrix} 17 & 27 \\ 8 & 12 \end{bmatrix}$.

_____

Chapter Assessment

Chapter 4, Form B, page 2

10. Find matrix $A = \begin{bmatrix} 2 & 3 & 4 & \vdots & 1 \\ 2 & 1 & 3 & \vdots & -1 \\ 6 & 2 & 0 & \vdots & 5 \end{bmatrix}$ after the row operation

$-3R_2 + R_3 \rightarrow R_3$. _____

11. a. Write an augmented matrix for the system $\begin{cases} x - 2z = 2 \\ -2x + 2y + 6z = 2. \\ 3y + 3z = 9 \end{cases}$ _____

   b. Write your matrix from part a in reduced row-echelon form. _____

   c. Classify the system as inconsistent, consistent and independent, or consistent and dependent. Write all solutions to the system.

   _____

12. Represent the network at right as an adjacency matrix A.

   _____

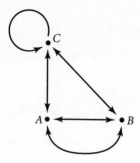

13. The measure of a triangle's largest angle is 6 times the measure of its smallest angle. The measure of the largest angle is also twice the sum of the measures of the other two angles.

   a. Write a system of three equations using the measures of the angles of the triangle. _____

   b. Find the measures of the angles. _____

14. A grocery store sells peanuts for $3.20 per pound and cashews for $8 per pound. The grocer wants to make 100 pounds of a mixture of peanuts and cashews that can be sold for $4.40 per pound. How many pounds of each type of nut should the grocer use? _____

Alternative Assessment

Matrices and Transformations, Chapter 4, Form A

TASK: Transform a geometric figure by using matrices.

HOW YOU WILL BE SCORED: As you work through the task, your teacher will be looking for the following:

- how well you perform matrix operations
- whether you understand how matrices are used to transform figures in the coordinate plane

1. a. Find the area of square *ABCD*. _____

   b. Represent *ABCD* as a matrix, *S*.

   _____

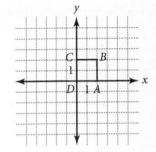

2. a. Let $T_1 = \begin{bmatrix} 1 & 0 \\ 0 & 3 \end{bmatrix}$. Find $T_1 S = S'$ and graph the resulting figure $A'B'C'D'$.

   _____

   b. What transformation does T_1 represent?

   _____

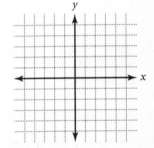

   c. Find the area of $A'B'C'D'$ and the determinant of T_1. How does the determinant of the transformation matrix seem to effect the area of the transformed figure? _____

   _____

   d. Find T_1^{-1}. What transformation does T_1^{-1} represent? Verify your answer by finding $T_1^{-1}S'$.

   _____

3. a. Let $T_2 = \begin{bmatrix} 2 & 0 \\ 0 & 3 \end{bmatrix}$. What transformation does T_2 represent? What

   transformation does T_2^{-1} represent? _____

   b. Find the determinant of T_2. Find the area of *ABCD* after it has

   been given the transformation represented by T_2. _____

SELF-ASSESSMENT: Find the matrix that represents a horizontal reflection.

Alternative Assessment
Applications of Matrix Algebra, Chapter 4, Form B

TASK: Solve a real-world problem by using matrices.

HOW YOU WILL BE SCORED: As you work through the task, your teacher will be looking for the following:

- whether you can solve systems of equations by using matrices
- how well you can interpret the solution to a real-world problem

Brett wants to buy a used car. A family member will lend Brett $800 at 12.5% interest each year, or Brett can borrow $1200 from a finance company at 5% interest each year.

1. Write a system of equations to represent Brett's options. Use the formula $A = Prt + P$, where A represents the total amount that Brett will owe, P represents the principal (the amount borrowed), r represents the annual rate of simple interest in decimal form, and t represents the time in years.

   _____

2. Write the system of equations in matrix form.

   _____

3. Solve the system of equations.

   _____

4. Explain the meaning of the solution.

   _____

5. Describe how to solve this system of equations by graphing. Then explain what the point of intersection represents. What would be the best choice for Brett if he wants to repay his debt in 5 years? 10 years? 15 years?

   _____

   _____

   _____

SELF-ASSESSMENT: Did you prefer solving this problem by using matrices or by using a graph? Think of a situation in which you might prefer to use the other method.

Quick Warm-Up: Assessing Prior Knowledge

5.1 *Introduction to Quadratic Functions*

Use the Distributive Property to find each product.

1. $(x + 1)(x - 1)$ _____

2. $(x + 2)(x + 9)$ _____

3. $(x + 5)(4x - 7)$ _____

4. $(3x - 1)(5x + 4)$ _____

5. $(-x - 3)(-2x - 3)$ _____

Lesson Quiz

5.1 *Introduction to Quadratic Functions*

Show that *f* represents a quadratic function by writing *f* in the form $f(x) = ax^2 + bx + c$. Identify *a*, *b*, and *c*.

1. $f(x) = (x - 5)(4x + 1)$

2. $f(x) = (x + 5)^2 - 10$

_____ _____

_____ _____

State whether the parabola opens up or down and whether the *y*-coordinate of the vertex is the maximum or minimum value of the function.

3. $f(x) = 12 - 5x^2 + 8x$

4. $f(x) = -7 + 3x + x^2$

_____ _____

5. Graph $f(x) = -2x^2 - 4x + 1$. Approximate the coordinates of the vertex.

_____

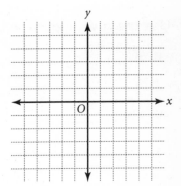

Quick Warm-Up: Assessing Prior Knowledge

5.2 *Introduction to Solving Quadratic Equations*

Simplify.

1. $\sqrt{81}$ _____

2. $-\sqrt{144}$ _____

3. $\pm\sqrt{1}$ _____

4. $\sqrt{25(9)}$ _____

5. $\sqrt{16} \cdot \sqrt{121}$ _____

6. $\sqrt{16} \cdot \sqrt{11}$ _____

Lesson Quiz

5.2 *Introduction to Solving Quadratic Equations*

Solve each equation. Give both exact solutions and approximate solutions to the nearest hundredth.

1. $5x^2 - 35 = 120$

2. $\frac{2}{5}(x + 5)^2 = 32.4$

3. $4(x^2 - 6) - 22 = 150$

_____   _____   _____

Find the unknown length in each triangle. Round answers to the nearest hundredth, if necessary.

4.

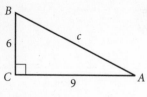

_____

5.

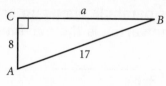

_____

Use the given figure to find each length.

6. AC _____

7. BC _____

8. AB _____

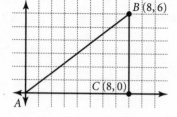

9. Find the length of $\overline{BC}$ in the diagram shown at right.

_____

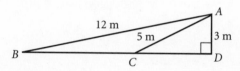

Quick Warm-Up: Assessing Prior Knowledge
5.3 Factoring Quadratic Expressions

List all the factors of each number.

1. 10 _____ 2. 48 _____ 3. 7 _____

Find the greatest common factor (GCF) of each set of numbers.

4. 6, 14 _____ 5. 12, 18, 30 _____ 6. 4, 8, 15, 20 _____

Lesson Quiz
5.3 Factoring Quadratic Expressions

Factor each expression.

1. $15bx + 25bx^2$

_____

2. $2ab + 4b + 3a + 6$

_____

3. $x^2 - 6x - 27$

_____

4. $3xy^2 + 27xy + 54x$

_____

5. $2x^2 + 5x - 12$

_____

6. $4x^2 - 20x + 25$

_____

7. $x^2 - 49$

_____

8. $16a^2 - 81$

_____

Use factoring and the Zero-Product Property to solve each equation.

9. $x^2 + 3x - 40 = 0$

_____

10. $4x^2 + 3x = 1$

_____

11. Find the zeros of the quadratic function $f(x) = x^2 - 9x.$ _____

12. Find the value of x in the diagram at right.

_____

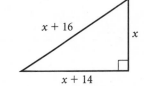

x + 16

x

x + 14

Quick Warm-Up: Assessing Prior Knowledge

5.4 Completing the Square

Factor each trinomial.

1. $x^2 + 14x + 49$ _____   2. $x^2 - 22x + 121$ _____   3. $x^2 - 12x - 64$ _____

Solve each equation.

4. $d^2 - 100 = 0$ _____   5. $z^2 - 2z + 1 = 0$ _____   6. $t^2 + 16 = -8t$ _____

Lesson Quiz

5.4 Completing the Square

Complete the square for each quadratic expression. Then rewrite the expression as a binomial squared.

1. $x^2 - 18x$

2. $x^2 + 9x$

_____   _____

Solve by completing the square. Round your answers to the nearest tenth, if necessary.

3. $x^2 + 4x - 32 = 0$

4. $x^2 = 5x + 2$

_____   _____

5. Solve $5x^2 + 6x - 8 = 0$ by any method. Round your answers to the nearest tenth, if necessary.

_____

6. Write the function $g(x) = x^2 - 6x + 13$ in vertex form and list the transformations of the graph of $f(x) = x^2$ that give the graph of g. Then give the coordinates of the vertex and the equation of the axis of symmetry.

_____

_____

Mid-Chapter Assessment

Chapter 5 (Lessons 5.1–5.4)

Write the letter that best answers the question or completes the statement.

_____ 1. Which of the following is not a quadratic function?

    a. $f(x) = (x + 3)(2x + 4)$ **b.** $g(x) = 5(x - 9)$

    c. $h(x) = 8 - 3x^2$ **d.** $j(x) = (x + 5)^2 + 7$

_____ 2. Which of the following are the coordinates of the vertex of the graph of $f(x) = (x - 7)^2 + 2$?

    a. $(-7, -2)$ **b.** $(7, -2)$ **c.** $(-7, 2)$ **d.** $(7, 2)$

_____ 3. Which of the following is the missing length in this triangle?

    a. $x = 6$ **b.** $x = \sqrt{24}$

    c. $x = 12$ **d.** $x = \sqrt{306}$

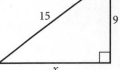

Solve each equation. Round your answers to the nearest hundredth, if necessary.

4. $8(x - 7)^2 = 200$ **5.** $\frac{4}{3}(x^2 + 12) - 25 = 11$

_____   _____

Factor each of the following expressions.

6. $x^2 - 4x - 45$ **7.** $49x^2 - 100$ **8.** $5x^2 + 11x - 12$

_____   _____   _____

9. Solve $x^2 - 13x + 42 = 0$ by factoring and applying the Zero-Product Property.

_____

10. Solve $2x^2 - 10x = 20$ by completing the square. Round your answers to the nearest tenth, if necessary.

_____

11. a. Does the graph of $f(x) = x^2 + 4x - 2$ open up or down? _____

    b. Write $f(x) = x^2 + 4 - 2$ in vertex form. Then write an equation for the axis of symmetry of the graph of f. _____

_____

Quick Warm-Up: Assessing Prior Knowledge
5.5 The Quadratic Formula

Solve each equation by factoring and then applying the Zero-Product Property.

1. $x^2 + 13x + 36 = 0$ _____ 2. $x^2 + 12x + 36 = 0$ _____

3. $x^2 = 4x + 21$ _____ 4. $2x^2 + 5x = 12$ _____

5. Solve $x^2 - 4x - 7 = 0$ by completing the square. Round to the

nearest tenth. _____

Lesson Quiz
5.5 The Quadratic Formula

Solve each equation by using the quadratic formula. Give exact and approximate answers to the nearest tenth.

1. $5x^2 - 9x + 3 = 0$ 2. $x^2 = 54 - 3x$

_____ _____

Find the equation of the axis of symmetry, the coordinates of the vertex, and the coordinates of the x-intercepts, if they exist, for each parabola.

3. $f(x) = 2x^2 - 3x - 14$ 4. $f(x) = x^2 + 8x + 17$

_____ _____

_____ _____

5. Chris is practicing long-range basketball shots. On one shot, the height of the basketball can be modeled by the function $h(t) = -16t^2 + 24t + 5$, where t is the number of seconds after the ball is released and $h(t)$ is the height in feet of the ball after t seconds. After how many seconds will the basketball reach a height of 10 feet? Round your answers to the nearest hundredth, if necessary.

_____

Quick Warm-Up: Assessing Prior Knowledge
5.6 *Quadratic Equations and Complex Numbers*

Use the quadratic formula to solve each equation.

1. $x^2 + 12x + 35 = 0$ _____

2. $x^2 + 81 = 18x$ _____

3. $x^2 + 4x - 9 = 0$ _____

4. $2x^2 = 5x + 9$ _____

Lesson Quiz
5.6 *Quadratic Equations and Complex Numbers*

Find the discriminant for each equation. Then write the number of real solutions for each equation.

1. $3x^2 - 12x + 12 = 0$

2. $8x^2 + 10x = 5$

3. $5x^2 = 6x - 2$

_____   _____   _____

4. Use the quadratic formula to solve the equation $2x^2 - 8x + 26 = 0$.

_____

Simplify each expression.

5. $(-5 + 7i) - (6 - 12i)$

6. $(4 + 5i)(2 - 3i)$

7. $\dfrac{2 + 6i}{3 - 4i}$

_____   _____   _____

8. a. Plot $-3 + 4i$ on the complex plane.

   b. Find $|-3 + 4i|$. _____

   c. Plot the conjugate of $-3 + 4i$ on the complex plane.

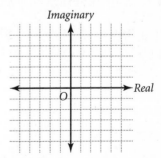

Quick Warm-Up: Assessing Prior Knowledge
5.7 Curve Fitting With Quadratic Models

1. Write the system of equations represented by $\begin{bmatrix} 2 & 2 \\ 1 & -3 \end{bmatrix}\begin{bmatrix} x \\ y \end{bmatrix} = \begin{bmatrix} 16 \\ -4 \end{bmatrix}$. _____

2. Write the matrix equation that represents $\begin{cases} x + y = 6 \\ 2x = 4 \end{cases}$. _____

3. Find the inverse of $\begin{bmatrix} -3 & 1 \\ 4 & -2 \end{bmatrix}$. _____

4. Solve $\begin{cases} x = 4 \\ -x + y = 5 \end{cases}$ by using a matrix inverse. _____

Lesson Quiz
5.7 Curve Fitting With Quadratic Models

1. Find a quadratic function whose graph contains the points $(-1, 13)$,

   $(1, -3)$, and $(3, 5)$. _____

2. Refer to the data in the table below.

x	1	2	3	4	5
y	-2	9	24	43	66

   a. Explain why a quadratic function provides a suitable model for

   the data. _____

   b. Find a quadratic function for y in terms of x. _____

   c. Use your function to predict y when $x = 12$. _____

3. The number of miles, M, that a car can travel on a gallon of gas
   depends on the average speed, v, of the car in miles per hour. A
   travel researcher has compiled the following data for his car.

v	44	50	53	56	60	70
M	35.9	37.5	38.0	38.3	38.4	37.1

   a. Find a quadratic model for M in terms of v. _____

   b. Use your model to predict M when $v = 65$. _____

Quick Warm-Up: Assessing Prior Knowledge

5.8 *Solving Quadratic Inequalities*

Solve each compound inequality. Graph the solution on a number line.

1. $-3p \le 6$ *and* $p - 3 \le 1$ _____

2. $5 + 2z < -1$ *or* $9z + 7 > 16$ _____

3. $8 \le 4t$ *or* $17 + 4t < 3 - 3t$ _____

Lesson Quiz

5.8 *Solving Quadratic Inequalities*

1. Solve $x^2 + 3x - 4 \le 0$. Graph the solution on the number line at right.

_____

2. Solve $3x^2 - 6x > 45$. Graph the solution on the number line at right.

_____

Solve each inequality.

3. $3(x - 7)^2 < 0$

4. $5(x - 4)^2 > 0$

_____   _____

5. Graph the solution to $y \le (x + 2)^2 - 5$.

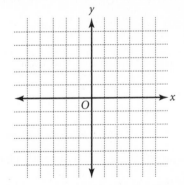

Chapter Assessment

Chapter 5, Form A, page 1

Write the letter that best answers the question or completes the statement.

_____ 1. The graph of which of the following quadratic functions opens down?

    a. $f(x) = -6 + 5x^2 - 8x$ **b.** $f(x) = 3(x - 3)^2 - 9$

    c. $f(x) = (5 + 2x)(3 - x)$ **d.** $f(x) = -3x(5 - x) + 7$

_____ 2. Find the solutions to the equation $2(x - 5)^2 + 7 = 79$.

    a. $x = 6$ or $x = -6$ **b.** $x = 31$ or $x = 41$

    c. $x = 11.56$ or $x = -1.56$ **d.** $x = 11$ or $x = -1$

_____ 3. Find the length of $\overline{BC}$.

    a. $\sqrt{500}$ meters

    b. $\sqrt{756}$ meters

    c. 14 meters

    d. 18 meters

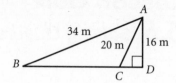

_____ 4. Factor $6x^2 - 17x + 12$.

    a. $(x + 6)(6x + 2)$ **b.** $(3x - 4)(2x + 3)$

    c. $(2x - 6)(3x - 2)$ **d.** $(2x - 3)(3x - 4)$

_____ 5. Factor $64x^2 - 49$.

    a. $(8x + 7)(8x - 7)$ **b.** $(8x - 7)(8x - 7)$

    c. $(-8x + 7)(-8x + 7)$ **d.** $(8x + 7)(8x + 7)$

_____ 6. Find the zeros of the quadratic function $f(x) = x^2 + 10x + 24$.

    a. 8 and 3   **b.** 5 and 2

    c. -12 and -2 **d.** -4 and -6

_____ 7. Which of the following completes the square for the expression $x^2 - 7x$?

    a. $\dfrac{7}{2}$ **b.** $\dfrac{49}{4}$ **c.** 49   **d.** -49

_____ 8. Find the equation of the axis of symmetry for the graph of
$f(x) = 3(x + 2)^2 - 5$.

    a. $x = -2$ **b.** $x = -3$ **c.** $x = -4$ **d.** $x = -5$

_____ 9. Find the vertex of $f(x) = 2x^2 - 20x + 18$.

    a. $(2, -20)$ **b.** $(-20, 18)$ **c.** $(5, -32)$ **d.** $(1, 9)$

_____ 10. Find the solutions to $3x^2 + 15x + 17 = 0$.

    a. $x = \dfrac{15 \pm \sqrt{429}}{6}$ **b.** $x = \dfrac{15 \pm \sqrt{765}}{6}$ **c.** $x = \dfrac{-15 \pm \sqrt{-429}}{6}$ **d.** $x = \dfrac{-15 \pm \sqrt{21}}{6}$

Chapter Assessment

Chapter 5, Form A, page 2

_____ 11. Find the discriminant for the equation $5x^2 = 3x - 7$.

    a. -131 b. -149 c. 131 d. 149

_____ 12. How many real solutions does the equation $36 = 24x - 4x^2$ have?

    a. 0 b. 1 c. 2 d. 3

_____ 13. Find the solutions to $2x^2 - 6x + 17 = 0$.

    a. $x = \dfrac{3}{2} \pm \dfrac{5}{2}i$ b. $x = 4$ or $x = -1$

    c. $x = \dfrac{6 \pm \sqrt{172}}{4}$ d. $x = 3 \pm 5i$

_____ 14. What is the complex conjugate of $-5 + 7i$?

    a. $5 - 7i$ b. $25 + 49i$ c. $-5 - 7i$ d. $7 - 5i$

_____ 15. Find the product $(3 + 6i)(4 - 7i)$.

    a. $12 - 42i$ b. $-30 + 45i$ c. $-44 - 45i$ d. $54 + 3i$

_____ 16. Find the quotient $\dfrac{4 + 6i}{2 - 3i}$.

    a. $-\dfrac{5}{26} - \dfrac{6}{13}i$ b. $2 - 2i$

    c. $-\dfrac{10}{13} + \dfrac{24}{13}i$ d. none of these

_____ 17. Which of the following is $|12 - 5i|$?

    a. 7 b. 13 c. 17 d. 60

_____ 18. Find the quadratic function whose graph contains the points $(1, -6)$, $(-2, 15)$, and $(3, 30)$.

    a. $f(x) = 2x^2 - 9x + 5$ b. $f(x) = 9x^2 - 2x - 5$

    c. $f(x) = 5x^2 - 9x - 2$ d. $f(x) = 5x^2 - 2x - 9$

_____ 19. Which of the following is the solution to the inequality $x^2 + 6x \geq 7$?

    a. $x \geq 7$ or $x \leq -1$ b. $x \leq -7$ or $x \geq 1$

    c. $x \leq 7$ and $x \geq -1$ d. $x \geq -7$ and $x \leq 1$

_____ 20. Which inequality is graphed at right?

    a. $y > (x - 3)^2 + 1$

    b. $y < (x + 3)^2 - 1$

    c. $y \geq (x - 3)^2 + 1$

    d. $y \leq (x + 3)^2 - 1$

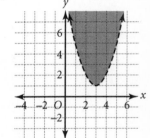

Chapter Assessment

Chapter 5, Form B, page 1

1. Solve $\frac{3}{5}(x^2 - 75) - 17 = 73$. _____

2. In the right triangle shown, find the length of the third side.

   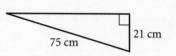

   75 cm   21 cm

   _____

Find the coordinates of the vertex and the equation of the axis of symmetry for each parabola.

3. $y = 5(x - 6)^2 + 12$

   _____

4. $y = 2x^2 + 12x + 10$

   _____

Find the *x*-intercepts for each parabola.

5. $y = 3x^2 - 9x + 12$

   _____

6. $y = 4x^2 + 7x - 15$

   _____

Simplify each expression.

7. $(5 + 3i)^2$

   _____

8. $\frac{2 + 5i}{6 - 8i}$

   _____

9. $2(4 + 3i) - (5 - 2i)$

   _____

Factor each expression.

10. $144x^2 - 25$

   _____

11. $x^2 - 3x - 40$

   _____

12. $3x^2 - 16x + 5$

   _____

13. Solve $3x^2 + 24x + 36 = 0$ by completing the square. _____

14. Write $f(x) = x^2 - 6x + 16$ in vertex form. _____

15. Find the discriminant and the number of real solutions for

   the equation $7x^2 = 10x - 9$. _____

Chapter Assessment

Chapter 5, Form B, page 2

Solve each equation by using the quadratic formula. Give exact answers and approximate answers to the nearest hundredth.

16. $5x^2 + 6x + 9 = 0$

17. $x^2 + 11 = 7x$

_____   _____

18. Find a quadratic model for y in terms of x that fits the data in the table below.

x	−1	1	2	4	7
y	−6	8	9	−1	−46

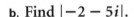

19. a. Graph $-2 - 5i$ on the complex plane.

   b. Find $|-2 - 5i|$.

_____

   c. Graph the conjugate of $-2 - 5i$ on the complex plane.

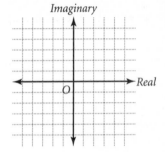

20. Solve $x^2 + 5x < 36$. Graph your answer on the number line at right.

_____

21. Graph $y \leq -2(x - 4)^2 - 1$.

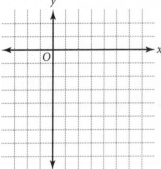

22. The manager of a factory has found that the output per worker at the factory can be modeled by the function $T(n) = -0.2n^2 + 8n - 24$, where n is the number of workers at the factory on a given day and $T(n)$ is the output per worker. Find the number of workers needed in order to maximize the output per worker. What is the maximum output per worker at this factory?

_____

Alternative Assessment

Graphs of Quadratic Functions, Chapter 5, Form A

TASK: Identify the transformations that result from changing the terms of a quadratic function.

HOW YOU WILL BE SCORED: As you work through the task, your teacher will be looking for the following:

- how well you can find the vertex and axis of symmetry for a quadratic function
- how well you can describe transformations of a quadratic function
- whether you can determine the values of x for which a quadratic function is increasing or decreasing

1. Find the coordinates of the vertex and the equation of the axis of symmetry for the graph of $f(x) = -(x - 2)^2 + 1$. Then find the x-intercepts, and explain how to find them.

_____

_____

2. Describe how you can obtain the graph of $g(x) = 3(x - 2)^2 + 1$ from the graph of $f(x) = 3x^2$.

_____

3. How does the graph of $f(x) = 4(x - 3)^2 + 1$ differ from the graph of $g(x) = 2(x - 3)^2 + 1$. Explain.

_____

_____

4. Compare the functions $f(x) = 2(x + 1)^2$ and $g(x) = -2(x + 1)^2$. For what values of x is f increasing and for what values of x is g increasing? For what values of x is f decreasing and for what values of x is g decreasing? Explain.

_____

_____

5. Create a quadratic function of the form $f(x) = ax^2$ that passes through the point $(1, 9)$.

_____

SELF-ASSESSMENT: Explain why the quadratic function is written in the form $f(x) = ax^2 + bx + c$, where $a \neq 0$.

Alternative Assessment
Writing a Quadratic Model, Chapter 5, Form B

TASK: Write a quadratic model that fits three data points from a real-world problem.

HOW YOU WILL BE SCORED: As you work through the task, your teacher will be looking for the following:

- whether you can find the quadratic model that fits three data points
- how well you can solve real-world problems

Different sizes of staples are used to hold together different amounts of paper. A $\frac{1}{4}$-inch staple can fasten about 30 sheets of paper, a $\frac{1}{2}$-inch staple can fasten about 100 sheets of paper, and a $\frac{5}{8}$-inch staple can fasten about 120 sheets of paper.

1. Explain why a quadratic function models this data.

   _____

   _____

2. Find the quadratic model that fits the points.

   _____

3. Find an approximation for the number of sheets that a $\frac{3}{8}$-inch staple can fasten. _____

4. According to this model, what is the maximum size for a staple? How many sheets of paper will this staple fasten?

   _____

   _____

5. Describe what restricted domain would be reasonable for this situation.

   _____

   _____

SELF-ASSESSMENT: Describe how you could check your solutions to this real-world problem.

Quick Warm-Up: Assessing Prior Knowledge
6.1 Exponential Growth and Decay

Write as a decimal.

1. 8% _____

2. 2.4% _____

3. 0.01% _____

Evaluate.

4. 3^6 _____

5. $3^4 \cdot 4^3$ _____

6. $24 \cdot 2^3$ _____

Lesson Quiz
6.1 Exponential Growth and Decay

Find the multiplier for each rate of exponential growth or decay.

1. 9% decay _____

2. 0.25% growth _____

3. In an experiment, bacteria are put into a petri dish and are allowed
to grow. The number of bacteria in the dish after n hours is found
to be $2000 \cdot 3^n$.

   a. How many bacteria were put into the dish at the beginning of the

   experiment? _____

   b. How fast is the population of bacteria growing? _____

   c. How many bacteria are in the dish after 5 hours? _____

4. The population of Rochester is 17,500 and is projected to grow at a
rate of 4.5% per decade.

   a. Write an expression for the projected population of Rochester

   after n decades. _____

   b. Predict the population, to the nearest hundred, of Rochester after

   40 years. _____

5. Pat bought a car for $9500. The salesperson projected that the value
of the car would decline by 20% per year for the next 5 years.

   a. Write an expression for the projected value of Pat's car after n years. _____

   b. Predict the value, to the nearest hundred dollars, of Pat's car after 5 years . _____

Quick Warm-Up: Assessing Prior Knowledge
6.2 Exponential Functions

Evaluate.

1. 3^4 _____

2. 3^0 _____

3. $(-4)^2$ _____

4. 4^{-2} _____

Evaluate each expression for $x = 2$.

5. x^5 _____

6. 5^x _____

7. 5^{-x} _____

8. $\left(\dfrac{1}{5}\right)^x$ _____

Lesson Quiz
6.2 Exponential Functions

Tell whether each function represents exponential growth or exponential decay, and give the *y*-intercept.

1. $f(x) = 5(1.2)^x$

2. $f(x) = 10(0.8)^x$

3. $f(x) = 7^{-x}$

_____   _____   _____

4. Find the final amount of a $1000 investment after 9 years at 8% interest compounded annually and compounded quarterly.

_____

5. Sam has a choice between an investment that pays 6% annual interest compounded monthly and an investment that pays 5.9% annual interest compounded daily. Which investment will earn Sam more money over the same period of time?

_____

6. A house was bought for $50,000 and was sold 15 years later for $95,000. Find the effective yield.

_____

7. Mal bought a computer for $4500. Mal sold the computer 4 years later for $1200. Use an exponential regression equation to find the percent by which the value of the computer declined per year.

_____

Quick Warm-Up: Assessing Prior Knowledge
6.3 Logarithmic Functions

Find the inverse of each function.

1. $f(x) = x + 10$ _____

2. $g(x) = 3x$ _____

3. $h(x) = 5x + 3$ _____

4. $j(x) = \frac{1}{4}x + 2$ _____

Lesson Quiz
6.3 Logarithmic Functions

Write each equation in logarithmic form.

1. $5^4 = 625$

_____

2. $9^{\frac{1}{2}} = 3$

_____

Write each equation in exponential form.

3. $\log_4 \frac{1}{64} = -3$

_____

4. $\log_2 64 = 6$

_____

Solve each equation for x. If necessary, round your answer to the nearest hundredth.

5. $10^x = 4720$ _____

6. $10^x = 0.01$ _____

7. $\log_g 1 = x$ _____

8. $\log_x 216 = 3$ _____

9. $\log_{64} x = \frac{1}{3}$ _____

10. $\log_2 128 = x$ _____

11. The pH of sea water is 8.5. What is the $[H^+]$ for sea water? _____

Quick Warm-Up: Assessing Prior Knowledge
6.4 *Properties of Logarithmic Functions*

Simplify each expression. Assume that no variable has a value of zero.

1. $z^3 \cdot z^4$ _____

2. $(t^3)^4$ _____

3. $\dfrac{c^5}{c^2}$ _____

4. $\left(\dfrac{m}{n}\right)^3$ _____

5. $(ab)^6$ _____

6. $(r^2s)^4$ _____

Lesson Quiz
6.4 *Properties of Logarithmic Functions*

Write each expression as a single logarithm. Then simplify, if possible.

1. $\log_4 a + \log_4 bc$

2. $\log_6 24 + \log_6 3 - \log_6 2$

Write each expression as a sum or a difference of logarithms. Then simplify, if possible.

3. $\log_5\left(\dfrac{m}{np}\right)$

4. $\log_3(27ab)$

Evaluate each expression.

5. $\log_{12} 12^8$

6. $\log_2 16^6$

7. $9^{\log_9 32}$

8. $7^{\log_7 12} + \log_2 64$

Solve for x.

9. $\log_8(3x - 7) = \log_8(48 - 8x)$

10. $\log_7(x^2 + 6x) = \log_7(4x + 15)$

Mid-Chapter Assessment
Chapter 6 (Lessons 6.1–6.4)

Write the letter that best answers the question or completes the statement.

_____ 1. What is the multiplier for a growth rate of 15%?

    a. 0.15   **b.** 1.15   **c.** 1.50   **d.** 15

_____ 2. Find the y-intercept of $f(x) = -5(0.7)^x$.

    a. $(0, 1)$ **b.** $(0, -1)$ **c.** $(0, 0.7)$ **d.** $(0, -5)$

_____ 3. What is another way to write $\log_3 a^2 b^3$?

    a. $2 \log_3 a + 3 \log_3 b$ **b.** $(2 \log_3 a)(3 \log_3 b)$

    c. $6 \log_3 ab$ **d.** $6 \log_3 a + 6 \log_3 b$

4. Write $\log_7 2401 = 4$ in exponential form. _____

5. Write $5^{-3} = \frac{1}{125}$ in logarithmic form. _____

Evaluate each expression.

6. $\log_8 64^7$ **7.** $5^{\log_5 17}$ **8.** $\log_5 10 + \log_5 50 - \log_5 4$

_____   _____   _____

9. Write $3(2 \log_9 a - 3 \log_9 b - \log_9 c)$ as a single logarithm. _____

Solve each equation for x. If necessary, round your answer to the nearest hundredth.

10. $10^x = 453{,}672$ **11.** $\log_2 x = 5$ **12.** $\log_x \frac{1}{8} = 3$

_____   _____   _____

13. $\log_2(2x) + \log_2 5 = \log_2(24 - 2x) - \log_2 3$ _____

14. Find the final amount of a $2000 investment after 7 years at 7.5%

interest compounded quarterly and monthly. _____

15. An antique was bought for $3000 and was sold 10 years later for

$6000. Find the effective yield. _____

16. The population of Knox is 48,500 and is declining at a rate of 2.5% per year.

    a. Write an expression for the projected population of Knox after n years. _____

    b. Predict the population of Knox, to the nearest hundred, after 8 years. _____

Quick Warm-Up: Assessing Prior Knowledge
6.5 Applications of Common Logarithms

Solve each equation for *x*. Round your answers to the nearest hundredth.

1. $10^x = 32$ _____

2. $10^x = 1.76$ _____

3. $10^x = \dfrac{1}{200}$ _____

Find the value of *v* in each equation.

4. $-3 = \log_{10} v$ _____

5. $2 = \log_v 49$ _____

6. $v = \log_{16} 4$ _____

Lesson Quiz
6.5 Applications of Common Logarithms

1. Suppose that a person is playing music at an intensity 32,000,000 times as loud as the threshold of sound. Find the relative intensity, *R*, of this music in decibels.

_____

Solve each exponential equation for *x*. Round your answers to the nearest hundredth.

2. $12^x = 400$

_____

3. $0.25^x = 10$

_____

4. $8^{x+5} = 120$

_____

5. $12 + 5(1.07^x) = 80$

_____

Evaluate each logarithmic expression. Round your answers to the nearest hundredth.

6. $\log_{15} 200$

_____

7. $\log_4\left(\dfrac{5}{2}\right)$

_____

Quick Warm-Up: Assessing Prior Knowledge
6.6 The Natural Base, e

Evaluate log x for each value.

1. $x = 10$ _____   2. $x = \frac{1}{10}$ _____   3. $x = -10$ _____   4. $x = 1$ _____

Find the final amount for each investment.

5. $1000 earning 4% annual interest compounded annually for 10 years _____

6. $1000 earning 4% annual interest compounded quarterly for 10 years _____

Lesson Quiz
6.6 The Natural Base, e

Evaluate $f(x) = e^x$ to the nearest thousandth for each value of x.

1. $x = 4.2$ _____   2. $x = -2.5$ _____

Evaluate $f(x) = \ln x$ to the nearest thousandth for each value of x.

3. $x = 650$ _____   4. $x = 0.075$ _____

Simplify each expression.

5. $e^{\ln 9.5}$ _____   6. $\ln e^{2a}$ _____

7. Suppose that $500 is invested at an annual interest rate of 6.8%.
   Find the final amounts of the investment after 10 years
   for interest compounded monthly and continuously.

   _____

8. How long does it take an investment to double at an annual interest
   rate of 9.2% compounded continuously? Round your answer to the
   nearest hundredth.

   _____

9. Bones found in an ancient cave contain 62% of their original
   amount of carbon-14. Use the equation $N(t) = N_0 e^{-0.00012t}$ to
   estimate the age of the bones.

   _____

Quick Warm-Up: Assessing Prior Knowledge
6.7 Solving Equations and Modeling

Solve each equation for *x*. Round your answers to the nearest hundredth if necessary.

1. $\log x = 3$ _____

2. $\log x = 0.477$ _____

3. $\ln x = 0$ _____

4. $\ln x = 1.61$ _____

5. $10^x = 0.1$ _____

6. $10^x = 8$ _____

7. $e^x = 1$ _____

8. $e^x = 8$ _____

Lesson Quiz
6.7 Solving Equations and Modeling

1. On the Richter scale, the magnitude, M, of an earthquake depends on the amount of energy, E, in ergs released by the earthquake according to the formula $M = \frac{2}{3} \log\left(\frac{E}{10^{11.8}}\right)$. Find the amount of energy released by an earthquake that measures 7.6 on the Richter scale.

_____

Solve each equation for *x*. If necessary, round your answers to the nearest hundredth.

2. $\log_2 x + \log_2(x - 2) = 3$

3. $7e^{5x+3} = 4900$

_____   _____

4. The population of Marshall County after n years can be predicted by using the function $P(n) = 52{,}000e^{0.013n}$. How long will it take for the population of Marshall County to reach 60,000?

_____

5. The net profit of a leading computer company is modeled by $p(x) = -7.84 \ln x + 3.35$, where x is the number of years after 1990 and $p(x)$ is the net profit in billions of dollars. What is the net profit for 1995?

_____

Chapter Assessment

Chapter 6, Form A, page 1

Write the letter that best answers the question or completes the statement.

_____ 1. Which of the following is not an exponential function?

    a. $f(x) = 5(2.7)^x$ **b.** $f(n) = 125e^{0.12n}$

    c. $f(x) = 7x^2$ **d.** $f(x) = 6.5\left(\frac{3}{4}\right)^{-x}$

_____ 2. Which of the following is a model for exponential decay?

    a. $f(x) = 0.8(3)^x$ **b.** $f(x) = 10\left(\frac{1}{3}\right)^{-x}$

    c. $f(x) = 5 + 3x^{-3}$ **d.** $f(x) = 15(0.7)^x$

_____ 3. The population of Starke County is 72,000 and is growing at a rate of 4.8% per decade. Which of the following is an expression for the population of Starke county after n decades?

    a. $72{,}000(1.48)^n$ **b.** $72{,}000(1.048)^n$

    c. $72{,}000(4.8)^n$ **d.** $72{,}000 + (4.8)^n$

_____ 4. Kim invests \$3000 at 7.8% annual interest compounded monthly. Find the final amount of Kim's investment after 15 years.

    a. \$9557.74   **b.** \$9593.62   **c.** \$9629.45   **d.** \$9665.98

_____ 5. Jamie invests \$800 at 8.2% annual interest compounded continuously. Find the final amount of Jamie's investment after 20 years.

    a. \$3869.32   **b.** \$4124.14   **c.** \$4356.63   **d.** \$4409.87

_____ 6. Which of the following is the logarithmic form of $3^5 = 243$?

    a. $\log_5 243 = 3$ **b.** $\log_{243} 5 = 3$

    c. $\log 243 = 5$ **d.** $\log_3 243 = 5$

_____ 7. Find the solution to the equation $\log_2 x = -4$.

    a. $x = -8$ **b.** $x = -16$ **c.** $x = \frac{8}{3}$ **d.** $x = \frac{1}{16}$

_____ 8. Find the solution to the equation $\log_x 8 = \frac{1}{3}$.

    a. $x = 512$ **b.** $x = 24$ **c.** $x = \frac{1}{8}$ **d.** $x = 2$

_____ 9. Find the value of the expression $\log_3 81 - \log_3\left(\frac{1}{9}\right)$.

    a. 2   **b.** 3   **c.** 6   **d.** 9

_____ 10. Find the approximate solution to the equation $3(1.5^x) + 10 = 280$.

    a. $x = 0.1$ **b.** $x = 11.1$ **c.** $x = 34.8$ **d.** $x = 60$

Chapter Assessment

Chapter 6, Form A, page 2

_____ 11. Find the value of the expression $\log_5 125^{-3}$.

    a. -9 b. -6 c. -1 d. $-\dfrac{3}{5}$

_____ 12. Find the value of the expression $e^{\ln 2.5}$.

    a. 30   b. 12.2   c. 2.5   d. 0.9

_____ 13. Find the approximate value of the expression $\log_{16} 160$.

    a. 0.54   b. 1.83   c. 2.20   d. 10

_____ 14. What is another way to write $4 \log_3 a + 3 \log_3(2b) - \log_3 m$?

    a. $\log_3\left(\dfrac{4a + 6b}{m}\right)$ b. $\log_3\left(\dfrac{24ab}{m}\right)$

    c. $\log_3\left(\dfrac{2a^4b^3}{m}\right)$ d. $\log_3\left(\dfrac{8a^4b^3}{m}\right)$

_____ 15. Find the solution to the equation $2 \log_a 3 + \log_a(x - 4) = \log_a(x + 8)$.

    a. $x = 7.2$ b. $x = 6.4$ c. $x = 5.5$ d. $x = 4$

_____ 16. Find the approximate solution to the equation $8.4 = \frac{3}{4} \log\left(\dfrac{x}{10^{2.4}}\right)$.

    a. 3.98×10^{13} b. 5.01×10^8

    c. $1.12 \times 10^{3.4}$ d. $6.3 \times 10^{2.4}$

_____ 17. Find the solution to the equation $\ln(x^2 + 3x) - \ln 10 = 0$.

    a. $x = 5$ or $x = -2$ b. $x = -5$ or $x = 2$

    c. $x = 5$ d. $x = 2$

_____ 18. The amount of a pollutant, measured in parts per million, in Pine Lake can be modeled by the function $A(t) = 14e^{-0.16t}$, where t is the number of years since a program to clean up the lake began. Approximately how long will it take for the amount of the pollutant in Pine Lake to reach 7 parts per million?

    a. 83.51 years   b. 12.52 years   c. 7.85 years   d. 4.33 years

_____ 19. The number of industrial jobs in Fulton County is decreasing by 9% per year. If there are 12,600 industrial jobs in Fulton County this year, estimate the number of industrial jobs, to the nearest hundred, in 10 years.

    a. 29,800   b. 11,300   c. 4900   d. 1300

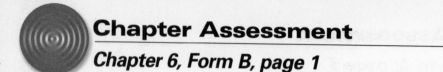

Chapter Assessment

Chapter 6, Form B, page 1

1. Write $4^5 = 1024$ in logarithmic form. _____

Evaluate each expression. If necessary, round your answer to the nearest tenth.

2. $\log_9 125$ _____   3. $5^{\log_5 7.2}$ _____   4. $\log_4 64^5$ _____

Write each expression as a single logarithm.

5. $3\log_7 x + 2\log_7(3y) + \log_7 w$

6. $3(\log_a n - 2\log_a m)$

_____   _____

7. Find the final amount of a $1500 investment after 25 years at 6.6% annual interest compounded quarterly and monthly.

_____

8. a. Find the final amount of a $200 investment after 18 years at

7.3% annual interest compounded continuously. _____

b. How long does it take for an investment to triple in value at an annual interest rate of 7.3% compounded continuously?

Round your answer to the nearest hundredth. _____

Solve each equation for x. If necessary, round your answers to the nearest hundredth.

9. $10^x = 8520$

_____

10. $14^x = 960$

_____

11. $\log_3 x = 6$

_____

12. $\log_x 5 = \frac{1}{4}$

_____

13. $\ln(5x - 3) + \ln 2 = \ln(24 - 2x)$

_____

14. $\log_5(3x + 10) - 3\log_5 4 = 2$

_____

15. $8 = 5 + 2\log\left(\frac{x}{4}\right)$

_____

16. $\log_6(x + 4) + \log_6(x - 1) = 2$

_____

Find the multiplier for each situation.

17. 24% growth _____   18. 0.8% decay _____

Chapter Assessment

Chapter 6, Form B, page 2

19. Find the y-intercept of the graph of $f(x) = -3(0.65)^{-x}$. _____

20. It cost Kurt $430 to maintain his car this year. Kurt's mechanic says that Kurt can expect his maintenance cost to increase by 15% per year for the next 8 years.

   a. Write a function for the maintenance cost per year for Kurt's

   car after n years. _____

   b. When will Kurt need to spend $1000 to maintain his car for the

   year? Round your answer to the nearest year. _____

   c. Use your function to predict how much it will cost Kurt to maintain

   his car in 8 years. _____

21. The managers of a lake resort decide to stock the lake with fish. The managers buy 3000 fish and put them into the lake. The fish suppliers tell the managers that the population of fish will decline by 9% per month for the next year.

   a. Write a function for the number of fish in the lake after n months.

   _____

   b. Predict the number of fish in the lake after 3 months. _____

   c. Predict how long it will be until half of the 3000 fish are left in the

   lake. Round your answer to the nearest tenth. _____

22. The remaining amount of a 100-milligram dose of a particular painkiller in a person's bloodstream after t hours can be modeled by the function $A(t) = 100e^{-0.21t}$.

   a. Find the remaining amount of the painkiller, to the nearest tenth

   of a milligram, after 4 hours. _____

   b. How long will it be until only 10 milligrams of the painkiller remain in the bloodstream? Round your answer to the nearest

   hundredth. _____

23. A vintage car was bought for $30,000 and was sold

   10 years later for $50,000. Find the effective yield. _____

Alternative Assessment

Exponential and Logarithmic Functions, Chapter 6, Form A

TASK: Identify the behavior of exponential functions and logarithmic functions by using inspection and graphing.

HOW YOU WILL BE SCORED: As you work through the task, your teacher will be looking for the following:

- whether you can identify an exponential growth or decay function
- how well you can describe the ways in which logarithmic functions and exponential functions are related

1. Graph $f(x) = 125\left(\frac{1}{5}\right)^x$.

2. What is the domain and range of this function?

_____

_____

3. Explain why f is an exponential function.

_____

_____

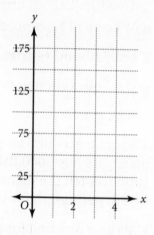

4. Describe how you can determine whether f is an exponential growth or decay function. _____

_____

5. Compare the graphs of $f(x) = \left(\frac{2}{3}\right)^x$ and $g(x) = \left(\frac{3}{2}\right)^x$. Describe how you can use the graph of f to graph g. _____

_____

6. Graph $f(x) = 3^{-x}$ and $g(x) = \log_{\frac{1}{3}} x$. Explain why the graphs are symmetrical with respect to the line $y = x$.

_____

_____

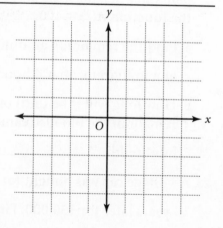

SELF-ASSESSMENT: Compare the graphs of linear, polynomial, and exponential functions. How are they alike? How are they different?

Alternative Assessment

Exponential and Logarithmic Equations, Chapter 6, Form B

TASK: Solve exponential and logarithmic equations.

HOW YOU WILL BE SCORED: As you work through the task, your teacher will be looking for the following:

- how well you can solve logarithmic and exponential equations by graphing
- whether you can solve logarithmic and exponential equations by using the Exponential-Logarithmic Inverse Properties

1. Describe how you would find the solution to $\log(x + 9) - \log x = 1$ by graphing. Then find the solution.

_____

_____

2. Solve $6^{x-1} = 216$. Describe how you can check your solution.

_____

_____

Solve each equation.

3. $\ln e^x = 2$

4. $\log x = \frac{1}{3} \log 27$

5. $2^{10-x} = 4^{2+x}$

_____   _____   _____

6. Solve $\log(3x + 1) - \log(2x + 3) = \log 2$ by graphing. Then solve the equation by using the Exponential-Logarithmic Properties. Explain the result.

_____

_____

_____

SELF-ASSESSMENT: For what values is $\log \frac{2x + 4}{3x}$ defined? For what values is the logarithm positive?

Quick Warm-Up: Assessing Prior Knowledge
7.1 An Introduction to Polynomials

Evaluate each expression for $x = -2$.

1. $-x + 1$ _____   2. $x^2 - 5$ _____   3. $-(x - 6)$ _____   4. $7 - x^3$ _____

Find the opposite of each expression.

5. $x - 3$ _____   6. $-x^2 + 5x + 1$ _____

Simplify each expression.

7. $8x - x$ _____   8. $(x + 5) + (2x + 3)$ _____

9. $(x + 9) - (4x + 6)$ _____   10. $(-x^2 - 2) - (x^2 - 2)$ _____

Lesson Quiz
7.1 An Introduction to Polynomials

Classify each polynomial by degree and number of terms.

1. $5x^5 + 2$ _____   2. $3 + 6x^2 - 3x^4$ _____

3. Evaluate $f(x) = 2x^3 + 4x^2 - 1$ for the given values of x.

a. $x = 2$ _____   b. $x = -3$ _____

4. Add $-5x^4 + 3x^2 - 6x$ and $3x^4 + 7x^3 - 9x + 4$. _____

5. Subtract $5x^2 + 7x - 8$ from $3x^2 - 4x + 5$. _____

Use a graphics calculator to graph each function. Describe the
general shape of the graph.

6. $f(x) = x^3 - x^2 - 6x + 1$ _____

7. $f(x) = x^4 - 6x^2 + 2$ _____

Quick Warm-Up: Assessing Prior Knowledge
7.2 *Polynomial Functions and Their Graphs*

Graph the function. Identify whether it has a maximum value or a minimum value, and approximate the coordinates of the vertex.

1. $g(x) = -3x^2 + 6x + 4$

_____

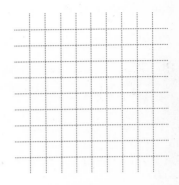

Lesson Quiz
7.2 *Polynomial Functions and Their Graphs*

1. Use a graphics calculator to graph $f(x) = x^4 - 4x^2 - 1$. Sketch the graph on the grid at right. Approximate the coordinates of any local maxima or minima to the nearest tenth. Then find the intervals for which the function is increasing and decreasing.

_____

_____

_____

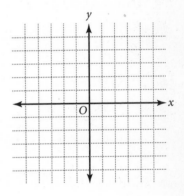

Describe the end behavior of each function.

2. $f(x) = 2 + 3x^2 - 2x^4$ _____

3. $g(x) = x^2 + x^5 - 4$ _____

4. Find a cubic regression model for the data in the table below.

x	-2	0	2	6	8
y	-25	-5	-9	7	75

_____

Quick Warm-Up: Assessing Prior Knowledge

7.3 Products and Factors of Polynomials

Factor each expression.

1. $6x^2 - 15x$

2. $x^2 + 3x - 28$

3. $x^2 - 64$

4. $4x^2 - 8x + 4$

5. $6x^2 - 5x - 6$

6. $16x^4 - 1$

Lesson Quiz

7.3 Products and Factors of Polynomials

1. Write $f(x) = (x - 4)(x^2 + 6x - 2)$ as a polynomial in standard form.

_____

Factor each polynomial expression.

2. $3x^3 - 9x^2 - 30x$

3. $x^3 + 343$

4. State whether each of the following binomials is a factor of
   $x^3 - 4x^2 - 4x + 16$.

   a. $x + 3$ _____

   b. $x - 4$ _____

5. Use long division to divide $x^3 + 7x^2 + 10x - 8$ by
   $x^2 + 3x - 2$.

6. Given that 2 is a zero of $P(x) = x^3 - x^2 - 14x + 24$,
   use synthetic division to factor $x^3 - x^2 - 14x + 24$.

Mid-Chapter Assessment

Chapter 7 (Lessons 7.1–7.3)

Write the letter that best answers the question or completes the statement.

_____ 1. Which of the following is not a polynomial?

     a. $\dfrac{x^2}{3} - 3x + 1$ b. $8 + 2x$

     c. $3^x + 3x + 2$ d. $1.5x^5 - 3.4$

_____ 2. The polynomial $6x + 5x^3 - 7x^5 + 9$ is

     a. quintic.   b. quartic.   c. cubic.   d. quadratic.

_____ 3. Which of the following is a factor of $3x^4 - 6x^3 - 15x^2 + 18x$?

     a. $x + 1$ b. $x - 4$ c. $x + 5$ d. $x + 2$

4. Describe the end behavior of $f(x) = 20 + x^4 - 144x^2$.

_____

5. Factor $27x^3 - 8$. _____

6. Use a graphics calculator to graph $f(x) = -2 + 6x + x^2 - x^3$. Sketch the graph on the grid at right. Approximate any local maxima or minima to the nearest tenth.

_____

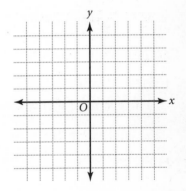

7. Find a quartic model for the data in the table below.

x	-2	0	1	3	4
y	74	-6	-10	84	410

_____

8. Divide by using long division.

    $(2x^3 + 11x^2 + 9x - 12) \div (x + 4)$

_____

9. Divide by using synthetic division.

    $(x^3 + 3x^2 - 5x - 15) \div (x + 3)$

_____

Quick Warm-Up: Assessing Prior Knowledge
7.4 Solving Polynomial Equations

Use factoring and the Zero-Product Property to solve each equation.

1. $x^2 - 5x - 14 = 0$ _____

2. $x^2 + 9x = 0$ _____

3. $x^2 - 121 = 0$ _____

4. $x^2 - 16 = 6x$ _____

5. Factor $2x^3 - 5x^2 - 7x$. _____

6. Find the quotient: $(x^3 - 2x^2 - 5x + 6) \div (x + 2)$ _____

Lesson Quiz
7.4 Solving Polynomial Equations

Use factoring to solve each equation.

1. $x^3 - 5x^2 - 14x = 0$

2. $5x^3 = 80x$

_____   _____

3. The graph of $f(x) = x^3 + 2x^2 - 5x - 6$ is shown at right.

   a. Write $x^3 + 2x^2 - 5x - 6$ in factored form.

   _____

   b. Find all solutions to $x^3 + 2x^2 - 5x - 6 = 0$.

   _____

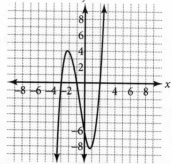

4. Use graphing, synthetic division, and factoring
   to find all the roots of $x^3 + 8x^2 + 5x - 50 = 0$.   _____

5. Use variable substitution and factoring
   to find all the roots of $x^4 - 12x^2 + 27 = 0$.   _____

Quick Warm-Up: Assessing Prior Knowledge

7.5 Zeros of Polynomial Functions

List all the factors of each number.

1. 21 _____   2. 60 _____

Solve each equation.

3. $x^2 - 4x + 2 = 0$ _____   4. $2x^2 + 3x - 5 = 0$ _____

State whether the given linear expression is a factor of the given polynomial.

5. $x^3 - 2x^2 - 5x + 6; x - 3$ _____   6. $3x^3 - 4x^2 - x + 5; x + 1$ _____

Lesson Quiz

7.5 Zeros of Polynomial Functions

1. Consider the equation $3x^3 - 18x^2 + 42x - 45 = 0$.

   a. List all possible rational roots of the equation.

   _____

   b. List all the actual rational roots of the equation. _____

2. Find all the zeros of $f(x) = 3x^3 + 27x^2 + 69x + 36$. _____

3. Find all the zeros of $f(x) = x^3 - 4x^2 + 9x - 10$. _____

4. The zeros of a third-degree polynomial, $P(x)$, are 5 (with a multiplicity of 2) and -2. In addition, $P(0) = 100$. Write $P(x)$ in factored form and in standard form.

   _____

5. The zeros of a third-degree polynomial, $P(x)$, with real-number coefficients include 4 and $2 + 5i$. In addition, $P(0) = -348$. Write $P(x)$ in factored form with real-number factors and in standard form.

   _____

Chapter Assessment

Chapter 7, Form A, page 1

Write the letter that best answers the question or completes the statement.

_____ 1. Which of the following is a quartic trinomial?

a. $4x^2 + 4x + 4$ b. $6x^4 - 5x^2$

c. $12x + 3x^4 - 25$ d. $3x^5 + 7x^4 + 6x^2$

_____ 2. Write $(2x^2 - 3x^4 - 6) - (5x^4 - 2x^2 + 4)$ in standard form.

a. $-3x^2 - x^4 - 10$ b. $4x^2 - 8x^4 - 10$

c. $-8x^4 - 4x^2 - 2$ d. $-8x^4 + 4x^2 - 10$

_____ 3. Write $(x - 3)(x + 2)^2$ in standard form.

a. $x^3 - x^2 + 8x - 12$ b. $x^3 - x^2 - 8x - 12$

c. $x^3 + x^2 - 8x + 12$ d. $x^3 + x^2 - 8x - 12$

_____ 4. Find the value of $\frac{2}{3}x^3 + \frac{3}{4}x^2 - 2x + 1$ when $x = -6$.

a. -104 b. -128 c. -158 d. 160

_____ 5. Which of the following is the end behavior of the graph of $f(x) = 3x^2 + 6 - 2x^5$?

a. The graph rises on the left and falls on the right.

b. The graph rises on the left and the right.

c. The graph falls on the left and the right.

d. The graph falls on the left and rises on the right.

_____ 6. Find the local minimum for $f(x) = x^3 - 5x^2 + 3x + 2$.

a. $(0.3, 2.5)$ b. $(0.3, -2.5)$ c. $(3, -7)$ d. $(-3, 7)$

_____ 7. Factor $8x^3 - 125$.

a. $(2x + 5)(4x^2 - 10x + 25)$ b. $(2x - 5)(4x^2 + 10x + 25)$

c. $(2x + 5)(4x^2 + 10x - 25)$ d. $(2x - 5)(4x^2 - 10x + 25)$

_____ 8. Find the remainder when $3x^3 - 9x^2 + 7x + 4$ is divided by $x - 3$.

a. -179 b. -17 c. 25   d. 142

_____ 9. Find the quotient when $4x^3 + 12x^2 - 14x + 8$ is divided by $x + 4$.

a. $4x^3 - 4x^2 + 2x$ b. $4x^2 + 4x - 2$

c. $4x^3 + 4x^2 - 2x$ d. $4x^2 - 4x + 2$

Chapter Assessment

Chapter 7, Form A, page 2

_____ 10. Find the quotient when $2x^3 + 5x^2 - 22x + 15$ is divided by $x^2 + 4x - 5$.

     a. $2x - 3$ b. $2x + 3$ c. $3x - 2$ d. $3x - 2$

_____ 11. Which of the following is not a factor of the polynomial function graphed at the right?

     a. x

     b. $x + 3$

     c. $x + 4$

     d. $x - 5$

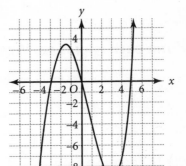

_____ 12. Find the solutions to the equation $8x^3 - 2x^2 - 43x + 30 = 0$.

     a. 2 and $\dfrac{3 \pm \sqrt{52}}{8}$ b. 2 and $\dfrac{2 \pm \sqrt{52}}{16}$

     c. $2, -\dfrac{5}{2},$ and $\dfrac{3}{4}$ d. 1, 2, and -3

_____ 13. Which of the following is a zero of the polynomial function graphed at the right?

     a. -3

     b. 3

     c. -6

     d. 6

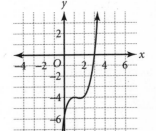

_____ 14. Find the zeros of the function $f(x) = x^3 + 6x^2 + 15x + 10$.

     a. $x = 1$ b. $x = -1$

     c. 1 and $\dfrac{-5 \pm \sqrt{15}}{2}$ d. -1 and $\dfrac{-5 \pm i\sqrt{15}}{2}$

_____ 15. If $P(x) = x^3 - 5x^2 + 24x - 20$ and one root of $P(x) = 0$ is $2 + 4i$, which of the following is another root?

     a. $2 - 4i$ b. $-2 - 4i$ c. $4 + 2i$ d. $4 - 2i$

_____ 16. Which of the following could not be a rational root of $12x^4 - 28x^3 + 13x^2 + 7x - 4 = 0$?

     a. 1   b. $\dfrac{4}{3}$ c. $\dfrac{3}{5}$ d. $\dfrac{1}{2}$

Chapter Assessment
Chapter 7, Form B, page 1

1. Classify $f(x) = 2x^5 + 6x^2 + 3$ by degree and number of terms. _____

2. Evaluate $f(x) = -\frac{3}{4}x^4 + \frac{5}{2}x^3 - \frac{5}{8}x^2 + 2$ when $x = -4$. _____

Perform each operation. Write your answer in standard form.

3. $(-4x^3 + 7x^2 - 3x - 2) - (6x^4 + 7x^3 - 5x^2 + 4)$ _____

4. $(x + 2)^2(x - 4)$ _____

Write in factored form.

5. $3x^3 - 6x^2 - 24x$

6. $x^3 + y^3$

7. $x^3 + 2x^2 - 19x - 20$

8. $125x^3 - 27$

9. Use a graphics calculator to graph $f(x) = x^4 - 2x^3 - 4x^2 + 6x + 5$. Sketch the graph on the grid at right. Approximate the coordinates of any local maxima and minima to the nearest tenth.

_____

_____

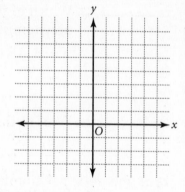

Describe the end behavior of the graph of each function.

10. $f(x) = 3x^2 + 4x^3 - 5x^4$ _____

11. $f(x) = -4x^7 + 6x^5 + 8x^3$ _____

12. Find the remainder when $P(x) = 2x^4 - 8x^3 - 3x + 7$ is divided by $x - 4$. _____

13. Find a cubic model for the data in the table below.

x	-2	0	2	4	6
y	-11	8	3	70	305

_____

Chapter Assessment

Chapter 7, Form B, page 2

14. Let $P(x) = x^3 - 3x^2 + 2$ and $Q(x) = x^2 - 6x + 11$.
Find all values of x such that $P(x) = Q(x)$. _____

Use synthetic division to find the quotient.

15. $(x^3 - 28x - 48) \div (x - 6)$

_____

16. $(x^4 + 6x^3 + 3x^2 - 23x - 12) \div (x + 4)$

_____

Use long division to find the quotient.

17. $(5x^3 - 17x^2 + 10x - 12) \div (x - 3)$

_____

18. $(3x^3 - 24) \div (x^2 + 2x + 4)$

_____

Find all roots to each equation.

19. $x^3 - 13x^2 + 56x - 78 = 0$

_____

20. $x^4 - 11x^2 + 18 = 0$

_____

21. List all possible rational zeros of the function $f(x) = 5x^7 - 7x^3 + 12x - 4$.

_____

22. Find all the zeros of the function $f(x) = 5x^3 + 14x^2 - 7x - 12$.

_____

23. A quadratic polynomial, $P(x)$, has zeros of -2 and 4. In addition,
$P(0) = 40$. Write $P(x)$ in factored form and in standard form.

_____

24. The zeros of a fourth-degree polynomial, $P(x)$, with real coefficients
include 3, with a multiplicity of 2, and $3 + 4i$. In addition,
$P(0) = 675$. Write $P(x)$ in factored form with real-number factors.

_____

Alternative Assessment

Exploring Polynomial Function Behavior, Chapter 7, Form A

TASK: Determine the basic shape of the graphs of polynomial functions of varying degrees.

HOW YOU WILL BE SCORED: As you work through the task, your teacher will be looking for the following:

- whether you can determine and classify the behavior of polynomials of varying degrees
- how well you can describe the behavior of polynomials of varying degrees

Let $f(x) = x^2(x + 2)$ and $g(x) = -x^2(x + 2)$.

1. What are the zeros and degree of f? What are the zeros and

   degree of g? _____

   _____

2. Where is f increasing? decreasing? What are its turning points?
   Where is g increasing? decreasing? What are its turning points?

   _____

   _____

3. Describe the effect of the sign of the leading coefficient of g on the

   shape of the graph of f. _____

Let $f(x) = x^4 - x^3 - 7x^2 + x + 6$.

4. Factor f into its linear factors by using its zeros. _____

5. Describe what happens at a turning point. Does f have any zeros

   that are turning points? _____

   _____

6. Describe what happens at a crossing point. How many crossing

   points does the graph of f have? _____

   _____

SELF-ASSESSMENT: Write an example of a third-degree polynomial in factored form that has two crossing-point zeros and no turning-point zeros.

Alternative Assessment

Factored Form of a Polynomial, Chapter 7, Form B

TASK: Write the factored form of a polynomial function.

HOW YOU WILL BE SCORED: As you work through the task, your teacher will be looking for the following:

- how well you can use the Factor Theorem to write a polynomial in factored form
- whether you can determine the number of complex zeros of a polynomial function
- how well you can write the factored form of a polynomial with complex component factors

1. Is $x(x - 1)(x + 2)(x - 3)$ the factored form of $f(x) = x^3 - 2x^2 - 5x + 6$?

   Why or why not? _____

   _____

2. Describe how you can determine whether $x + 2$ is a factor of $f(x) = 2x^4 - x^3 - 7x^2 + 6x$.

   _____

   _____

   _____

Write each function in factored form.

3. $f(x) = x^2 - x - 20$ _____ 4. $f(x) = 81x^3 - 16x$ _____

5. What is the relationship between the linear factors and the zeros of a polynomial?

   _____

   _____

6. The graph of the function $f(x) = x^3 - 3x^2 + x - 3$ intersects the x-axis at only one point. How many real and complex zeros does f have? What are the zeros of f? Graph f. Then write f in factored form with complex component factors.

   _____

   _____

SELF-ASSESSMENT: If the polynomial P is divided by $x - 2$, the degree of the quotient is 4, and the remainder is 3. What is the degree of P?

Quick Warm-Up: Assessing Prior Knowledge
8.1 *Inverse, Joint, and Combined Variation*

The variable *y* varies directly as *x*. Find the constant of variation, *k,*
and write an equation of direct variation that relates the two variables.

1. $y = -6$ when $x = 3$ 2. $y = 3$ when $x = -6$ 3. $y = 3.75$ when $x = 0.3$

_____   _____   _____

The variable *a* varies directly as *b*.

4. If *a* is 36 when *b* is −9, find *a* when *b* is 12. _____

5. If *a* is 36 when *b* is −9, find *b* when *a* is 12. _____

 # Lesson Quiz
8.1 *Inverse, Joint, and Combined Variation*

1. The variable *y* varies inversely as *x*, and $y = 80$ when $x = 25$.

   a. Find the constant of variation, and write an equation for the

     relationship. _____

   b. Find *y* when $x = 40$. _____

2. The variable *y* varies jointly as *x* and *z*, and $y = 50$ when $x = 20$ and
   $z = 5$.

   a. Find the constant of variation, and write an equation for the

     relationship. _____

   b. Find *y* when $x = 30$ and $z = 12$. _____

3. The variable *y* varies jointly as *x* and *z* and inversely as *w*. When
   $y = 120$, $x = 15$, $z = 16$, and $w = 3$.

   a. Find the constant of variation, and write an equation for the

     relationship. _____

   b. Find *y* when $x = 24$, $z = 20$, and $w = 8$. _____

4. A bicycle's pedal gear has 48 teeth and rotates at 50 revolutions per
   minute. A chain links the pedal gear to a rear-wheel gear that has
   20 teeth. How fast is the rear-wheel gear rotating? _____

Quick Warm-Up: Assessing Prior Knowledge

8.2 *Rational Functions and Their Graphs*

Solve each equation.

1. $x + 5 = 0$ _____

2. $5x = 0$ _____

3. $5x + 2 = 0$ _____

4. $x^2 - 5x = 0$ _____

5. $x^2 - 5x - 14 = 0$ _____

6. $x^3 + 3x^2 - 54x = 0$ _____

7. $-1 + 2x - x^2 = 0$ _____

Lesson Quiz

8.2 *Rational Functions and Their Graphs*

1. a. Find the domain of $f(x) = \dfrac{x + 1}{x^2 + 3x - 10}$. _____

   b. Find equations of all the vertical asymptotes of the graph of f. _____

Find the equations of all the horizontal asymptotes of the graph of each function.

2. $f(x) = \dfrac{x + 3}{x^2 + 1}$

3. $g(x) = \dfrac{3x^3 - 8}{5x - 6x^3}$

_____   _____

4. Sketch the graph of $f(x) = \dfrac{2x}{x - 3}$ showing all asymptotes.
   Write equations for the asymptotes.

   _____

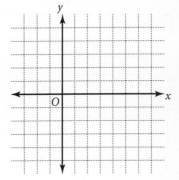

5. Where does the hole in the graph of $f(x) = \dfrac{(x + 2)(x - 5)}{(x + 3)(x - 5)(x - 2)}$

   occur? _____

Quick Warm-Up: Assessing Prior Knowledge

8.3 Multiplying and Dividing Rational Expressions

Evaluate.

1. $\dfrac{2}{3} \cdot \dfrac{3}{7}$ _____

2. $\dfrac{3}{4} \cdot \dfrac{8}{15}$ _____

3. $\dfrac{4}{9} \div \dfrac{5}{12}$ _____

4. $\dfrac{9}{10} \div \dfrac{3}{10}$ _____

Factor each expression.

5. $x^2 - 81$ _____

6. $x^2 - 16x - 36$ _____

Lesson Quiz

8.3 Multiplying and Dividing Rational Expressions

Simplify each expression.

1. $\dfrac{x^2 - 49}{x^2 - 5x - 14}$

2. $\dfrac{21x^2}{10} \cdot \dfrac{4}{x^4} \cdot \dfrac{5x^5}{7}$

3. $\dfrac{x - 1}{x^3(x + 3)} \cdot \dfrac{x(x + 3)}{(x + 2)(x - 1)}$

4. $\dfrac{x^2 + 3x}{x^2 - 6x + 8} \cdot \dfrac{x^2 - 7x + 12}{x^2 - 9}$

5. $\dfrac{8x^3}{x^2(x - 2)} \div \dfrac{5x}{3(x - 2)}$

6. $\dfrac{x^2 + 4x - 5}{x^3} \div \dfrac{x^2 + 7x + 10}{x^3 + 2x^2}$

7. $\dfrac{\dfrac{x^2 - 16}{x + 3}}{\dfrac{x - 4}{x^2 + 6x + 9}}$

8. $\dfrac{\dfrac{x^2 + 6xy + 5y^2}{x^2 + 4xy + 4y^2}}{\dfrac{x + y}{x + 2y}}$

9. $\dfrac{x^2 - 1}{x^2 + 2x + 1} \cdot \dfrac{1 + x}{1 - x}$

10. $\dfrac{x^3 - 6x^2 + 8x}{x^2 - 8x + 16} \div \dfrac{2x - 4}{10x^2 - 40x}$

NAME _____ CLASS _____ DATE _____

 Quick Warm-Up: Assessing Prior Knowledge

8.4 *Adding and Subtracting Rational Expressions*

Simplify.

1. $-\frac{5}{8} - \left(-\frac{1}{8}\right)$ _____

2. $-\frac{2}{3} + \frac{1}{9}$ _____

3. $\frac{1}{x} + \frac{1}{x}$ _____

4. $\frac{1}{2n} + \frac{1}{2n}$ _____

5. $\frac{1}{a} + \frac{1}{b}$ _____

6. $\frac{x}{y} + \frac{x}{y}$ _____

 Lesson Quiz

8.4 *Adding and Subtracting Rational Expressions*

Simplify each expression. Write your answer in simplest form.

1. $\frac{3x - 7}{3x + 5} + \frac{4x - 3}{3x + 5}$

2. $\frac{3x}{x - 4} - \frac{12}{x - 4}$

3. $\frac{3}{x + 3} + \frac{2}{x}$

4. $\frac{7}{x + 3} - \frac{x - 9}{x^2 + 5x + 6}$

5. $\frac{3x}{x + 5} + \frac{5x}{2x - 3}$

6. $\frac{2}{1 + \frac{1}{x}} + \frac{3}{1 - \frac{1}{x}}$

7. $\frac{3x + 1}{x - 2} - \frac{4x + 1}{x - 3}$

8. $\frac{x}{x - y} - \frac{2x}{x + y} - \frac{2xy}{x^2 - y^2}$

9. $\dfrac{\dfrac{1}{x - y} - 1}{2 - \dfrac{x}{x - y}}$

10. $\dfrac{1}{\dfrac{1}{x} + \dfrac{1}{y} + \dfrac{1}{z}}$

NAME _____ CLASS _____ DATE _____

Mid-Chapter Assessment

Chapter 8 (Lessons 8.1–8.4)

Write the letter that best answers the question or completes the statement.

_____ 1. If y varies inversely as x and $y = 20$ when $x = 10$, then find the constant of variation.

    a. $k = 200$ b. $k = 10$ c. $k = 2$ d. $k = \frac{1}{2}$

_____ 2. Find the equation of the horizontal asymptote of the graph of $f(x) = \frac{4x}{2x^2 - 2x + 4}$.

    a. $y = 2$ b. $y = -2$ c. $y = 0$ d. $x = 0$

_____ 3. Where does the hole in the graph of $f(x) = \frac{x^2 + 6x + 8}{x^2 - 2x - 8}$ occur?

    a. $x = 1$ b. $x = -2$ c. $x = -3$ d. $x = 4$

_____ 4. Which of the following is the simplest form of $\frac{4x + 1}{4x + 3} - \frac{2x - 8}{4x + 3}$?

    a. $\frac{2x - 7}{4x + 3}$ b. $\frac{x + 3}{2x + 1}$

    c. $\frac{x - 7}{2x + 3}$ d. $\frac{2x + 9}{4x + 3}$

5. Sketch the graph of $f(x) = \frac{-3x + 1}{x + 2}$, showing all asymptotes. Write equations of the asymptotes.

_____

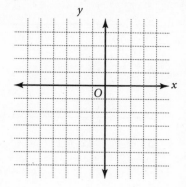

6. If y varies jointly as x and z and $y = 100$ when $x = 5$ and $z = 4$, find y when $x = 15$ and $z = 6$.

_____

7. Find the domain of $f(x) = \frac{3x + 5}{x^2 + 3x - 18}$. _____

Simplify.

8. $\frac{x^2 - 36}{x^2 + 6x} \div \frac{x^2 - 4x - 12}{x^3 + 4x^2}$

9. $\frac{3}{x^2 + 2x} + \frac{5x}{x^2 - 4}$

_____   _____

Quick Warm-Up: Assessing Prior Knowledge

8.5 *Solving Rational Equations and Inequalities*

Solve.

1. $-6 < 8c$ _____

2. $-2r \geq 15$ _____

3. $x^2 + 5x - 36 = 0$ _____

4. $3x^2 - 4 = x$ _____

5. $\dfrac{16}{5} = \dfrac{m}{3}$ _____

6. $\dfrac{15}{g} = \dfrac{2.5}{4}$ _____

7. $\dfrac{5}{4} = \dfrac{3}{2a}$ _____

8. $\dfrac{1}{x} + \dfrac{1}{2x} = \dfrac{1}{3}$ _____

Lesson Quiz

8.5 *Solving Rational Equations and Inequalities*

1. Sam is taking a trip that consists of 192 miles on highways and 48 miles in towns. Sam is able to drive twice as fast on the highway as in towns. Write a rational function to represent the total time, T, in hours that Sam needs to complete the trip in terms of his speed in towns, x, in miles per hour.

_____

Solve each equation or inequality. Check your answers.

2. $\dfrac{x + 3}{8} = \dfrac{3x - 5}{4}$

3. $\dfrac{2}{x - 2} + \dfrac{x}{x + 4} = \dfrac{24}{x^2 + 2x - 8}$

4. $\dfrac{3x}{x - 2} > 6$

5. $\dfrac{x - 2}{x + 2} < \dfrac{x}{x - 2}$

6. $\dfrac{3x + 1}{2} - \dfrac{3x - 4}{3} = \dfrac{3x + 1}{4}$

7. $\dfrac{x - 1}{2} - \dfrac{3x - 4}{2} = \dfrac{5x - 3}{8}$

8. $\dfrac{x - 2}{x + 2} < 3$

9. $\dfrac{2x}{x + 2} - \dfrac{x}{x - 3} < \dfrac{9}{x^2 - x - 6}$

Quick Warm-Up: Assessing Prior Knowledge

8.6 Radical Expressions and Radical Functions

Identify each transformation of the parent function $f(x) = x^2$.

1. $f(x) = x^2 + 5$ _____

2. $f(x) = (x + 5)^2$ _____

3. $f(x) = 5x^2$ _____

4. $f(x) = -5x^2$ _____

5. $f(x) = (5x)^2$ _____

6. $f(x) = \left(\frac{1}{5}x\right)^2$ _____

Lesson Quiz

8.6 Radical Expressions and Radical Functions

1. Find the domain of $f(x) = \sqrt{3x + 6}$. _____

For each function, describe the transformations applied to
$f(x) = \sqrt{x}$.

2. $f(x) = 3\sqrt{x - 4} - 2$

_____

_____

3. $g(x) = \sqrt{2x + 6} + 5$

_____

_____

4. Find the inverse of $y = x^2 + 3$. Then graph the function and
its inverse on the same set of axes.

_____

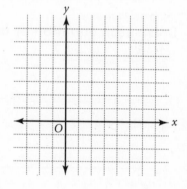

Evaluate each expression. Give exact answers.

5. $12 - 4\sqrt[3]{125}$

_____

6. $-3\left(\sqrt[3]{-27}\right)^2 + 10$

_____

Quick Warm-Up: Assessing Prior Knowledge
8.7 Simplifying Radical Expressions

Evaluate each expression.

1. $36^{\frac{1}{2}}$ _____

2. $-125^{\frac{2}{3}}$ _____

Simplify each expression.

3. $(ab^4)(a^2b)$ _____

4. $(m^2n)^3$ _____

5. $\dfrac{r^2s^3}{r^5s}$ _____

6. $\left(\dfrac{cd^2}{c^4d^3}\right)^2$ _____

7. $(2x-1)(3x+2)$ _____

Lesson Quiz
8.7 Simplifying Radical Expressions

Simplify each expression.

1. $\sqrt{81x^4y^9z^2}$

2. $\sqrt[3]{-125x^9y^8z^4}$

Simplify each expression. Assume that the value of each variable is positive.

3. $(20x^3y)^{\frac{1}{2}}\sqrt{5x^4y}$

4. $\dfrac{12\sqrt[3]{24x^8y^6}}{3(3x^2y^2)^{\frac{1}{3}}}$

5. $\left(10+\sqrt{20}\right)-\left(4-\sqrt{45}\right)$

6. $\left(5+3\sqrt{7}\right)\left(-4+5\sqrt{7}\right)$

Write each expression with a rational denominator.

7. $\dfrac{3}{\sqrt{5}}$

8. $\dfrac{4}{2-\sqrt{6}}$

Quick Warm-Up: Assessing Prior Knowledge

8.8 *Solving Radical Equations and Inequalities*

Solve.

1. $2(a + 9) = 10$

2. $6 - t = t - 3$

3. $y^2 + 4y = 0$

_____

_____

_____

4. $m^2 - 2m - 15 = 0$

5. $x^2 + 2x = 4x + 7$

6. $\dfrac{2}{x - 1} + \dfrac{x}{x + 1} = \dfrac{4}{x^2 - 1}$

_____

_____

_____

Lesson Quiz

8.8 *Solving Radical Equations and Inequalities*

Solve each equation for *x*. Check your solutions.

1. $5\sqrt{x - 12} = 30$

2. $\sqrt[3]{5x + 12} = \sqrt[3]{3x + 18}$

_____

_____

3. $\sqrt{3x + 1} + 1 = x$

4. $\sqrt{2x + 3} = \sqrt{x + 1} + 1$

_____

_____

5. $\sqrt{4x^2 - 1} = 2x + 3$

6. $\sqrt{x + 4} + \sqrt{x - 4} = 4$

_____

_____

Solve each inequality for *x*. Check your solutions.

7. $5 \le \sqrt{4x - 3}$

8. $2\sqrt[3]{4x - 3} > x$

_____

_____

9. $6 - \sqrt{2x + 1} < 3$

10. $\sqrt{x + 9} - \sqrt{x} > \sqrt{3}$

_____

_____

11. $\sqrt{x - 5} - \sqrt{x + 7} \le 4$

12. $\sqrt{x + 5} + \sqrt{x + 10} > 2$

_____

_____

Chapter Assessment

Chapter 8, Form A, page 1

Write the letter that best answers the question or completes the statement.

_____ 1. If y varies jointly as x and z and $y = 144$ when $x = 8$ and $z = 4$, then find the constant of variation.

    a. $k = 22.5$ **b.** $k = 18$ **c.** $k = 12$ **d.** $k = 4.5$

_____ 2. Which function is graphed at right?

    a. $f(x) = \dfrac{5x}{x-3}$

    b. $f(x) = \dfrac{5x}{x+3}$

    c. $f(x) = \dfrac{5}{x-3}$

    d. $f(x) = \dfrac{5}{x+3}$

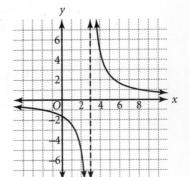

_____ 3. Where does the hole in the graph of $f(x) = \dfrac{x^2 - 2x - 3}{x^2 + 2x - 15}$ occur?

    a. $x = -1$ **b.** $x = 3$ **c.** $x = -5$ **d.** $x = 15$

_____ 4. Find the equation of the horizontal asymptote of $f(x) = \dfrac{3 + 2x^2 + 5x^3}{3x^3 - 8x}$.

    a. $y = 0$ **b.** $y = \dfrac{5}{8}$ **c.** $y = 1$ **d.** $y = \dfrac{5}{3}$

_____ 5. Which of the following is the simplest form of $\dfrac{5x}{x^4} \cdot \dfrac{4x^5}{8x^2} \cdot \dfrac{x^6}{2}$?

    a. $4x^2$ **b.** $\dfrac{5x^2}{4}$ **c.** $\dfrac{5x^5}{4}$ **d.** $\dfrac{5x^6}{4}$

_____ 6. Which of the following is the simplest form of $\dfrac{x^2 + 2x}{x^2 - 9} \div \dfrac{x^2}{x^2 + 5x + 6}$?

    a. $\dfrac{(x+2)^2}{x(x-3)}$

    b. $\dfrac{x^3}{(x-3)(x+3)^2}$

    c. $\dfrac{10x + 6}{-9}$

    d. $-\dfrac{4}{3}$

_____ 7. Write $\dfrac{5}{\sqrt{7} + 2}$ with a rational denominator.

    a. $\dfrac{5\sqrt{7}}{9}$ **b.** $\dfrac{5\sqrt{7} - 10}{3}$ **c.** $\dfrac{5\sqrt{7} + 10}{3}$ **d.** $\dfrac{5\sqrt{7} - 10}{9}$

_____ 8. If y varies inversely as x and $y = 12$ when $x = 3$, find x when $y = 18$.

    a. $x = 1.5$ **b.** $x = 2$ **c.** $x = 36$ **d.** $x = 45$

_____ 9. Which of the following is the simplest form of $\sqrt[3]{-64x^5 y^{12}}$?

    a. $-4x^2 y^4$ **b.** $-4|x|y^4\sqrt[3]{x}$ **c.** $-4xy^4\sqrt[3]{x^2}$ **d.** $-4xy^3\sqrt[3]{2xy}$

Chapter Assessment

Chapter 8, Form A, page 2

_____ 10. Which of the following is the simplest form of $\dfrac{5}{x+2} - \dfrac{8}{x+4}$?

    a. $\dfrac{-3x+36}{x^2+6x+8}$ **b.** $\dfrac{-3x+4}{x^2+6x+8}$ **c.** $\dfrac{-5}{x+4}$ **d.** $\dfrac{-3x+4}{x^2+8}$

_____ 11. If the value of each variable is positive, then which of the following is the

    simplest form of $\dfrac{(36x^7y^9)^{\frac{1}{2}}}{\sqrt{2x^2y^3}}$?

    a. $18x^5y^6$ **b.** $3x^2y\sqrt{xy}$ **c.** $3x^4y^2\sqrt{2xy}$ **d.** $3x^2y^3\sqrt{2x}$

_____ 12. Multiply $(3 + \sqrt{6})(4 - 2\sqrt{6})$.

    a. $-2\sqrt{6}$ **b.** $12 - 2\sqrt{12}$ **c.** $24 - 2\sqrt{6}$ **d.** 0

_____ 13. Which of the following is the domain of $f(x) = \sqrt{x^2 - 4}$?

    a. $x \geq 4$ **b.** $-2 \leq x \leq 2$ **c.** $x \leq -2 \text{ or } x \geq 2$ **d.** $x \leq 2$

_____ 14. Which transformation was not applied to $f(x) = \sqrt{x}$ to obtain
    $f(x) = -3\sqrt{2(x+3)}$?

    a. reflection across the x-axis   **b.** vertical translation of 3 units up

    c. vertical stretch by a factor of 3   **d.** horizontal compression by a factor
    of $\frac{1}{2}$

_____ 15. Which of the following is the solution to the equation $\dfrac{x+3}{x} - \dfrac{7}{x+2} = \dfrac{14}{x^2+2x}$?

    a. $x = 4$ **b.** $x = -10$ **c.** $x = 4 \text{ or } x = -2$ **d.** $x = -10 \text{ or } x = 2$

_____ 16. Which of the following is the solution to the equation $\sqrt{x + 17} + 3 = x$?

    a. $x = 8$ **b.** $x = -17$ **c.** $x = 3 \text{ or } x = -17$ **d.** $x = 8 \text{ or } x = -1$

_____ 17. Which of the following is the solution to the inequality $\dfrac{15}{x+4} > 3$?

    a. $-4 < x < 1$ **b.** $x < -4$ **c.** $x > 1 \text{ or } x < -4$ **d.** $x > 1$

_____ 18. Which of the following is the solution to the inequality $4 < \sqrt{2x + 6}$?

    a. $-3 < x < 5$ **b.** $x < -3$ **c.** $x < -3 \text{ or } x > 5$ **d.** $x > 5$

_____ 19. If a motorcycle driver travels 40 miles at m miles per hour and then 50 miles at
    $m + 10$ miles per hour, find the average speed, $s(m)$.

    a. $s(m) = \dfrac{40}{m} + \dfrac{50}{m+10}$ **b.** $s(m) = \dfrac{9m^2 + 90m}{9m + 40}$

    c. $s(m) = \dfrac{8100m + 3600}{m^2 + 10m}$ **d.** $s(m) = \dfrac{90}{m^2 + 10m}$

Chapter Assessment

Chapter 8, Form B, page 1

1. If y varies inversely as x and $y = 15$ when $x = 24$, find the constant of variation. Then find y when $x = 9$.

_____

2. Write the equations of all asymptotes of the graph of the function
$f(x) = \dfrac{x^2 + 7x + 10}{4x^2 - 9}$.

_____

3. Graph $f(x) = \dfrac{x^2 + 5x + 6}{x + 3}$ on the grid at right.

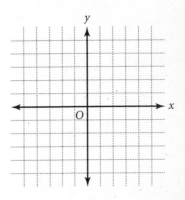

Simplify each expression.

4. $\left(3 + 2\sqrt{5}\right)\left(2 - 3\sqrt{5}\right) + \left(15 + \sqrt{20}\right)$

5. $\sqrt[3]{27x^8y^{15}}$

_____

6. $\dfrac{x^2 + 7x + 10}{x^2 - 6x} \div \dfrac{x^3 - 4x}{x^2 - 8x + 12}$

7. $\dfrac{3x}{2x + 1} - \dfrac{5}{3x + 2}$

_____

8. $\dfrac{\dfrac{x + 2}{x^2 + 9x + 20}}{\dfrac{x + 2}{x + 5}}$

9. $\dfrac{\left(24x^8y^6\right)^{\frac{1}{2}}}{\sqrt{3x^2y^4}}$

_____

10. Describe the transformations applied to $f(x) = \sqrt{x}$ in order to obtain $g(x) = 5\sqrt{-3(x + 2)} - 4$.

_____

_____

_____

Chapter Assessment

Chapter 8, Form B, page 2

Find the domain of each function.

11. $f(x) = \dfrac{3x^2 + 8x + 12}{x^2 - 3x - 28}$

12. $g(x) = \sqrt{4x - 2}$

_____   _____

13. Evaluate $-5\left(\sqrt[4]{81}\right)^3 + 25$. Give an exact answer. _____

14. Write $\dfrac{5}{4 - \sqrt{10}}$ with a rational denominator. _____

Solve each equation.

15. $\dfrac{5x + 4}{5} = \dfrac{12 - 2x}{6}$

16. $\sqrt[3]{5x - 8} = \sqrt[3]{12 - 3x}$

_____   _____

17. $1 + \dfrac{4}{x} = \dfrac{12}{x^2}$

18. $\sqrt{2x - 3} = x - 3$

_____   _____

19. $\dfrac{2}{x + 7} + \dfrac{5}{x - 7} = \dfrac{x^2 + 3}{x^2 - 49}$

20. $\sqrt{2x + 1} = \sqrt{x + 7}$

_____   _____

Solve each inequality.

21. $\dfrac{4x}{3x - 6} < 2$

22. $6 > \sqrt{9 - 3x}$

_____   _____

23. Find the inverse of the function $f(x) = x^2 + 3x$. _____

24. The amount of interest earned by a bank account varies jointly as
the amount left in the account and the time for which it is left in
years. If $400 is left in the account for 3 years and earns $90 in
interest, find the amount of interest earned if $500 is left in the
account for 8 years.

_____

25. Construct a rational function with horizontal asymptote $y = 2$ and
vertical asymptote $x = -2$.

_____

Alternative Assessment

Reciprocals of Polynomial Functions, Chapter 8, Form A

TASK: Graph the reciprocals of polynomial functions.

HOW YOU WILL BE SCORED: As you work through the task, your teacher will be looking for the following:

- whether you can describe how to graph reciprocal functions as transformations
- whether you can identify characteristics of a reciprocal function

1. Explain how you can determine the horizontal and vertical asymptotes of $f(x) = \frac{1}{x + 2}$ without graphing.

_____

_____

2. Sketch the graphs of $f(x) = \frac{2x - 5}{x - 3}$ and $g(x) = 2 + \frac{1}{x - 3}$ on the same coordinate plane. Describe how the graphs are related. How can you determine the asymptotes of f by using g?

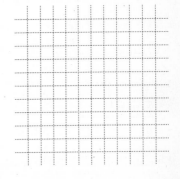

_____

_____

_____

_____

3. Graph the functions $p(x) = x^2 - 2x - 3$ and $q(x) = \frac{1}{x^2 - 2x - 3}$ on the grid at right.

4. What are the zeros of p and the vertical asymptotes of q? What is the domain of q?

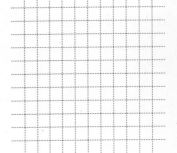

_____

_____

SELF-ASSESSMENT: Create a quadratic function. Find the inverse relation or inverse function. Find the reciprocal function. How are they alike? How are they different?

Alternative Assessment

Solving Rational Equations, Chapter 8, Form B

TASK: Solve rational equations.

HOW YOU WILL BE SCORED: As you work through the task, your teacher will be looking for the following:

- how well you can solve rational equations by graphing
- whether you can solve rational equations by algebraic means

1. Describe how to solve $\frac{x-3}{x} = \frac{x-4}{x-2}$ by graphing. Then find the solution.

_____

_____

2. Describe how to solve $\frac{1}{x^2} + \frac{4}{x} + 1 = 6$ by algebraic means. Find the possible solutions. Explain why it is important to check the possible solutions.

_____

_____

3. Solve $\frac{2x+3}{x-1} - \frac{2x-3}{x+1} = \frac{10}{x^2-1}$ by algebraic means. Then solve the equation by graphing. Compare the two methods.

_____

_____

Let $f(x) = \frac{2x+1}{3x}$ and $g(x) = \frac{x-1}{3x}$.

4. Give the domains for f and g.

_____

5. Find $f + g$ in simplified form. Then use a graphics calculator to graph $h(x) = f(x) + g(x)$. Describe what you notice about the domain of h. Explain.

_____

_____

_____

SELF-ASSESSMENT: Construct a rational function that has a hole in its graph at $x = 2$.

Quick Warm-Up: Assessing Prior Knowledge
9.1 Introduction to Conic Sections

Solve each equation for *y*.

1. $3x + y = 7$ _____

2. $6x + 3y = -15$ _____

3. $2x - 2y = 8$ _____

Solve each equation for *x*.

4. $x^2 = 16$ _____

5. $x^2 = 7$ _____

6. $x^2 - 4 = 11$ _____

Find the unknown lengths. Round your answers to the nearest hundredth.

7.

_____

8.

_____

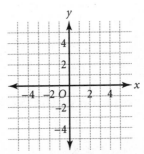

Lesson Quiz
9.1 Introduction to Conic Sections

1. Graph $x^2 + y^2 = 9$.

Find *PQ* and the coordinates of *M*, the midpoint of $\overline{PQ}$. When appropriate, give exact answers and approximate answers to the nearest hundredth.

2. $P(3, 7)$ and $Q(15, 12)$

3. $P(-4, 7)$ and $Q(-8, -3)$

_____   _____

4. One endpoint of $\overline{PQ}$ is $P(2, 3)$ and the midpoint, *M*, is $(6, 8)$. Find the coordinates of Q.

_____

5. The endpoints of the diameter of a circle have coordinates $A(4, 1)$ and $B(12, 7)$. Find the center, radius, and circumference of the circle.

_____

Quick Warm-Up: Assessing Prior Knowledge
9.2 Parabolas

The graph of each function given below is a parabola. For each parabola, find an equation for the axis of symmetry and the coordinates of the vertex, state whether the parabola opens up or down, and whether the y-coordinate of the vertex is the minimum or maximum value of the function.

1. $f(x) = -x^2$ _____

2. $f(x) = x^2 - 4x$ _____

3. $f(x) = 3 - 8x - 4x^2$ _____

Lesson Quiz
9.2 Parabolas

1. Graph $x = \frac{1}{12}y^2$. Write the coordinates of the focus and the equation of the directrix.

_____

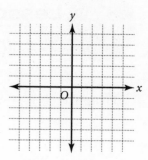

Write the standard equation of the parabola with the following characteristics.

2. focus: $(0, 0)$; directrix: $x = 4$

3. focus: $(2, 1)$; vertex: $(2, -3)$

_____   _____

4. Graph $x^2 - 6x - 8y - 7 = 0$. Write the coordinates of the vertex and the focus and the equation of the directrix.

_____

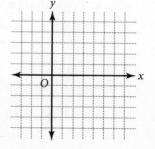

Quick Warm-Up: Assessing Prior Knowledge
9.3 Circles

Find the distance between *P* and *Q*.

1. $P(-4, 10)$ and $Q(5, -2)$ _____

2. $P(1, 2)$ and $Q(3, 5)$ _____

Solve by completing the square.

3. $x^2 - 4x = 12$ _____

4. $x^2 + 6x + 1 = 0$ _____

Graph each equation on your own paper and identify the conic section.

5. $x^2 + 9y^2 = 9$ _____

6. $x^2 + y^2 = 49$ _____

Lesson Quiz
9.3 Circles

1. Write an equation for the circle whose center is at the origin and whose radius is 6. Graph the circle.

_____

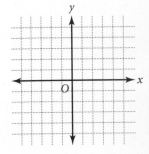

2. Write the standard equation for the circle graphed at right.

_____

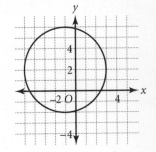

3. Write the standard equation for the circle defined by $x^2 - 8x + y^2 + 6y - 24 = 0$. Give the radius and the coordinates of the center of the circle.

_____

Mid-Chapter Assessment
Chapter 9 (Lessons 9.1–9.3)

Write the letter that best answers the question or completes the statement.

_____ 1. Find the length of the segment with endpoints $P(3, -8)$ and $Q(7, -2)$.

    a. $\sqrt{52}$ b. 52 c. $\sqrt{116}$ d. 116

_____ 2. Find the midpoint of the segment with endpoints $P(-12, 8)$ and $Q(-6, -2)$.

    a. $(-2, -4)$ b. $(-3, 5)$ c. $(-9, 3)$ d. $(-18, 6)$

_____ 3. Find the standard equation of the parabola with its vertex at $(0, 0)$ and directrix $x = 5$.

    a. $y = \frac{1}{20}x^2$ b. $x = \frac{1}{20}y^2$ c. $y = -\frac{1}{20}x^2$ d. $x = -\frac{1}{20}y^2$

_____ 4. Find the standard equation of the circle with a radius of 9 and its center at $(5, -8)$.

    a. $(x + 5)^2 + (y - 8)^2 = 9$ b. $(x - 5)^2 + (y + 8)^2 = 3$

    c. $(x + 5)^2 + (y - 8)^2 = 81$ d. $(x - 5)^2 + (y + 8)^2 = 81$

5. Graph $y + 3 = -\frac{1}{12}(x - 1)^2$. Write the coordinates of the vertex and the focus and the equation of the directrix.

    _____

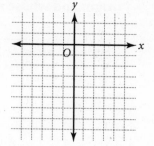

6. Graph the circle defined by the equation $x^2 + 6x + y^2 - 4y + 9 = 0$. Give the coordinates of the center and the radius.

    _____

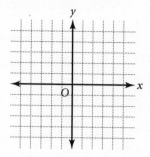

7. Write the standard equation of the parabola with directrix $x = 1$ and its vertex at $(6, 2)$. _____

8. The endpoints of a diameter of a circle have coordinates $A(2, 5)$ and $B(18, 17)$. Write the standard equation of the circle.

    _____

Quick Warm-Up: Assessing Prior Knowledge
9.4 Ellipses

Write the standard equation of the circle with the given radius and center.

1. 9; $(0, 0)$ _____

2. 1; $(0, 5)$ _____

3. 4; $(-8, -1)$ _____

4. 5; $(-4, 2)$ _____

Write the standard equation of the circle defined by the given equation. Then state the coordinates of its center and give its radius.

5. $x^2 + y^2 + 2x - 6y = 6$ _____

Lesson Quiz
9.4 Ellipses

Find the center, vertices, and co-vertices of each ellipse.

1. $\dfrac{x^2}{49} + \dfrac{y^2}{9} = 1$

2. $\dfrac{(x + 2)^2}{16} + \dfrac{(y - 5)^2}{25} = 1$

_____ _____

_____ _____

3. Write the standard equation of the ellipse centered at the origin with foci at $(12, 0)$ and $(-12, 0)$ and a minor axis of 10.

_____

4. Write the standard equation of the ellipse with its center at $(-4, 1)$, a vertical major axis of 8, and a minor axis of 4. Graph the ellipse.

_____

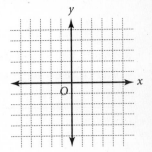

5. Write the standard form of the ellipse defined by the equation $9x^2 + 18x + 4y^2 - 27 = 0$. Find the coordinates of the center and foci.

_____

_____

Quick Warm-Up: Assessing Prior Knowledge
9.5 *Hyperbolas*

Graph the equation on your own paper and identify the conic section.

1. $x^2 + y^2 = 4$ _____   2. $x^2 + y = 4$ _____

3. $x^2 + 4y^2 = 4$ _____

4. Write the standard equation for the ellipse defined by
$4x^2 + 9y^2 + 16x - 54y = -61$. Identify the coordinates of the
center, vertices, co-vertices, and foci.

_____

 Lesson Quiz
9.5 *Hyperbolas*

**Find the coordinates of the vertices and the equations of the
asymptotes of each hyperbola.**

1. $\dfrac{y^2}{25} - \dfrac{x^2}{64} = 1$ 2. $\dfrac{x^2}{9} - \dfrac{y^2}{49} = 1$

_____   _____

3. Write the standard equation of the hyperbola whose vertices are at
$(7, 0)$ and $(-7, 0)$ and whose co-vertices are at $(0, 9)$ and $(0, -9)$.

_____

4. Write the standard equation of the hyperbola with foci at $(2, 2)$ and
$(2, 10)$ and with vertices at $(2, 4)$ and $(2, 8)$.

_____

5. Graph $\dfrac{(x-1)^2}{9} - \dfrac{(y-3)^2}{4} = 1$. Write the coordinates of the center
and the vertices.

_____

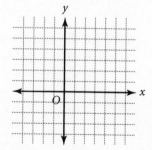

Quick Warm-Up: Assessing Prior Knowledge
9.6 Solving Nonlinear Systems

Solve each system.

1. $\begin{cases} x + y = 6 \\ x - y = -4 \end{cases}$ _____

2. $\begin{cases} x + y = -3 \\ 3x - 3y = 9 \end{cases}$ _____

3. $\begin{cases} 2x - y = -3 \\ 4x - 2y = 6 \end{cases}$ _____

4. $\begin{cases} 2x + y = -7 \\ 3x + 2y = 9 \end{cases}$ _____

5. $\begin{cases} -2x + 3y = 1 \\ 3x - 4y = -2 \end{cases}$ _____

Lesson Quiz
9.6 Solving Nonlinear Systems

Use the substitution method to solve each system.

1. $\begin{cases} y = 2x \\ 5x^2 - y^2 = 16 \end{cases}$

2. $\begin{cases} x^2 = 2y - 4 \\ x^2 + y^2 = 4 \end{cases}$

_____   _____

Use the elimination method to solve each system.

3. $\begin{cases} 2x^2 + 9y^2 = 18 \\ 5x^2 - 9y^2 = 45 \end{cases}$

4. $\begin{cases} 3x^2 + 2y^2 = 44 \\ x^2 + y^2 = 20 \end{cases}$

_____   _____

5. Classify the conic section defined by the equation
   $9x^2 + 36x + 16y^2 - 96y + 36 = 0$. Write the standard
   equation and sketch the graph of the conic section.

   _____

   _____

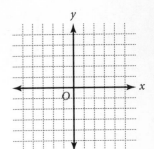

Chapter Assessment

Chapter 9, Form A, page 1

Write the letter that best answers the question or completes the statement.

_____ 1. Find the length of the segment with endpoints $P(6, -2)$ and $Q(3, 4)$.

     a. $\sqrt{117}$ b. $\sqrt{65}$ c. $\sqrt{45}$ d. $\sqrt{13}$

_____ 2. One endpoint of $\overline{PQ}$ is $P(9, 3)$ and the midpoint, M, is $(1, 5)$. Find the coordinates of Q.

     a. $Q(5, 4)$ b. $Q(4, -1)$ c. $Q(-4, 1)$ d. $Q(-7, 7)$

_____ 3. If a diameter of a circle has endpoints $(2, 5)$ and $(-8, 29)$, then find the center and radius of the circle.

     a. center: $(-3, 17)$; radius: 13   b. center: $(-5, 17)$; radius: 26

     c. center: $(5, 12)$; radius: 13   d. center: $(-3, 17)$; radius: $\sqrt{612}$

_____ 4. Find the equation of a circle with its center at $(5, -2)$ and a radius of 16.

     a. $(x + 5)^2 + (y - 2)^2 = 256$ b. $(x + 5)^2 + (y - 2)^2 = 4$

     c. $(x - 5)^2 + (y + 2)^2 = 256$ d. $(x - 5)^2 + (y + 2)^2 = 4$

_____ 5. Find the equation of the parabola shown at right.

     a. $x + 2 = -\frac{1}{8}y^2$

     b. $x - 2 = \frac{1}{8}y^2$

     c. $y = \frac{1}{8}(x + 2)^2$

     d. $y = -\frac{1}{8}(x - 2)^2$

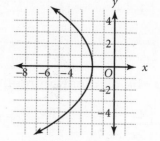

_____ 6. Find the equation of the parabola with its focus at $(-4, 7)$ and directrix $y = 1$.

     a. $y - 7 = \frac{1}{24}(x + 4)^2$ b. $y - 4 = \frac{1}{12}(x + 4)^2$

     c. $y + 4 = -\frac{1}{12}(x - 4)^2$ d. $y - 3 = \frac{1}{24}(x + 4)^2$

_____ 7. Find the equation of the ellipse shown at right.

     a. $\dfrac{(x - 1)^2}{4} - \dfrac{(y + 4)^2}{25} = 1$

     b. $\dfrac{(x + 1)^2}{4} + \dfrac{(y - 4)^2}{25} = 1$

     c. $\dfrac{(x - 1)^2}{25} - \dfrac{(y + 4)^2}{4} = 1$

     d. $\dfrac{(x - 1)^2}{25} + \dfrac{(y + 4)^2}{4} = 1$

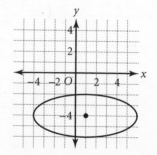

Chapter Assessment

Chapter 9, Form A, page 2

_____ 8. Find the equation of the ellipse centered at the origin with foci at $(0, -3)$ and $(0, 3)$, and a major axis of 10.

    a. $\dfrac{x^2}{25} + \dfrac{y^2}{16} = 1$ b. $\dfrac{x^2}{16} + \dfrac{y^2}{25} = 1$

    c. $\dfrac{x^2}{25} + \dfrac{y^2}{9} = 1$ d. $\dfrac{x^2}{9} + \dfrac{y^2}{25} = 1$

_____ 9. Find the equation of the hyperbola shown at right.

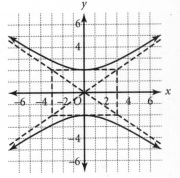

    a. $\dfrac{x^2}{9} - \dfrac{y^2}{4} = 1$

    b. $\dfrac{x^2}{4} + \dfrac{y^2}{9} = 1$

    c. $\dfrac{y^2}{4} - \dfrac{x^2}{9} = 1$

    d. $\dfrac{y^2}{9} - \dfrac{x^2}{4} = 1$

_____ 10. Find the equation of the hyperbola with vertices at $(5, 4)$ and $(-3, 4)$ and co-vertices at $(1, 1)$ and $(1, 7)$.

    a. $\dfrac{(x-1)^2}{16} - \dfrac{(y-4)^2}{9} = 1$ b. $\dfrac{(x+1)^2}{9} + \dfrac{(y+4)^2}{16} = 1$

    c. $\dfrac{(x+1)^2}{9} - \dfrac{(y+4)^2}{16} = 1$ d. $\dfrac{(x-1)^2}{16} + \dfrac{(y+4)^2}{9} = 1$

_____ 11. Find the asymptotes of the hyperbola $\dfrac{y^2}{9} - \dfrac{x^2}{81} = 1$.

    a. $y = \pm 9x$ b. $y = \pm\dfrac{1}{9}x$ c. $y = \pm 3x$ d. $y = \pm\dfrac{1}{3}x$

_____ 12. Which conic section is defined by the equation $4x^2 + 7x = 24 + 4y^2$?

    a. parabola   b. circle   c. ellipse   d. hyperbola

_____ 13. How many solutions does the system $\begin{cases} 4x^2 + 4y^2 = 100 \\ y - 2 = 2(x-3)^2 \end{cases}$ have?

    a. 0   b. 1   c. 2   d. 3

_____ 14. Write the standard equation of the circle defined by $x^2 + y^2 + 8x - 12y + 43 = 0$.

    a. $(x-6)^2 + (y+4)^2 = 9$ b. $(x+4)^2 + (y-6)^2 = 95$

    c. $(x+4)^2 + (y-6)^2 = 7$ d. $(x+4)^2 + (y-6)^2 = 9$

Chapter Assessment
Chapter 9, Form B, page 1

1. For $\overline{PQ}$ with endpoints $P(1, 7)$ and $Q(9, -8)$, find PQ and the midpoint, M, of the segment.

_____

2. One endpoint of $\overline{PQ}$ is $P(-6, 3)$ and the midpoint, M, is $(2, -12)$. Find the coordinates of Q.

_____

3. Graph the circle defined by the equation $(x + 2)^2 + y^2 = 16$. Find the radius and coordinates of the center.

_____

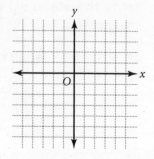

4. Graph $x - 3 = -\frac{1}{8}(y + 2)^2$. Write the coordinates of the vertex and the focus and the equation of the directrix.

_____

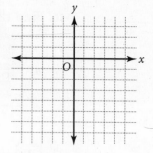

5. Graph $\dfrac{(x + 4)^2}{4} + \dfrac{(y + 1)^2}{25} = 1$. Write the coordinates of the center, vertices, and co-vertices.

_____

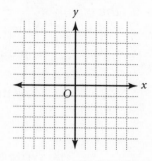

Find all solutions to each system of equations algebraically.

6. $\begin{cases} x^2 + y^2 = 25 \\ 3x^2 + 2y^2 = 59 \end{cases}$

7. $\begin{cases} x^2 + y^2 = 10 \\ 3y = x^2 + 8 \end{cases}$

_____   _____

8. Graph $\dfrac{(y+1)^2}{16} - \dfrac{(x-2)^2}{9} = 1$. Write the coordinates of the center and the vertices.

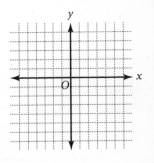

_____

Write the standard equation of the conic section with the given characteristics.

9. circle with diameter endpoints at $(-8, 5)$ and $(4, 21)$

10. parabola with focus at $(6, 8)$ and directrix $y = -2$

_____

11. ellipse with center at $(5, -7)$, a major axis of 16, and foci at $(-1, -7)$ and $(11, -7)$

12. ellipse with vertices at $(2, 11)$ and $(2, -3)$ and co-vertices at $(7, 4)$ and $(-3, 4)$

_____

13. hyperbola with foci at $(2, 0)$ and $(14, 0)$ and vertices at $(12, 0)$ and $(4, 0)$

14. hyperbola with vertices at $(3, -1)$ and $(3, -9)$ and co-vertices at $(-6, -5)$ and $(12, -5)$

_____

15. Find the equations of the asymptotes of the hyperbola defined by the equation $\dfrac{x^2}{49} - \dfrac{y^2}{100} = 1$. _____

Write the equation of each conic section in standard form.

16. $x^2 + y^2 - 10x + 6y + 18 = 0$

17. $x^2 + 9y^2 + 8x + 36y + 43 = 0$

_____

18. Find the point(s) of intersection between the circle $x^2 + y^2 = 25$ and the line $x - y = -1$.

_____

19. If the circle $(x - 1)^2 + (y + 3)^2 = 16$ is translated 4 units to the left and 2 units upward, write the equation of the resulting circle.

_____

Alternative Assessment

Relationships Between Equations and Graphs, Chapter 9, Form A

TASK: Determine the relationship between the equation of a conic section and the characteristics of its graph.

HOW YOU WILL BE SCORED: As you work through the task, your teacher will be looking for the following:

- whether you can use the equation of a parabola to find its vertex, focus, and directrix
- whether you can graph a circle by using its standard equation
- whether you can write the standard equation of an ellipse and find the coordinates of its center, vertices, and foci

1. Explain how to find the vertex, focus, and directrix for the parabola represented by $8y - x^2 + 6x = 25$. Then find the vertex, focus, and directrix. _____

_____

_____

2. Explain how you can graph the circle represented by the equation $x^2 + y^2 - 6x - 2y + 6 = 0$. _____

_____

_____

3. The equation $4x^2 + 3y^2 = 48$ represents an ellipse. Write the equation of the ellipse in standard form. Then find the coordinates of the center, vertices, and foci. How can you determine whether the major axis is horizontal or vertical? _____

_____

_____

_____

4. Write the equation of the ellipse that has vertices at $(5, 0)$ and $(-5, 0)$ and co-vertices at $(0, 3)$ and $(0, -3)$. _____

SELF-ASSESSMENT: Compare the types of symmetry determined by the graphs of a parabola, a circle, and an ellipse.

Alternative Assessment

Solving Nonlinear Systems, Chapter 9, Form B

TASK: Solve nonlinear systems of equations.

HOW YOU WILL BE SCORED: As you work through the task, your teacher will be looking for the following:

- how well you can use graphs to determine the number of real solutions of a nonlinear system and to estimate the solutions
- whether you can use algebraic methods to find solutions of a nonlinear system

1. In the space at right, draw all the possible intersections that can occur between a circle and an ellipse. How many intersections are possible?

   _____

   _____

2. In the space at right, draw all the possible intersections that can occur between the graphs of a first-degree equation and a second-degree equation. How many intersections are possible?

   _____

   _____

3. Describe how to solve the nonlinear system at right by graphing. Then solve the system.

$$\begin{cases} y^2 - x^2 = 16 \\ x^2 + y^2 = 34 \end{cases}$$

   _____

   _____

   _____

4. Solve the nonlinear system at right by using algebra.

$$\begin{cases} x^2 - y^2 = 6 \\ xy = 4 \end{cases}$$

   _____

SELF-ASSESSMENT: Write and graph a system of nonlinear equations with only nonreal solutions.

Quick Warm-Up: Assessing Prior Knowledge
10.1 Introduction to Probability

Write as a percent. If necessary, round to the nearest tenth of a percent.

1. 0.157 _____   2. 10.122 _____   3. $\frac{2}{5}$ _____

4. $\frac{17}{50}$ _____   5. $\frac{133}{200}$ _____   6. $\frac{3}{7}$ _____

Find the area of a circle with the given measure.

7. radius: 5 centimeters   8. diameter: 6 inches

_____   _____

Lesson Quiz
10.1 Introduction to Probability

1. If one person is randomly selected from a class that has 6 sophomores, 12 juniors, and 7 seniors, find the probability that the person selected is a senior. _____

2. Assume that a dart thrown at the rectangular board shown at right will hit the board and that each point on the board is equally likely to be hit. Find the probability that the dart will hit the shaded rectangle.

_____

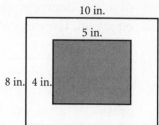

3. The table below shows how many bottles of each type of fruit juice were sold from a vending machine on a randomly selected day.

Orange	Apple	Grape	Cranberry
22	18	12	8

How many of the next 500 people who buy from this machine can be expected to buy apple juice? _____

4. A car electronics store sells 6 different radios, 10 different CD players, and 8 different speaker packages. In how many ways can you choose a radio, a CD player, and a speaker package for your car? _____

5. How many different ways can 5 people be seated in 3 chairs with 2 people left standing? _____

Quick Warm-Up: Assessing Prior Knowledge
10.2 Permutations

Find the number of passwords possible if the following patterns are used:

1. 1 letter followed by 3 digits _____

2. 2 digits, excluding 1, followed by 2 letters, excluding *B* _____

3. 1 digit followed by 3 letters followed by 2 digits _____

4. 2 digits, excluding 0, followed by 1 letter, excluding *Z*, followed by

   3 digits _____

Lesson Quiz
10.2 Permutations

Evaluate each expression.

1. $5! + 3!$

2. $_9P_4$

3. $\dfrac{8! \times 0!}{4! \times 2!}$

_____ _____ _____

4. There are 6 runners in a race. If there are no ties, in how many different orders can the runners finish the race? _____

5. The 20 members of the math club must choose officers. In how many different ways can the club choose a president, a vice-president, a secretary, and a treasurer? _____

6. A grocery store has 6 cash registers. In how many different ways can the manager of the store assign 12 cashiers to the 6 cash registers? _____

Find the number of permutations of the letters in each of the following words.

7. algebra

8. pepper

_____ _____

9. The 6 members of the Smith family go to a restaurant and are seated at a circular table with 6 chairs. In how many different ways can the Smith family be seated in the 6 chairs? _____

Quick Warm-Up: Assessing Prior Knowledge
10.3 Combinations

Evaluate each expression.

1. $6!$ _____

2. $4! \times 5!$ _____

3. $\frac{8!}{3!}$ _____

4. $\frac{9!}{4!5!}$ _____

5. $_7P_3$ _____

6. $_5P_2 \times _6P_4$ _____

In how many different ways can 8 students be assigned to 8 seats that are arranged

7. in a line? _____

8. in a circle? _____

Lesson Quiz
10.3 Combinations

Evaluate each expression.

1. $_{43}C_0$

2. $_{15}C_5$

3. $\frac{_{10}C_{10} \times _{12}C_8}{_9C_1 \times _6C_3}$

_____   _____   _____

4. The manager of a factory needs 7 workers to work overtime. If there are 15 workers at the factory, in how many ways can the manager select 7 people to work overtime? _____

5. There are 20 people competing in a talent show for $300 in prizes.

   a. Suppose that the judges decide to award a $150 first prize, a $100 second prize, and a $50 third prize. In how many ways can the judges award the prize money? _____

   b. Suppose that the judges decide to choose the top 3 contestants and give them each $100. In how many ways can the judges award the prize money? _____

6. A mall has 12 clothing stores, 9 shoe stores, and 5 electronics stores. In how many ways can a person shopping at this mall go to 5 clothing stores, 4 shoe stores, and 3 electronics stores? _____

7. The history club consists of 15 boys and 14 girls. The club decides to randomly select the 5 people needed to organize the club dance. Find the probability that 3 boys and 2 girls are selected to organize the dance. _____

Quick Warm-Up: Assessing Prior Knowledge
10.4 Using Addition With Probability

Swiss cheese was on sale at a local market. The
table at right shows the cheese purchases of
150 customers at this market. Find the
experimental probability of each event.

Swiss cheese	35
Other cheese	55
No cheese	60

1. A customer buys Swiss cheese _____

2. A customer buys no cheese _____

Of 600 customers at this market, how many can be expected to buy

3. Swiss cheese? _____

4. another type of cheese? _____

Lesson Quiz
10.4 Using Addition With Probability

1. An engineering consulting firm employs engineers, accountants,
   and secretaries. The manager of the firm is interested in the
   methods of transportation that the employees use to travel to work.
   The table below summarizes the results.

	Engineer	Accountant	Secretary	Total
Car	9	4	5	18
Bus	5	4	4	13
Train	4	2	3	9
Total	18	10	12	40

   a. Find the probability that a randomly selected employee is an
      engineer or a secretary.

      _____

   b. Find the probability that a randomly selected employee is an
      accountant or rides a bus to work.

      _____

2. The girls' varsity softball, basketball, and volleyball teams
   at Greenfield High have 13 players, 10 players, and 11
   players, respectively. Some players are on more than one
   team, as indicated in the diagram. If one of these players
   is randomly selected, find the probability that the player
   is on at least two teams.

   _____

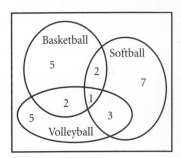

Mid-Chapter Assessment

Chapter 10 (Lessons 10.1–10.4)

Write the letter that best answers the question or completes the statement.

_____ 1. Students are choosing the 4 call letters for a school's new radio station. In how many ways can the students choose the letters if the first letter must be *W*?

   a. 78   b. 9,564   c. 17,576   d. 456,976

_____ 2. How many permutations of the letters of *indiana* are possible?

   a. 630   b. 840   c. 2520   d. 5040

_____ 3. A restaurant serves appetizers on a circular platter that rotates. If there are 7 appetizers, in how many ways can they be arranged on the platter?

   a. 823,543   b. 40,320   c. 5040   d. 720

_____ 4. If $P(A^c) = \frac{2}{3}$, find $P(A)$.

   a. $-\frac{2}{3}$ b. $\frac{3}{2}$ c. $\frac{1}{3}$ d. $\frac{5}{3}$

5. Assume that a dart thrown at the circular board shown at right will hit the board and that each point on the board is equally likely to be hit. To the nearest percent, find the probability that the dart will hit a shaded area.

_____

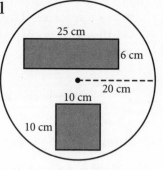

6. Dana has decided to apply to 7 colleges and wants to visit 4 of them over spring break. In how many ways can Dana choose the 4 colleges to visit?   _____

7. In how many ways can the coaches of a basketball team select a most valuable player, a most improved player, and a best defensive player from the 12 players on the team?   _____

8. A student council has 9 seniors, 10 juniors, and 7 sophomores. In how many ways can 4 seniors, 3 juniors, and 2 sophomores be chosen to visit the state capitol?   _____

9. A restaurant has 17 tables in the nonsmoking section and 8 tables in the smoking section. There are 6 tables by a window, 3 in each section. If one table in the restaurant is randomly selected, find the probability that the table is in the smoking section or by a window.   _____

Quick Warm-Up: Assessing Prior Knowledge
10.5 Independent Events

A bag contains 2 black marbles, 7 white marbles, 6 green marbles, and 5 blue marbles. Find the probability of drawing the following:

1. 1 green marble _____

2. 1 yellow marble _____

3. 1 marble that is not blue _____

4. 1 marble that is not red _____

5. 1 black marble *or* 1 white marble _____

Lesson Quiz
10.5 Independent Events

1. If *A* and *B* are independent events and *P*(*A*) = 0.5 and
   P(*A and B*) = 0.2, find *P*(*B*).   _____

2. If a number cube is rolled and a fair coin is flipped, find
   the probability that the number cube shows a 3 and the
   coin shows heads.   _____

3. If a number cube is rolled 4 times, find the probability
   that an even number is rolled all 4 times.   _____

4. All of the sections of the spinner at right are equal in size.
   Suppose the spinner is spun 3 times.

   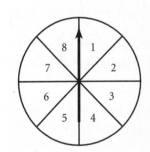

   a. To the nearest percent, find the probability that all
      3 numbers spun are greater than 5.

   _____

   b. To the nearest percent, find the probability that the
      same number is spun 2 or more times.

   _____

5. A school has 2 computer networks, network *A* and network *B*.
   Network *A* does not work 6% of the time, network *B* does not work
   8% of the time, and both networks do not work 2% of the time. Do
   networks *A* and *B* operate independently? Explain.

   _____

Quick Warm-Up: Assessing Prior Knowledge
10.6 *Dependent Events and Conditional Probability*

Two number cubes are rolled. Find the probability of rolling each sum below.

1. a sum of 7 _____

2. a sum of 8 _____

3. a sum of 7 *or* a sum of 8 _____

4. a sum less than 7 _____

5. a sum less than 7 *or* a sum greater than 8 _____

6. a sum less than 12 *or* a sum greater than 7 _____

Lesson Quiz
10.6 *Dependent Events and Conditional Probability*

1. If $P(A) = 0.8$ and $P(A \text{ and } B) = 0.2$, find $P(B|A)$. _____

2. If a fair coin is flipped twice, find the probability that the second flip results in heads, given that the first flip resulted in heads. _____

3. The Spanish club at Culver High has 18 members. The math club has 15 members, including 6 members who are also in the Spanish club. If a single student is randomly selected from these two clubs, find the probability that the student is in the Spanish club if it is known that the student is in the math club. _____

4. The table below shows the numbers of juniors and seniors taking science classes at Culver High.

	Biology	Chemistry	Physics
Juniors	9	21	20
Seniors	6	18	16

If one student is randomly selected from among the students in the table, find the probability that the student is taking chemistry, given that the student is a junior. _____

5. In a test for a disease, 96% of the people who have the disease test positive and 98% of the people who do not have the disease test negative. Suppose that 4% of the population has the disease. Find the probability that a randomly selected person who tests positive for the disease actually has the disease. _____

Quick Warm-Up: Assessing Prior Knowledge
10.7 *Experimental Probability and Simulation*

A coin is tossed. What is the theoretical probability of

1. heads? _____   2. tails? _____

The coin is tossed 20 times with the results at right. Using these results, what is the experimental probability of

H H H T T T T H T T
H H T T H T H H H H

3. heads? _____   4. tails? _____

In 1000 tosses of this coin, how many heads can you expect

5. theoretically? _____

6. based on the results of the experiment? _____

Lesson Quiz
10.7 *Experimental Probability and Simulation*

1. The probabilities that a car salesperson will sell from 0 to 8 cars in a week are given in the table below. How would you distribute random integers from 1 to 100 among these values so that the corresponding random integers could be used to simulate the number of cars the salesperson sells in a week?

Number	0	1	2	3	4	5	6	7	8
Probability	0.01	0.07	0.12	0.18	0.19	0.17	0.13	0.08	0.05
Random numbers									

2. Use the distribution you constructed in Exercise 1 to simulate the weekly sales for 10 consecutive weeks. Record your results in the table below.

Trial	1	2	3	4	5	6	7	8	9	10
Car sales										

3. Use your simulation to estimate the probability that the salesperson sells more than 4 cars in a week. _____

Chapter Assessment

Chapter 10, Form A, page 1

Write the letter that best answers the question or completes the statement.

_____ 1. A bag contains 8 red marbles, 12 blue marbles, and 17 green marbles. If one marble is randomly selected from the bag, what is the probability that the marble is red or green?

a. $\frac{8}{17}$ b. $\frac{25}{12}$ c. $\frac{25}{37}$ d. $\frac{20}{37}$

_____ 2. If a point is randomly selected from the points inside the square shown below, find the probability that the point is inside the circle.

a. 0.314   b. 0.628

c. 0.785   d. 3.142

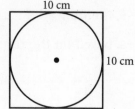

10 cm

10 cm

_____ 3. If $P(B) = \frac{3}{8}$, find $P(B^c)$.

a. $\frac{5}{8}$ b. $\frac{11}{8}$ c. $-\frac{3}{8}$ d. $\frac{8}{3}$

_____ 4. If A and B are independent events and $P(A) = 0.5$ and $P(B) = 0.4$, find $P(B|A)$.

a. 0.6   b. 0.5   c. 0.4   d. 0.2

_____ 5. If A and B are independent events and $P(A) = 0.4$ and $P(B) = 0.25$, find $P(A \ or \ B)$.

a. 0.15   b. 0.55   c. 0.65   d. 0.75

_____ 6. The menu at a restaurant has 11 appetizers, 15 entrees, 10 desserts, and 8 beverages. The restaurant offers a dinner special that includes 1 appetizer, 1 entree, 1 dessert, and 1 beverage. In how many ways can a person order a dinner special at this restaurant?

a. 45,644   b. 13,200   c. 870   d. 44

_____ 7. A CD has 10 songs on it. If a CD player randomly selects the order in which the songs are played, in how many different orders can the 10 songs be played?

a. 10   b. 34,670   c. 100,000   d. 3,628,800

_____ 8. How many different permutations of the letters in *September* are possible?

a. 362,880   b. 60,480   c. 720   d. 6

_____ 9. A baseball league that has 8 teams decides to add 3 new teams. The league then decides to divide into 2 divisions, one with 6 teams and the other with 5 teams. In how many ways can the 6 teams be chosen for the larger division?

a. 39,916,800   b. 332,640   c. 55,440   d. 462

Chapter Assessment

Chapter 10, Form A, page 2

_____ 10. A pizzeria has 6 meat toppings and 9 vegetable toppings. In how many different ways can a pizza with 2 meat toppings and 3 vegetable toppings be ordered from this pizzeria?

    a. 324   b. 924   c. 1260   d. 15,120

_____ 11. If there are 16 students in a classroom that has 25 chairs, how many different seating arrangements are possible?

    a. 25!   b. $\dfrac{25!}{16!}$ c. $_{25}C_{16}$ d. $_{25}P_{16}$

_____ 12. In how many different ways can 8 magazines be arranged on a circular carousel?

    a. 362,880   b. 40,320   c. 5040   d. 720

_____ 13. There are 15 dogs and 10 cats at an animal shelter. If a family decides to randomly select 5 animals to adopt, find the probability that the family selects 3 dogs and 2 cats.

    a. 0.04   b. 0.167   c. 0.2   d. 0.385

_____ 14. If two number cubes are rolled and the numbers that result are added, find the probability that the sum is an even number or a number less than 5.

    a. $\dfrac{5}{9}$ b. $\dfrac{3}{8}$ c. $\dfrac{2}{3}$ d. $\dfrac{1}{2}$

_____ 15. All of the sections on the circular spinner shown at right are equal in size. If the spinner is spun 3 times, what is the probability that an even number is spun all 3 times?

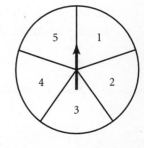

    a. $\dfrac{6}{5}$ b. $\dfrac{3}{10}$

    c. $\dfrac{6}{25}$ d. $\dfrac{8}{125}$

_____ 16. There are 38 members on the basketball teams and 54 members on the track teams at Central High. There are 13 people who are on both a basketball team and a track team. If one member of these teams is randomly selected, find the probability that the person is on a track team given that the person is on a basketball team.

    a. $\dfrac{13}{38}$ b. $\dfrac{13}{92}$ c. $\dfrac{54}{38}$ d. $\dfrac{38}{54}$

_____ 17. If a number cube is rolled 4 times, what is the probability that the same number is rolled at least twice?

    a. 0.09   b. 0.28   c. 0.72   d. 0.91

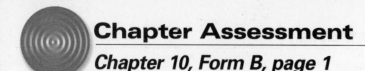

Chapter Assessment

Chapter 10, Form B, page 1

For Exercises 1–3, evaluate each expression.

1. $_{14}P_0$ _____

2. $_{25}C_{10}$ _____

3. $\dfrac{15!}{5! \times 3!}$ _____

4. A car dealer has 8 exterior colors, 12 interior colors, and 7 options packages available for new cars. In how many different ways can a person buying a new car from this dealer select an exterior color, an interior color, and an options package? _____

5. A restaurant has a dinner special in which a party of four can order any 12 of the 40 items on the restaurant's menu for a fixed price. In how many different ways can a party of four order the dinner special in this restaurant? _____

6. How many permutations of the letters in *interstate* are possible? _____

7. A newspaper editor needs to cover stories in Paris, New York, and Lubbock. If the editor has 8 reporters available, in how many different ways can the editor assign reporters to the stories? _____

8. A bakery has 6 different kinds of cake and 12 different kinds of pie. If John and Mary come to this bakery, in how many different ways can they select 3 different cakes and 4 different pies for a party? _____

9. If one point is randomly selected from the points inside the rectangle shown at right, find the probability, to the nearest percent, that the point is in a shaded area.

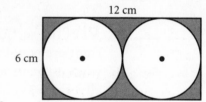

12 cm

6 cm

_____

10. If A and B are mutually exclusive events and $P(A) = 0.3$ and $P(B) = 0.2$, find the following:

a. $P(A \text{ and } B)$

b. $P(A^C)$

c. $P(A \text{ or } B)$

_____   _____   _____

11. If A and B are independent events and $P(A) = 0.6$ and $P(B) = 0.5$, find the following:

a. $P(A \text{ and } B)$

b. $P(B|A)$

c. $P(A \text{ or } B)$

_____   _____   _____

12. A math teacher decides to grade 5 randomly selected problems from among the 20 assigned. If you completed only 8 of the problems, find the probability that the teacher will select 3 of the problems you completed and 2 of the problems you did not complete. _____

Chapter Assessment

Chapter 10, Form B, page 2

13. **a.** An anthropologist has trained a monkey to place sticks that are the same length end to end. The anthropologist then gives the monkey 5 sticks of different lengths. In how many ways can the monkey place the sticks of different lengths end to end? _____

b. If the monkey cannot distinguish between the different lengths of the sticks, what is the probability that the monkey will place the sticks in order from shortest to longest? _____

14. For medical purposes, the managers of a company decide to record the blood type of all the employees. The results are shown in the table below.

	O	A	B	AB
Women	8	5	4	2
Men	12	6	2	1

Suppose that a single person is randomly selected from the people in this company.

a. Find the probability that the person has type O blood or type A blood. _____

b. Find the probability that the person is a woman or has type A blood. _____

c. Find the probability that the person is a man, given that the person has type O blood. _____

15. A wheel used on a game show has 7 spaces with dollar amounts written on them and 3 spaces with "Lose a Turn" written on them. All of the spaces on the wheel are equal in size. If a contestant on this show spins the wheel 3 times, find the probability that the contestant spins "Lose a Turn" all 3 times. _____

16. The area of the rectangle shown at right is 1. The areas of the other regions are given in each region. Suppose that a point is randomly selected from the points in the rectangle.

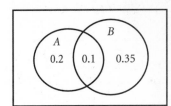

a. Find $P(B|A)$. _____

b. Are picking a point in A and picking a point in B independent events? Explain. _____

_____

Alternative Assessment
Combinations and Permutations, Chapter 10, Form A

TASK: Describe the difference between a permutation and a combination.

HOW YOU WILL BE SCORED: As you work through the task, your teacher will be looking for the following:

- whether you can determine if a real-world counting problem represents a combination or permutation
- how well you can communicate your responses in writing

For each problem, identify whether it is a permutation or combination. Explain. Then solve each problem.

1. a. A supermarket advertises two job openings—one for a cashier and the other for a deli clerk. Twelve students who are qualified for both positions apply. In how many ways can the positions be filled?

   _____

   b. A supermarket advertises two job openings for cashiers. Twelve students who are qualified apply. In how many ways can the positions be filled?

   _____

2. a. Ten students compete for 3 different trophies. In how many different ways can a trophy be awarded to a winner, a runner-up, and a second runner-up?

   _____

   b. Ten students compete for 3 identical trophies. In how many different ways can these trophies be awarded?

   _____

3. a. How many ways are there to choose a committee of 2 from a group of 8 people?

   _____

   b. How many ways are there to choose a chairperson and a secretary from a group of 8 people?

   _____

SELF-ASSESSMENT: How can you derive the formula for $_nC_r$ from the formula for $_nP_r$?

Alternative Assessment

Exploring Two-Event Probabilities, Chapter 10, Form B

TASK: Describe the relationships between two events.

HOW YOU WILL BE SCORED: As you work through the task, your teacher will be looking for the following:

- whether you can calculate probabilities concerning two events
- how well you can interpret and explain your results

Of the 170 members in a town's recreation program, 110 signed up for tennis lessons, 70 signed up for golf lessons, and 20 signed up for both.

1. Fill in the numbers in the diagram at right to represent the situation described above.

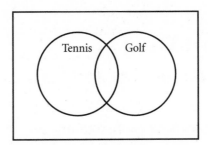

2. Find the probability that a randomly selected member of the town's recreation program signed up for both tennis lessons and golf lessons.

_____

3. Are the events "signing up for tennis lessons" and "signing up for golf lessons" independent events? Explain.

_____

4. Are the events, "signing up for tennis lessons" and "signing up for golf lessons" mutually exclusive events? Explain.

_____

5. Find the probability that a randomly selected member of the town's recreation program signed up for tennis lessons or golf lessons. What is the complement of this event? What is its probability?

_____

SELF-ASSESSMENT: Explain the difference between the probability that two independent events A and B will both occur and the probability that B will occur only if event A occurs.

NAME _____ CLASS _____ DATE _____

Quick Warm-Up: Assessing Prior Knowledge
11.1 Sequences and Series

Write the next three numbers in each pattern.

1. $15, 11, 7, 3, -1, \ldots$

2. $-12, -7, -2, 3, 8, \ldots$

3. $10, 11, 13, 16, 20, \ldots$

4. $2, 6, 18, 54, 162, \ldots$

5. $96, 48, 24, 12, 6, \ldots$

6. $1, 4, 9, 16, 25, \ldots$

Lesson Quiz
11.1 Sequences and Series

Write the first four terms of each sequence.

1. $t_n = 25 - 5n$

2. $\begin{cases} a_1 = 5 \\ a_n = a_{n-1} + 7 \end{cases}$, where $n \geq 2$

3. The first five terms of a sequence are $15, 8, 1, -6,$ and -13.

   a. Write the next three terms of the sequence. _____

   b. Write a recursive formula for the sequence. _____

Write the terms of each series. Then evaluate.

4. $\sum_{k=1}^{4} -5k$

5. $\sum_{k=1}^{6} 12$

6. $\sum_{k=1}^{5} (5k - 2)$

Evaluate the sum.

7. $\sum_{k=1}^{8} (3k^2 + 5k - 2)$

8. $\sum_{k=1}^{5} (k^2 + 2k + 1)$

9. $\sum_{k=1}^{6} (2k^2 + k + 7)$

Quick Warm-Up: Assessing Prior Knowledge
11.2 *Arithmetic Sequences*

Write the first five terms of each sequence.

1. $t_n = 3n$

_____

2. $t_n = 6n - 7$

_____

3. $t_n = -9n + 1$

_____

4. $a_1 = 2; a_n = -3a_{n-1}$

_____

5. $a_1 = 9; a_n = a_{n-1} - 4$

_____

6. $a_1 = -1; a_n = 3a_{n-1} + 5$

_____

Lesson Quiz
11.2 *Arithmetic Sequences*

State whether each sequence is arithmetic. If so, identify the common difference, *d*.

1. $\frac{1}{3}, \frac{1}{2}, \frac{2}{3}, \frac{5}{6}, 1, \ldots$

_____

2. $4, 9, 16, 25, 36, \ldots$

_____

3. Write an explicit formula for the arithmetic sequence that has a first

term of 20 and a common difference of –8. _____

4. Write an explicit formula for the sequence $-12, -3, 6, 15, 24, \ldots$ _____

5. Find the 12th term of the sequence $\begin{cases} t_1 = 16 \\ t_n = t_{n-1} + 15 \end{cases}$, where $n \geq 2$.

_____

6. Jamie buys a car for $7550. If the car depreciates at a rate of $725

per year, find the value of the car after 6 years. _____

7. Find the 10th term of the arithmetic sequence in which $t_3 = 15$ and $t_6 = 39$.

_____

8. Find five arithmetic means between 7 and 43. _____

Quick Warm-Up: Assessing Prior Knowledge
11.3 *Arithmetic Series*

Find the sum of each series.

1. $\sum_{n=1}^{4} 6$

2. $\sum_{k=1}^{6} (k + 2)$

3. $\sum_{i=1}^{5} 4i$

4. $\sum_{m=1}^{9} (2m - 5)$

_____   _____   _____   _____

Find the indicated term of each arithmetic sequence.

5. 12th term, given $t_2 = 6$ and $t_8 = 24$ _____

6. 7th term, given $t_5 = 22$ and $t_{11} = 46$ _____

Lesson Quiz
11.3 *Arithmetic Series*

1. Find S_{30} in the arithmetic series with $t_1 = 15$ and $t_{30} = 521$. _____

2. Given 4, 12, 20, 28, . . . , find S_{40}. _____

Find each sum.

3. $9 + 20 + 31 + 42 + \cdots + 141$

4. $50 + 45 + 40 + 35 + \cdots + 0$

_____   _____

5. $\sum_{k=1}^{35} (12 - 5k)$

6. $\sum_{n=1}^{20} [8 + 6(n - 1)]$

_____   _____

7. Each row of seats in a theater has 3 more seats than the previous
row, and the first row has 16 seats. If there are 25 rows in the
theater, find the total number of seats. _____

8. In the month of June, Rebecca saved 1 quarter the 1st day, 2
quarters the 2nd day, 3 quarters the 3rd day, and so on.
How much money did she save in June? _____

Quick Warm-Up: Assessing Prior Knowledge
11.4 Geometric Sequences

Find the fifth term of each arithmetic sequence.

1. $t_1 = 4$ and $t_n = t_{n-1} + 6$ _____

2. $t_1 = -7$ and $t_n = t_{n-1} - 3$ _____

Find the indicated term of each arithmetic sequence.

3. 11th term, given $t_2 = 10$ and $t_7 = 35$ _____

4. 15th term, given $t_6 = 5$ and $t_{12} = -19$ _____

5. Find three arithmetic means between -15 and 37. _____

6. Find three arithmetic means between 1 and -27. _____

Lesson Quiz
11.4 Geometric Sequences

Determine whether each sequence is geometric. If so, identify the common ratio, *r*.

1. $4, -12, 36, -108, \ldots$

2. $128, 96, 72, 54, \ldots$

_____ _____

3. Write an explicit formula for the geometric sequence that has a first term of 6 and a common ratio of -4. _____

4. Write an explicit formula for the sequence $16, 24, 36, 54, \ldots$ _____

5. Find the 10th term of the sequence $\begin{cases} t_1 = 0.25 \\ t_n = 4t_{n-1} \end{cases}$, where $n \geq 2$. _____

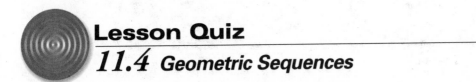

6. A new computer costs $4000 and retains 60% of its value each year.

Find the value of the computer after 5 years. _____

7. Find the ninth term of the geometric sequence in which $t_3 = 5$ and $t_6 = 320$.

_____

8. Find two geometric means between 64 and 125. _____

Mid-Chapter Assessment

Chapter 11 (Lessons 11.1–11.4)

Write the letter that best answers the question or completes the statement.

_____ 1. Find the fifth term of the sequence $\begin{cases} t_1 = 4 \\ t_n = 3t_{n-1} - 7 \end{cases}$, where $n \geq 2$.

a. 8   b. 17   c. 44   d. 125

_____ 2. For the arithmetic sequence in which $t_5 = 20$ and $t_9 = 4$, find t_{20}.

a. -48 b. -40 c. -32 d. -20

_____ 3. What is the value of r in the geometric sequence 250, 100, 40, 16, ...?

a. 2.5   b. -2.5 c. 0.4   d. -0.4

Write an explicit formula for each sequence.

4. 3, 24, 192, 1536, ...

5. 16.5, 25.1, 33.7, 42.3, ...

Find each sum.

6. $\displaystyle\sum_{k=1}^{12} 9k$

7. $\displaystyle\sum_{k=1}^{24} (8 + 7k)$

8. $\displaystyle\sum_{k=1}^{6} (k^2 + 7k - 3)$

9. Find t_{12} in the geometric sequence in which $t_5 = 32$ and $t_7 = 8$. _____

10. Find seven arithmetic means between 42 and 142.

_____

11. Given the sequence $-10, -4, 2, 8, \ldots$, find S_{100}. _____

12. Suppose a cook earns $25,000 the first year on the job. Each year after the first year the cook earns $1200 more than the previous year.

a. How much will the cook earn in the 10th year? _____

b. Find the total amount a cook will earn after 20 years. _____

13. An antique car is increasing in value. At the end of each year, the car's value is 110% of its value at the end of the previous year. If the car was purchased for $30,000, find its value after 6 years. _____

Quick Warm-Up: Assessing Prior Knowledge
11.5 *Geometric Series and Mathematical Induction*

Find each sum.

1. $\displaystyle\sum_{m=1}^{8} 6$

2. $\displaystyle\sum_{j=1}^{5} 4j$

3. $\displaystyle\sum_{k=1}^{7} (10 - 2k)$

4. $\displaystyle\sum_{n=1}^{6} (n^2 - n + 1)$

_____   _____   _____   _____

Find the indicated sum for each arithmetic series.

5. $3 + 6 + 9 + 12 + 15 + \cdots; S_{12}$ _____

6. $9 + 2 - 5 - 12 - 19 - \cdots; S_{20}$ _____

Lesson Quiz
11.5 *Geometric Series and Mathematical Induction*

1. Approximate S_{12} to the nearest tenth for the geometric series in which $t_1 = 10$ and $r = 1.6$. _____

2. Given the series $64 + 48 + 36 + 27 + \cdots$, approximate S_{20} to the nearest tenth. _____

Evaluate. If necessary, approximate answers to the nearest tenth.

3. $\displaystyle\sum_{k=1}^{9} 0.5(4^{k-1})$

4. $\displaystyle\sum_{k=1}^{16} 2(-1.5)^{k-1}$

_____   _____

5. If a family deposits $500 at the beginning of each year into a bank account that pays 7% annual interest, how much will the family have in the account after 15 years? _____

6. Use mathematical induction to prove that $1 + 3 + \cdots + (2n - 1) = n^2$ is true for all natural numbers, n.

_____

_____

_____

_____

Quick Warm-Up: Assessing Prior Knowledge
11.6 Infinite Geometric Series

Evaluate.

1. $\displaystyle\sum_{k=1}^{5}(7-k)$

2. $\displaystyle\sum_{k=1}^{6}\left(\frac{1}{2}\right)^{k-1}$

3. $\displaystyle\sum_{k=1}^{4}5(-2)^{k-1}$

_____   _____   _____

Find the indicated sum.

4. $4-8+16-32+64-\cdots; S_{15}$ _____

5. $\dfrac{1}{5}+\dfrac{1}{10}+\dfrac{1}{20}+\dfrac{1}{40}+\cdots; S_{11}$ _____

Lesson Quiz
11.6 Infinite Geometric Series

1. Find the sum of the infinite geometric series in which $t_1 = 10$ and $r = 0.2$. _____

Find the sum of each infinite geometric series, if it exists.

2. $60 + 24 + 9.6 + 3.84 + \cdots$

3. $6 + 4 + \dfrac{8}{3} + \dfrac{16}{9} + \cdots$

_____

4. $\displaystyle\sum_{k=1}^{\infty}0.8(1.1)^{k-1}$

5. $\displaystyle\sum_{k=1}^{\infty}\dfrac{10}{6^{k-1}}$

_____

Write each decimal as a fraction in simplest form.

6. $0.4\overline{5}$ _____

7. $0.\overline{25}$ _____

8. A baseball is initially hit a distance of 210 feet. It then bounces ahead $\frac{2}{5}$ of the distance of its previous bounce. How far does it travel before coming to rest? _____

Quick Warm-Up: Assessing Prior Knowledge
11.7 *Pascal's Triangle*

Evaluate each expression.

1. $_{11}C_4$ _____

2. $_{11}C_1$ _____

3. $_8C_8$ _____

4. $_8C_0$ _____

5. $_7C_2$ _____

6. $_7C_5$ _____

A fair coin is tossed 3 times.

7. What is the total number of possible outcomes? _____

8. What is the probability of tossing

    a. exactly 3 heads? _____

    b. exactly 2 heads? _____

    c. exactly 1 heads? _____

    d. 0 heads? _____

Lesson Quiz
11.7 *Pascal's Triangle*

1. How many entries are in row 18 of Pascal's triangle? _____

2. a. Find the fifth entry in row 14 of Pascal's triangle. _____

    b. Which other entry in row 14 will have the same value as the fifth entry? _____

3. Find the sum of all the entries in row 10 of Pascal's triangle. _____

4. Suppose that 9 fair coins are tossed.

    a. In how many ways can 5 heads appear? _____

    b. Find the probability that exactly 5 heads appear. Round your answer to the nearest hundredth. _____

    c. Find the probability that exactly 5 heads or exactly 6 heads appear. Round your answer to the nearest hundredth. _____

    d. Find the probability that 2 or fewer heads appear. Round your answer to the nearest hundredth. _____

5. Suppose that a family has 6 children. Assume that giving birth to a boy and giving birth to a girl are equally likely.

    a. Find the probability that the family has 3 boys and 3 girls. Round your answer to the nearest hundredth. _____

    b. Find the probability that the family has 4 or more boys. Round your answer to the nearest hundredth. _____

Quick Warm-Up: Assessing Prior Knowledge
11.8 The Binomial Theorem

Simplify.

1. $(x - 5)^2$ _____

2. $(x + y)^2$ _____

3. $(4m + 3n)^2$ _____

4. $(a + 3)(a^2 - 2a + 4)$ _____

5. $(r + 2)^3$ _____

Evaluate.

6. $\begin{pmatrix} 8 \\ 6 \end{pmatrix}$ _____

7. $\begin{pmatrix} 10 \\ 0 \end{pmatrix}$ _____

8. $\begin{pmatrix} 4 \\ 1 \end{pmatrix}$ _____

Lesson Quiz
11.8 The Binomial Theorem

1. How many terms are in the expansion of $(a + b)^{21}$? _____

Expand each binomial raised to a power.

2. $(c + d)^5$

_____

3. $(x - 3y)^4$

_____

4. In the expansion of $(x + y)^9$, find the term containing $x^6 y^3$. _____

5. In the expansion of $(x + 3)^{12}$, find the term containing x^9. _____

6. The probability that a basketball player makes a shot from a particular spot is 0.42. Suppose that the player takes 10 shots from that spot. Find the following probabilities. Round your answers to the nearest hundredth.

   a. Find the probability that the player makes exactly 4 of the 10 shots. _____

   b. Find the probability that the player makes 5 or 6 of the 10 shots. _____

   c. Find the probability that the player makes 2 or fewer of the 10 shots. _____

Chapter Assessment

Chapter 11, Form A, page 1

Write the letter that best answers the question or completes the statement.

_____ 1. Find the value of $\sum_{k=1}^{8} (2k^2 + 3k - 5)$.

    a. 329   **b.** 476   **c.** 556   **d.** 660

_____ 2. Find a recursive formula for the sequence $5, 9, 17, 33, \ldots$

    a. $t_n = 2^{n+1} + 1$ **b.** $t_n = 5 + 2(n - 1)$

    c. $\begin{cases} t_1 = 5 \\ t_n = t_{n-1} + 4 \end{cases}$, where $n \geq 2$ **d.** $\begin{cases} t_1 = 5 \\ t_n = 2t_{n-1} - 1 \end{cases}$, where $n \geq 2$

_____ 3. Find the 60th term of the arithmetic sequence in which $t_5 = -8$ and $t_{11} = -38$.

    a. -251 **b.** -283 **c.** -288 **d.** -342

_____ 4. Find three geometric means between 2 and 2592.

    a. 3, 120, 1500   **b.** 16, 92, 624   **c.** 12, 72, 432   **d.** 649.5, 1297, 1944.5

_____ 5. Which of the following is t_{120} in the sequence $-60, -46, -32, -18, \ldots$?

    a. 1606   **b.** 1620   **c.** 1634   **d.** 1648

_____ 6. Which of the following is a formula for the sequence $8, -20, 50, -125, \ldots$?

    a. $t_n = 8 + (n - 1)(-2.5)$ **b.** $t_n = 8 + (-2.5)^{n+1}$

    c. $t_n = 8(-2.5)^{n-1}$ **d.** $t_n = 8(-2.5^{n-1})$

_____ 7. Which of the following is S_{80} in the series $250 + 217 + 184 + 151 + \cdots$?

    a. $-84,280$ **b.** $-72,600$ **c.** $-54,300$ **d.** $-42,100$

_____ 8. Suppose that the population of fish in a lake is decreasing by 40% per year because of the increase of pollution in the lake. If there are about 75,000 fish in the lake now, predict the number of fish in the lake after 7 years.

    a. 3500   **b.** 2100   **c.** 1200   **d.** 300

_____ 9. Sally decides to start doing sit-ups as part of her daily workout. She decides to do 15 sit-ups the first day and then increase the number by 4 each day after that. Find the total number of sit-ups Sally will do in the next 3 weeks if she sticks to her plan.

    a. 95   **b.** 625   **c.** 1155   **d.** 1435

_____ 10. It cost Kip \$12 to maintain his car during the first month he owned it. Since then the cost has increased by \$2.25 a month. If the cost continues to increase by the same amount each month, how much will it cost Kip to maintain his car during the 40th month he owns it?

    a. \$120   **b.** \$104.40   **c.** \$102   **d.** \$99.75

Chapter Assessment

Chapter 11, Form A, page 2

_____ 11. Find the value of $\sum_{k=1}^{30} -4(1.08^{k-1})$ to the nearest tenth.

     a. 349.8   b. 123.4   c. -415.9 d. -453.1

_____ 12. Which of the following infinite series has a sum?

     a. $12 + 10.25 + 8.5 + 6.75 + \cdots$ b. $-8 + (-12) + (-18) + (-27) + \cdots$

     c. $20 + (-16) + 12.8 + (-10.24) + \cdots$ d. $\frac{2}{3} + \frac{1}{2} + \frac{3}{4} + \frac{5}{8} + \cdots$

_____ 13. Find the sum of the infinite series $1300 + 455 + 159.25 + \cdots$

     a. 2000   b. 2952.6   c. 3714.3   d. 3000

_____ 14. Which of the following is the eighth entry in row 17 of Pascal's triangle?

     a. 12,870   b. 19,448   c. 24,310   d. 98,017,920

_____ 15. Find the sum of the terms in row 12 of Pascal's triangle.

     a. 144   b. 924   c. 2048   d. 4096

_____ 16. In the expansion of $(a + b)^{13}$, which term contains b^9?

     a. $715a^9b^9$ b. $1287a^9b^9$ c. $715a^4b^9$ d. $1287a^4b^9$

_____ 17. In the expansion of $(3x - y)^7$, which term contains y^5?

     a. $189x^2y^5$ b. $-189x^2y^5$ c. $63x^2y^5$ d. $-63x^5y^5$

_____ 18. If 12 fair coins are tossed, in how many ways can 8 heads appear?

     a. 96   b. 495   c. 792   d. 1264

_____ 19. If a family deposits $2000 at the beginning of each year into a bank account that pays 6% annual interest, how much will the family have in the account after 18 years?

     a. $5708.68   b. $38,160   c. $61,811.31   d. $65,519.98

_____ 20. If a number cube is rolled 7 times, what is the probability that an even number occurs exactly 5 times?

     a. 0.164   b. 0.225   c. 0.417   d. 0.523

_____ 21. When Amy bowls, the probability that she will bowl one strike in a frame is 0.35. What is the probability that Amy will bowl exactly 4 strikes in the next 7 frames?

     a. 1.40   b. 0.57   c. 0.27   d. 0.14

_____ 22. The probability of being stopped at a particular traffic light is 0.21. If you go through this traffic light 10 times, what is the probability that you will be stopped 2 or fewer times?

     a. 0.21   b. 0.30   c. 0.55   d. 0.65

Chapter Assessment

Chapter 11, Form B, page 1

1. Find the fourth term of the sequence $\begin{cases} t_1 = 5 \\ t_n = 3t_{n-1} - 12 \end{cases}$, where $n \geq 2$. _____

Write an explicit formula for each sequence.

2. $\dfrac{1}{2}, \dfrac{7}{8}, \dfrac{5}{4}, \dfrac{13}{8}, 2, \ldots$ _____   3. $500, 100, 20, 4, \ldots$ _____

Find each sum. If necessary, round your answer to the nearest hundredth.

4. $\displaystyle\sum_{k=1}^{40} 8(-1.25)^{k-1}$ _____   5. $\displaystyle\sum_{n=1}^{85} (3 + 5n)$ _____

6. $\displaystyle\sum_{n=1}^{\infty} 12(0.7^{n-1})$ _____   7. $\displaystyle\sum_{k=1}^{9} (4k^2 - 5k + 1)$ _____

8. Find t_{12} in the geometric sequence in which $t_3 = 5$ and $t_6 = 320$. _____

9. Find S_{52} in the series $428 + 407 + 386 + 365 + \cdots$ _____

10. Write $0.\overline{72}$ as a fraction in simplest form. _____

11. a. Find the seventh entry in row 17 of Pascal's triangle. _____

   b. Which other entry in row 17 has the same value as the seventh entry? _____

   c. Find the sum of all the entries in row 17 of Pascal's triangle. _____

Expand each binomial.

12. $(r - t)^7$

_____

13. $(3x + 2y)^4$

_____

14. In the expansion of $(x + 5)^{10}$, find the term containing x^8. _____

15. a. If 12 fair coins are tossed, in how many ways can 9 heads appear? _____
   b. If 12 fair coins are tossed, find the probability that 9 heads appear. _____

16. Marie has just bought a new car for $14,000. She will make monthly
   payments on the car for 5 years.

   a. If the car retains 80% of its value each year,
      how much will Marie's car be worth after 5 years? _____

   b. If the value of the car decreases by $1600 per year,
      how much will Marie's car be worth after 5 years? _____

Chapter Assessment

Chapter 11, Form B, page 2

17. If, at the beginning of each year, a family puts $1500 into a bank account that pays 9% annual interest, how much money will the family have in the account after 12 years? _____

18. Bill has decided to start taking a daily walk in order to improve his health. He decides to walk 0.5 mile the first day and then increase the distance by 0.25 mile per day.

   a. If Bill sticks to his plan, how far will he walk on the 15th day? _____

   b. If Bill sticks to his plan for 4 weeks, find the total distance he will walk. _____

19. The owner of a new restaurant is disappointed because only 150 people came to the restaurant during the first week it was open. However, the owner believes that the number of people who come to the restaurant will increase by 10% per week.

   a. If the owner is correct, how many people will come to the restaurant during the 20th week it is open? _____

   b. If the owner is correct, find the total number of people that will come to the restaurant during the first year it is open. _____

20. If a person reserves a seat on a flight, the probability that the person shows up is 0.86. Suppose that 20 people have reserved seats on this flight. Find the following probabilities. Round your answers to the nearest hundredth.

   a. Find the probability that exactly 16 of the 20 people show up. _____

   b. Find the probability that 18 or more of the 20 people show up. _____

21. Use mathematical induction to prove that $3 + 7 + 11 + \cdots + (4n - 1) = n(2n + 1)$ is true for all natural numbers, n.

   _____

   _____

   _____

   _____

   _____

Alternative Assessment

Creating Sequences, Chapter 11, Form A

TASK: Create a sequence that is arithmetic or geometric and supply the missing terms.

HOW YOU WILL BE SCORED: As you work through the task, your teacher will be looking for the following:

- how well you can create sequences
- whether you can write the rule used to define a sequence

1. Create an arithmetic sequence. What rule did you use to define your sequence? What is d for your sequence?

_____

_____

2. Create a geometric sequence. What rule did you use to define your sequence? What is r for your sequence?

_____

_____

3. Create a sequence that is neither geometric nor arithmetic. What rule did you use to define your sequence?

_____

_____

4. Consider the linear function $f(x) = 3x - 1$ for $x = 1, 2, 3, \ldots$ Does this function generate an arithmetic or a geometric sequence? Describe how the function is related to the sequence.

_____

_____

5. Consider the exponential function $g(x) = 9\left(\frac{1}{3}\right)^x$ for $x = 1, 2, 3, \ldots$

Does this function generate an arithmetic or a geometric sequence? Describe how the function is related to the sequence.

_____

_____

SELF-ASSESSMENT: Describe examples of patterns in the real world that are made up of arithmetic sequences or geometric sequences.

Alternative Assessment

Binomial Powers and Pascal's Triangle, Chapter 11, Form B

TASK: Describe the relationship between binomial powers and Pascal's triangle.

HOW YOU WILL BE SCORED: As you work through the task, your teacher will be looking for the following:

- how well you can compare the expanded form of a binomial with Pascal's triangle
- how well you can describe patterns

1. Expand $(a + b)^0$, $(a + b)^1$, $(a + b)^2$, and $(a + b)^3$.

_____

2. Describe how the number of terms in the expanded forms of Exercise 1 compare with the exponents of the binomials.

_____

3. Examine the algebraic terms of the expanded form. Describe the pattern in the exponents as you read them from left to right. What happens to the exponents of a? What happens to the exponents of b?

_____

_____

4. Write the first 4 rows of Pascal's triangle. Then compare the values of each row with the expanded form of the binomials in Exercise 1. Explain how you can use Pascal's triangle to expand $(a + b)^6$.

_____

_____

_____

_____

5. A quiz consists of 3 true-false questions. Suppose that you guess the answer to each question. Using R for the event "right" and W for the event "wrong," list the possible outcomes for each of the following events: (a) 3 answers are correct, (b) 2 answers are correct, (c) 1 answer is correct, and (d) no answers are correct. Describe how the numbers of possible outcomes for these events relate to Pascal's triangle.

_____

_____

SELF-ASSESSMENT: Write the Binomial Theorem by using sigma notation.

Quick Warm-Up: Assessing Prior Knowledge
12.1 *Measures of Central Tendency*

Find the average of each pair of numbers.

1. 10 and 16 _____

2. 12 and 23 _____

3. 42 and 42 _____

4. 0 and 208 _____

5. 1.9 and 3.6 _____

6. 5 and 2.3 _____

Arrange the set of numbers in order from least to greatest.

7. 6.4, 0.8, 3.7, 1.5, 2.6, 3.9 _____

Lesson Quiz
12.1 *Measures of Central Tendency*

1. Find the mean, median, and mode for the data set below.
   12, 18, 32, 18, 22, 24, 52, 18, 25, 20

_____

2. The frequency table at right shows the number of children in a randomly selected sample of families. Find the mean, median, and mode for the number of children in a family.

   mean: _____

   median: _____

   mode(s): _____

Children	Frequency
1	3
2	9
3	4
4	3
5	1

3. The grouped frequency table at right shows the number of hours of TV watched in a week by a randomly selected sample of students. Estimate the mean number of hours of TV these students watch in a week.

_____

Hours	Frequency
1–7	6
8–14	10
15–21	7
22–28	2

4. The mean of 6 pieces of data is $7\frac{2}{3}$. Five of the data values are 9, 4, 8, 8, and 7. What is the sixth data value? _____

5. The mean of 5 pieces of data is 0.21. Four of the data values are 0.12, 0.36, 0.15, and 0.17. What is the fifth data value? _____

Quick Warm-Up: Assessing Prior Knowledge

12.2 Stem-and-Leaf Plots, Histograms, and Circle Graphs

Refer to the data set at right.   17, 22, 8, 23, 20, 22, 21, 17, 19, 20, 22, 18

1. Find the mean. _____   2. Find the median. _____   3. Find the mode(s). _____

4. Make a grouped frequency table for the data.

Number					
Frequency					

5. Use your grouped frequency table from Exercise 4
to estimate the mean.   _____

Lesson Quiz

12.2 Stem-and-Leaf Plots, Histograms, and Circle Graphs

1. In the space at right, make a stem-and-leaf plot of this
data set.

56   67   85   62   73   69   70   65   53   74
81   68   59   65   47   75   60   77   65   71

2. In the space at right, make a histogram of this data set.

5   4   6   1   2   3   5   1   2   2   3   4   3   2   1
4   3   5   1   1   2   2   2   3   5   4   4   3   2   1

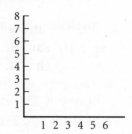

3. In the space at right, make a circle graph to represent the table
below, which shows how a randomly selected sample of students
travels to school.

Method	Number
Bus	21
Car	27
Walk	12

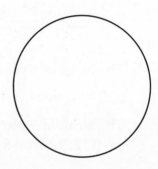

Quick Warm-Up: Assessing Prior Knowledge

12.3 *Box-and-Whisker Plots*

Find the mean, median, and mode(s) of each data set.

1. 2, 3, 9, 4, 5, 7 _____

2. 8.2, 8.2, 8.2, 8.3, 8.3, 8.3 _____

3. 10, 11, 12, 13, 14 _____

4. 1.6, 1.6, 1.6, 1.6, 1.6, 1.6 _____

 Lesson Quiz

12.3 *Box-and-Whisker Plots*

1. a. Find the quartiles, range, and interquartile range for
   the data below, which shows the number of runs
   scored by a softball team in games this season.

   1 4 8 2 1 2 4 8 6 3 5 2 5 7 15 5 7

   _____

   b. In the space at right, make a box-and-whisker plot
   for the data.

   c. Find any outliers in the data. _____

2. The box-and-whisker plots below show the time a randomly
   selected sample of students spent studying for a math test and for
   an English test.

   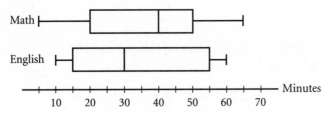

   a. Find the IQR for each set of data. _____

   b. What percent of students studied for more than 20 minutes for the math test? _____

   c. In which set of data is the median higher? _____

Mid-Chapter Assessment

Chapter 12 (Lessons 12.1–12.3)

Write the letter that best answers the question or completes the statement.

_____ 1. Find the median for this set of data: 13, 17, 31, 24, 46, 29, 50.

     a. 24   **b.** 29   **c.** 30   **d.** 35

_____ 2. Find the mean for the data at right, which shows the number of cars owned by families in a neighborhood.

     a. 6.25   **b.** 4.75

     c. 3.16   **d.** 2.24

Cars	Frequency
1	3
2	15
3	5
4	2

_____ 3. Find Q_3 for this set of data: 16, 24, 26, 31, 33, 37, 45, 54.

     a. 25   **b.** 32   **c.** 41   **d.** 45

4. a. Make a stem-and-leaf plot of the data below, which shows the heights, in inches, of randomly selected students.

    72   64   68   71   67   58   63   67   74   65
    59   62   70   66   61   67   76   80   63

b. Find the mean, median, and mode for the heights.

5. a. Make a histogram of the data below, which shows the number of times randomly selected families go out to eat in a week.

    3   5   8   5   4   3   6   3   4   7   4   5   4   5   5
    4   7   8   7   5   4   5   7   3   5   6   5   3   4   6

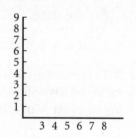

b. If one of the families in this sample is randomly selected, find the probability that the family eats out at least 6 times a week. _____

6. a. Find the quartiles, range, and interquartile range for this data on the number of CDs owned by a randomly selected group of students.

    25   42   54   33   65   37   75   47   58
    64   58   72   44   35   61   28   60   73

b. Make a box-and-whisker plot of the data.

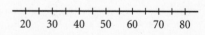

    20   30   40   50   60   70   80

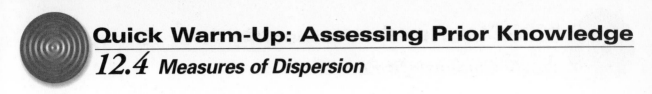

Quick Warm-Up: Assessing Prior Knowledge
12.4 Measures of Dispersion

Find the indicated statistical measure for the data below. Round
to the nearest tenth when necessary.

45, 21, 39, 52, 37, 44, 40, 36, 37, 43, 51, 45

1. mean _____   2. median _____   3. mode(s) _____   4. range _____

5. Q_1 _____   6. Q_2 _____   7. Q_3 _____   8. IQR _____

Lesson Quiz
12.4 Measures of Dispersion

1. Will the standard deviation of daily high temperatures in March be
greater in Chicago, Illinois, or in Nairobi, Kenya, which is near the
equator? Explain.

_____

_____

2. Find the range and the mean deviation for the following set of data:

3   16   10   12   15   20   24   25   28   30   37

_____

3. Find σ^2 and σ for the following set of data. Round your answers to
the nearest hundredth.

132   145   111   157   160   162   176   187   210

_____

4. Find the standard deviation for a data set that has a variance of 57.76. _____

5. The approximate percentages of women in the work force for the
years 1988 through 1993 are given in the table below.

Year	1988	1989	1990	1991	1992	1993
Percentage	54	56	56	55	56	57

Find the range, mean, median, and standard deviation for the data.

_____

Quick Warm-Up: Assessing Prior Knowledge
12.5 *Binomial Distributions*

Evaluate.

1. $_{10}C_4$ _____

2. $_8C_1$ _____

3. $_{12}C_{12}$ _____

A fair coin is tossed 4 times. Find the probability of tossing

4. 4 heads. _____

5. fewer than 4 heads. _____

6. 4 heads *or* 3 heads. _____

7. 4 heads *or* 4 tails. _____

Lesson Quiz
12.5 *Binomial Distributions*

Solve each problem. Round all your answers to the nearest thousandth.

1. A family has 6 children. If the probability of having a boy is equal to the probability of having a girl, find the probability that the family has 4 boys and 2 girls. _____

2. A basketball player makes 75% of the free throws he attempts in a game. Suppose that the player attempts 10 free throws in a game. Find the probability that

   a. the player makes exactly 7 of the 10 free throws. _____

   b. the player makes at least 8 of the 10 free throws. _____

3. A cold medication relieves sinus congestion in 60% of the people with colds that take the medication. Suppose 8 people with colds take this medication. Find the probability that

   a. exactly 5 have their sinus congestion relieved. _____

   b. 3 or fewer have their sinus congestion relieved. _____

4. On a multiple choice test each question has 5 possible answers. A person taking the test does not know the answer to 12 of the questions and decides to guess on all of them. Each question has one correct answer. Find the probability that

   a. the person guesses correctly exactly 2 times. _____

   b. the person guesses correctly 2 or fewer times. _____

Quick Warm-Up: Assessing Prior Knowledge
12.6 *Normal Distributions*

Find each statistical measure for the data below. Round to the nearest thousandth when necessary.

2.0, 1.3, 2.1, 2.8, 1.8, 2.6, 1.9, 2.3

1. mean _____

2. median _____

3. mode(s) _____

4. quartiles _____

5. range _____

6. mean deviation _____

7. variance _____

8. standard deviation _____

Lesson Quiz
12.6 *Normal Distributions*

1. Find each probability by using a standard normal curve area table or a graphics calculator.

   a. $P(x \leq 1.74)$ b. $P(x > 2.05)$ c. $P(-2.35 \leq x < 0.65)$

   _____ _____ _____

2. The length of time it takes to assemble a VCR in a factory is normally distributed with a mean of 37 minutes and a standard deviation of 2.5 minutes.

   a. Find the probability that a randomly selected VCR takes less than 33 minutes to assemble. _____

   b. If 2000 VCRs are assembled each day in this factory, how many can the managers expect to be assembled each day in less than 33 minutes? _____

3. The number of miles per gallon for a particular car model is normally distributed with a mean of 36 miles per gallon and a standard deviation of 1.2 miles per gallon.

   a. Find the probability that a randomly selected car of this model gets 37.5 miles per gallon or more. _____

   b. Find the probability that a randomly selected car of this model gets between 35.1 and 36.9 miles per gallon. _____

Chapter Assessment

Chapter 12, Form A, page 1

Write the letter that best answers the question or completes the statement.

_____ 1. Find the median of this set of data: 52, 45, 34, 67, 21, 54, 67, 34, 89, 43, 50, 31.

   a. 37.6   b. 47.5   c. 48.9   d. 60.5

_____ 2. Find the mean of the data shown in the stem-and-leaf plot at right.

Stem	Leaf
6	0 3 7
5	4 4 6 8 9
4	1 3 5
3	3 4

   a. 4.4   b. 17.8

   c. 34.2   d. 51.3

_____ 3. A video store surveyed its customers to find the number of movies they rent per month. The results are shown in the grouped frequency table at right. Estimate the mean number of movies per month rented by the customers of this video store.

Movies Rented	Frequency
1–5	8
6–10	10
11–15	7
16–20	5

   a. 7.5   b. 8.5

   c. 9.5   d. 10.5

_____ 4. Find Q_1 in this set of data: 17, 21, 24, 32, 45, 46, 51, 52, 63, 72, 81.

   a. 24   b. 28   c. 46   d. 63

_____ 5. The data from a survey on the number of pieces of junk mail people in a town receive is summarized in the box-and-whisker plot at right. Find the IQR for the data.

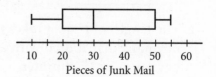

Pieces of Junk Mail

   a. 10   b. 20

   c. 30   d. 45

_____ 6. A teacher surveyed his class to find the number of minutes students spend traveling to school each morning. The results in minutes are shown below.

   10 25 15 20 15 5 22 15 20 18

   Find σ for the data.

   a. 5.6 minutes   b. 9.2 minutes   c. 16.5 minutes   d. 31.1 minutes

_____ 7. Find the variance of a data set with a standard deviation of 16.

   a. 4   b. 32   c. 128   d. 256

_____ 8. Find the mean deviation of this set of data: 15, 25, 28, 35, 33, 17, 22.

   a. 6   b. 7   c. 12   d. 25

Chapter Assessment

Chapter 12, Form A, page 2

_____ 9. Find $P(x \geq 1.54)$ using a standard normal curve area table or a graphics calculator.

   a. 0.9382   b. 0.7438   c. 0.2754   d. 0.0618

_____ 10. The scores for a statistics test are shown below.

   84 93 67 84 53 73 73 67 95 84 72 85 78 71 87 90 64

   Find the range and the mode for the test scores.

   a. range = 42; mode = 84   b. range = 40; mode = 73

   c. range = 67; mode = 84   d. range = 84; mode = 73

_____ 11. The results of a survey on the number of television sets owned by households in a town are shown in the histogram at right. If one of the households in the survey were randomly selected, find the probability that the household has 4 or more television sets.

   a. 40%   b. 50%

   c. 60%   d. 70%

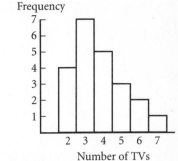

_____ 12. If a person rolls a number cube 7 times, find the probability that an even number results exactly 5 times.

   a. 0.714   b. 0.418   c. 0.164   d. 0.031

_____ 13. A restaurant has found that 55% of their customers have coffee with their meals. If 12 people eat at this restaurant, find the probability that exactly 7 of them will have coffee with their meals.

   a. 0.015   b. 0.222   c. 0.4242   d. 0.577

_____ 14. A set of data is normally distributed with a mean of 12 and a standard deviation of 4. Find the z-score for 6 in this set of data.

   a. 1.5   b. −1.5   c. 0.17   d. −0.17

_____ 15. The weights of the fish in a lake are normally distributed with a mean of 9.4 pounds and a standard deviation of 3.2 pounds. If a person catches a fish in this lake, find the probability that the fish weighs 15 pounds or less.

   a. 0.0401   b. 0.1038   c. 0.8962   d. 0.9599

Chapter Assessment

Chapter 12, Form B, page 1

1. A principal takes a random sample of the classes at her school and finds the number of students in each class. The data is shown below.

   17 23 25 31 14 19 27 33 20 23
   11 30 23 35 16 25 17 28 32 21

   a. In the space at right, make a stem-and-leaf plot of the data.

   b. Find the mean, median, and mode for the data.

   _____

2. A travel agent is interested in the length of time people in a town go on vacation. The results from a random sample of people in the town are shown below.

   5 3 4 5 7 6 5 3 3 4 5 7 3
   4 4 6 3 5 7 5 4 5 6 5 4

   a. In the space at right, make a histogram of the data.

   b. If one person from the sample is randomly selected, find the probability that the person spends at least 5 days on vacation.

   _____

3. The data below represents the number of people that stopped at a display in a mall during a random sample of days.

   45 56 67 32 43 85 67 54 35 62 60
   55 74 41 78 63 35 48 65 39 58

   a. Find the quartiles and the IQR for the data.

   _____

   b. In the space at right, make a box-and-whisker plot of the data.

4. The data below represents the number of inches of rain that fell in Knox during 10 consecutive months.

   6.3 5.7 7.3 4.7 5.3 3.7 6.8 7.6 4.2 3.4

   Find the range, variance, standard deviation, and mean deviation for the data. Round your answers to the nearest hundredth.

   _____

5. Make a circle graph of the data below, which shows the favorite fast food of a randomly selected sample of people at a mall.

Food	Frequency
Pizza	15
Hamburgers	18
Tacos	15
Chicken Nuggets	12

Find each probability by using a standard normal curve area table or a graphics calculator.

6. $P(x \geq -0.67)$

7. $P(x < 2.33)$

8. $P(-1.65 < x \leq -1.29)$

_____

_____

_____

9. If a fair coin is tossed 14 times, find the probability that tails results exactly 10 times. Round your answer to the nearest thousandth. _____

10. An insurance agent has found that 7% of drivers in Plymouth have an accident in any given year. If the insurance agent has insured 14 drivers in Plymouth, find the probability that 3 or fewer will have an accident this year. Round your answer to the nearest thousandth. _____

11. The scores on a reading test are normally distributed with a mean of 150 and a standard deviation of 20.

a. Find the z-score of a test score of 175. _____

b. If a randomly selected person takes this reading test, find the probability that the person scores 175 or lower on the test. _____

12. The amount of soda a machine dispenses into cups is normally distributed with a mean of 250 milliliters and a standard deviation of 8 milliliters. If one cup of soda dispensed by this machine is randomly selected, find the following probabilities:

a. Find the probability that the cup contains more than 238 milliliters of soda. _____

b. Find the probability that the cup contains between 234 and 262 milliliters of soda. _____

Alternative Assessment

Using Statistics, Chapter 12, Form A

TASK: Compare two sets of data.

HOW YOU WILL BE SCORED: As you work through the task, your teacher will be looking for the following:

- whether you can find measures of central tendency and measures of dispersion
- whether you can construct box-and-whisker plots

Chris and Pat both play basketball in a summer league. The number of points they have scored in each game is shown below.

Chris: 16 19 22 23 14 28 19 20 17 26 15 24 30 21 18 31 24 22 19 16 17
Pat: 13 21 26 17 30 11 32 33 14 15 32 19 15 38 14 25   9 20 22 28   7

1. Find the mean and median number of points scored for both Chris and Pat. Is it possible to tell who is the better player by looking at the mean and median?

   _____

2. Find Q_1, Q_3, the range, and the IQR for the number of points scored by each player.

   _____

3. In the space below, make box-and-whisker plots for both Chris and Pat. Put them on the same graph.

4. Which player would you rather have on your team? Explain.

   _____

   _____

   _____

SELF ASSESSMENT: Are the mean, median, and quartiles of a data set always values in the set? Create sample data sets to demonstrate your answer.

Alternative Assessment

Exploring Binomial Distributions, Chapter 12, Form B

TASK: Describe characteristics of a binomial experiment and find the probability of a binomial experiment.

HOW YOU WILL BE SCORED: As you work through the task, your teacher will be looking for the following:

- whether you can recognize a binomial experiment
- whether you can describe the characteristics of a binomial experiment
- whether you can find the probability of *r* successes in *n* trials of a binomial experiment

Decide whether the binomial probability distribution can be applied to each of the following experiments. If the experiment is a binomial experiment, describe the characteristics that make it a binomial experiment. Then find the probability.

1. The integers 1, 2, 3, 4, and 5 are each written on a card, and the five cards are placed in a hat. Three cards are drawn at random, one at a time, and replaced after each draw. Find the probability that exactly three odd integers are drawn.

_____

2. Two number cubes, one red and one blue, are tossed. Find the probability that both numbers rolled are greater than 3.

_____

3. Two cards are drawn from a deck of 52 cards, one after the other, without replacement. Find the probability that exactly two cards are queens.

_____

4. Georgette has a $\frac{9}{20}$ chance of winning any one game of "mines." If she plays seven games, what is the probability that she wins exactly one of the seven games?

_____

SELF-ASSESSMENT: Design your own probability experiment by using the binomial probability distribution.

Quick Warm-Up: Assessing Prior Knowledge
13.1 Right-Triangle Trigonometry

Rewrite as a decimal rounded to the nearest ten-thousandth.

1. $\dfrac{13}{24}$ _____

2. $\dfrac{24}{13}$ _____

Solve each equation.

3. $0.3 = \dfrac{m}{8}$ _____

4. $1.25 = \dfrac{7}{y}$ _____

5. Find the unknown length in the right
   triangle ABC. _____

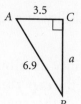

Lesson Quiz
13.1 Right-Triangle Trigonometry

1. Find the values of the six trigonometric functions of θ
   for the right triangle shown. Give exact answers and
   answers rounded to the nearest ten-thousandth.

   _____

   _____

   _____

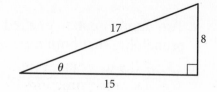

2. Find x and y in the triangle shown. Round your answers
   to the nearest hundredth.

   _____

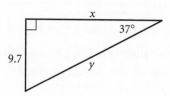

3. Solve $\triangle ABC$. Round $m\angle A$ and $m\angle B$ to the nearest
   degree and round AB to the nearest tenth.

   _____

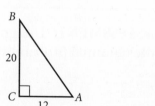

Quick Warm-Up: Assessing Prior Knowledge
13.2 Angles of Rotation

Find the values of each trigonometric function for angle θ.
Give exact answers and answers rounded to the nearest
ten-thousandth.

1. sin θ _____   2. cos θ _____   3. tan θ _____

4. csc θ _____   5. sec θ _____   6. cot θ _____

Lesson Quiz
13.2 Angles of Rotation

Find the coterminal angle, θ, for each angle such that
$-360° < \theta < 360°$.

1. 125° _____   2. −215° _____

Find the reference angle, θ_{ref}, for each angle.

3. 305° _____   4. −100° _____   5. 168° _____

6. Using the diagram at right, find the exact values of the six
trigonometric functions of θ.

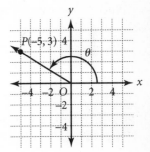

_____

_____

7. The terminal side of θ lies in Quadrant IV and $\cos \theta = \frac{5}{13}$.

Find $\sin \theta$ and $\tan \theta$. _____

8. Give two positive and two negative angles that are coterminal with

112°. _____

Quick Warm-Up: Assessing Prior Knowledge

13.3 *Trigonometric Functions of Any Angle*

Find the reference angle, θ_{ref}, for each angle.

1. $\theta = 163°$ _____   2. $\theta = -163°$ _____   3. $\theta = -280°$ _____   4. $\theta = 311°$ _____

The point $(1, -2)$ is located on the terminal side of θ. Find the exact value of each trigonometric function of θ.

5. $\sin \theta$ _____   6. $\cos \theta$ _____   7. $\tan \theta$ _____

8. $\csc \theta$ _____   9. $\sec \theta$ _____   10. $\cot \theta$ _____

Lesson Quiz

13.3 *Trigonometric Functions of Any Angle*

Find the exact values of the sine and the cosine of each angle.

1. $750°$ _____   2. $-945°$ _____

3. $-1260°$ _____   4. $1140°$ _____

5. In the diagram at right, $\theta = 240°$ and $x = -8$. Find exact values for r and the coordinates of P.

_____

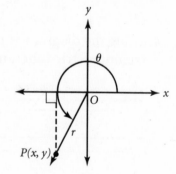

6. In the illustration at right, point P is the intersection of a circle with a radius of 7 and the terminal side of a $135°$ angle. Find the exact coordinates of P.

_____

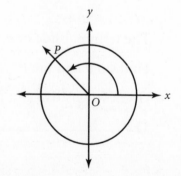

Mid-Chapter Assessment
Chapter 13 (Lessons 13.1–13.3)

Write the letter that best answers the question or completes the statement.

_____ 1. Which of the following is sec θ?

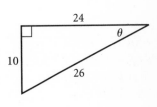

    a. $\frac{12}{13}$ **b.** $\frac{13}{5}$

    c. $\frac{13}{12}$ **d.** $\frac{5}{13}$

_____ 2. Which of the following angles is coterminal with $-140°$?

    a. $-220°$ **b.** $220°$ **c.** $-40°$ **d.** $40°$

_____ 3. Point P is located at the intersection of a circle with a radius of 10 and the terminal side of a 330° angle. Find the exact coordinates of P.

    a. $P\left(-5, \frac{10\sqrt{3}}{2}\right)$ **b.** $P\left(5, -\frac{10\sqrt{3}}{2}\right)$

    c. $P\left(-\frac{10\sqrt{3}}{2}, 5\right)$ **d.** $P\left(\frac{10\sqrt{3}}{2}, -5\right)$

Solve each triangle. Give the measure of each angle to the nearest degree and the length of each side to the nearest tenth.

4.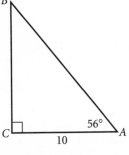

5.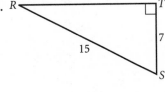

_____   _____

Find the reference angle, θ_{ref}, for each angle.

6. 95° _____   7. 250° _____   8. $-35°$ _____

9. Find the exact values of the six trigonometric functions of θ if θ is in standard position and $(7, -24)$ is on the terminal side of θ.

_____

10. Find exact values for sin 1305° and tan 1305°. _____

Quick Warm-Up: Assessing Prior Knowledge
13.4 Radian Measure and Arc Length

Find each trigonometric value. Give exact answers.

1. sin 60° _____   2. cos 135° _____   3. tan(−30°) _____   4. sin(−150°) _____

5. cos 360° _____   6. sin(−90°) _____   7. tan(−180°) _____   8. tan 270° _____

Find the number of rotations represented by each angle.

9. 720° _____   10. 90° _____   11. −60° _____   12. −540° _____

Lesson Quiz
13.4 Radian Measure and Arc Length

Convert each degree measure to radian measure. Give exact answers.

1. 135° _____   2. 450° _____

Convert each radian measure to degree measure. Round answers to the nearest tenth.

3. $\dfrac{2\pi}{3}$ _____   4. 2.5 _____

Evaluate each expression. Round answers to the nearest ten-thousandth.

5. sin 3.5 _____   6. $\tan\left(\dfrac{5\pi}{6}\right)$ _____

7. A central angle in a circle with a radius of 20 meters measures 1.6 radians. Find the length of the arc on the circle that this angle intercepts.

_____

8. A central angle in a circle with a diameter of 30 meters measures 60°. To the nearest tenth, find the length of the arc on the circle that this angle intercepts.

_____

9. A central angle in a circle with a radius of 50 meters intercepts an arc 12 meters long. Find the measure of the central angle in radians.

_____

10. Find the radius of a circle if the length of the arc intercepted by a 45° central angle is π meters.

_____

Quick Warm-Up: Assessing Prior Knowledge
13.5 Graphing Trigonometric Functions

Identify the transformation(s) applied to the parent function $f(x) = \sqrt{x}$.

1. $f(x) = \sqrt{x} - 2$ _____

2. $f(x) = \sqrt{x - 2}$ _____

3. $f(x) = -3\sqrt{x}$ _____

4. $f(x) = \sqrt{-x}$ _____

5. $f(x) = \sqrt{6x + 1}$ _____

Lesson Quiz
13.5 Graphing Trigonometric Functions

1. Graph one period of $y = \sin(x + 90°) - 1$.

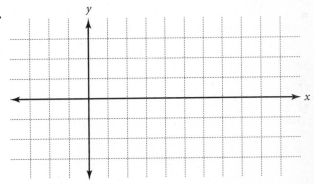

2. Graph one period of $y = 3\cos\left(\frac{3}{2}x\right)$.

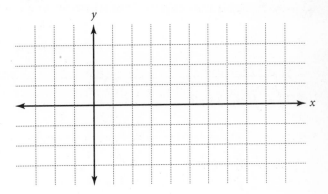

3. Find the phase shift, vertical translation, amplitude, and period of the function $y = 2.5\cos[3(\theta - 20°)] + 6$.

_____

Quick Warm-Up: Assessing Prior Knowledge
13.6 Inverses of Trigonometric Functions

Find the inverse of each function.

1. $f(x) = x - 4$ _____

2. $g(x) = -5x$ _____

3. $h(x) = 2x + 6$ _____

4. $j(x) = 3^x$ _____

5. $k(x) = \ln x$ _____

 # Lesson Quiz
13.6 Inverses of Trigonometric Functions

Evaluate each trigonometric expression. Give answers in degrees rounded to the nearest hundredth.

1. $\text{Sin}^{-1}\left(\frac{3}{4}\right)$ _____ 2. $\text{Tan}^{-1} 7.5$ _____

Evaluate each trigonometric expression. Give answers in radians rounded to the nearest hundredth.

3. $\text{Cos}^{-1}(-0.27)$ _____ 4. $\text{Tan}^{-1}\left(\sqrt{3}\right)$ _____

Evaluate each composite trigonometric expression.

5. $\sin\left[\text{Cos}^{-1}\left(\frac{\sqrt{3}}{2}\right)\right]$ 6. $\tan\left[\text{Sin}^{-1}\left(-\frac{\sqrt{2}}{2}\right)\right]$

_____ _____

7. $\text{Tan}^{-1}(\sin 330°)$ 8. $\text{Cos}^{-1}(\cos 225°)$

_____ _____

9. A 30-foot-tall building casts a 40-foot-long shadow on the ground. Find the angle of elevation of the sun to the nearest tenth of a

degree. _____

Chapter Assessment

Chapter 13, Form A, page 1

Write the letter that best answers the question or completes the statement.

_____ 1. Find the value of x in the figure at right.

    a. 8.73   b. 9.98

    c. 12.42   d. 15.74

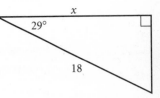

_____ 2. Find the value of θ in the figure at right.

    a. 23.6°   b. 25.9°

    c. 64.1°   d. 66.4°

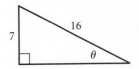

_____ 3. Which of the following is coterminal with 112°?

    a. 148°   b. 68°   c. $-22°$ d. $-248°$

_____ 4. Which of the following is the reference angle for 230°?

    a. 40°   b. 50°   c. 130°   d. 180°

_____ 5. Using the diagram at right, find $\csc \theta$.

    a. $-\dfrac{5}{4}$ b. $-\dfrac{3}{4}$

    c. $\dfrac{5}{3}$ d. $\dfrac{3}{7}$

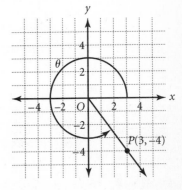

_____ 6. If θ is an angle in standard position with its terminal side in Quadrant III and $\cot \theta = \dfrac{15}{8}$, find $\cos \theta$.

    a. $-\dfrac{17}{8}$ b. $-\dfrac{17}{15}$ c. $-\dfrac{15}{17}$ d. $-\dfrac{8}{17}$

_____ 7. Point P is the intersection of a circle with a radius of 15 and the terminal side of a 200° angle in standard position. Find the coordinates of P.

    a. $P(12.7, -6.4)$ b. $P(-5.1, -14.1)$

    c. $P(6.4, -12.7)$ d. $P(-14.1, -5.1)$

_____ 8. Convert 38° to radian measure.

    a. 0.66   b. 12.10   c. 320.86   d. 2177.24

_____ 9. Convert $\frac{5\pi}{4}$ radians to degree measure.

     a. 115°   **b.** 225°   **c.** 315°   **d.** 405°

_____ 10. A central angle in a circle with a radius of 80 meters intercepts an arc that is 120 meters long. What is the measure of the central angle?

     a. 40°   **b.** 15°   **c.** 1.5 radians   **d.** 0.67 radians

_____ 11. A central angle in a circle with a radius of 20 meters measures 43°. Find the length of the arc on the circle that the angle intercepts.

     a. 860 meters   **b.** 430 meters   **c.** 65 meters   **d.** 15 meters

_____ 12. Find the amplitude and period of the function $y = 4\sin(2\theta) + 3$.

     a. amplitude: 4; period: 720°   **b.** amplitude: 3; period: 180°

     c. amplitude: 4; period: 180°   **d.** amplitude: 2; period: 90°

_____ 13. Identify the phase shift and the vertical translation in the function $y = 5\cos[3(\theta - 20°)] + 7$.

     a. phase shift: 20°; vertical translation: −7

     b. phase shift: −20°; vertical translation: 7

     c. phase shift: 20°; vertical translation: 7

     d. phase shift: −20°; vertical translation: −7

_____ 14. Which of the following equations is graphed at right?

     a. $y = \cos(x + 60°) - 3$

     b. $y = 3\cos(x - 60°)$

     c. $y = \cos(x + 60°) + 3$

     d. $y = \cos(3x) - 60°$

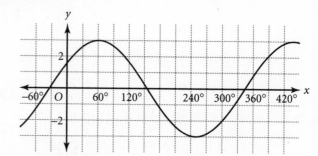

_____ 15. Which of the following is $\cos\left[\text{Tan}^{-1}\left(-\frac{\sqrt{3}}{3}\right)\right]$?

     a. $\frac{1}{2}$ **b.** $\frac{\sqrt{3}}{2}$ **c.** $-\frac{1}{2}$ **d.** $-\frac{\sqrt{3}}{2}$

_____ 16. Which of the following is $\text{Sin}^{-1}(\cos 30°)$?

     a. 60°   **b.** 30°   **c.** 0.5   **d.** −0.5

_____ 17. The angle of depression from the top of a cliff to a ship is 12°. If the cliff is 50 feet high, about how far from the bottom of the cliff is the ship?

     a. 10 feet   **b.** 50 feet   **c.** 125 feet   **d.** 235 feet

Chapter Assessment

Chapter 13, Form B, page 1

1. Find x and y to the nearest tenth in the triangle at right.

   _____

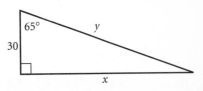

2. Find θ to the nearest tenth of a degree in the triangle at right.

   _____

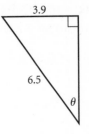

Find the reference angle, θ_{ref}, for each angle.

3. $-74°$ _____

4. $105°$ _____

5. $275°$ _____

Evaluate each expression. Round answers to the nearest ten-thousandth.

6. $\tan\left(-\dfrac{2\pi}{5}\right)$

7. $\cos 274°$

8. $\sin 6.2$

_____   _____   _____

9. The point P is the intersection of a circle with a radius of 30 and the terminal side of a 310° central angle. Find the coordinates of P to

   the nearest tenth. _____

10. The terminal side of θ lies in Quadrant II, and $\sin\theta = \dfrac{20}{29}$.

    Find exact values for $\tan\theta$ and $\sec\theta$. _____

11. Find exact values for $\csc\theta$ and $\cot\theta$ if θ is in standard position and

    $(-12, 5)$ is on the terminal side of θ. _____

12. Find the exact values for the sine and cosine of 1650°. _____

13. Find an angle between $-360°$ and 360° that is coterminal with 250°. _____

Convert to radian measure. Give exact answers.

14. $240°$ _____

15. $315°$ _____

Convert to degree measure. Round answers to the nearest degree.

16. $\dfrac{7\pi}{2}$ _____

17. 2.6 _____

Chapter Assessment
Chapter 13, Form B, page 2

18. A central angle in a circle with a radius of 60 centimeters intercepts an arc that is 75 centimeters long. Find the measure of the central angle in radians. _____

19. A central angle in a circle with a radius of 25 meters measures 200°. Find the length of the arc on the circle that the angle intercepts to the nearest tenth of a meter. _____

20. Graph one period of $y = 5\cos(x + 30°)$.

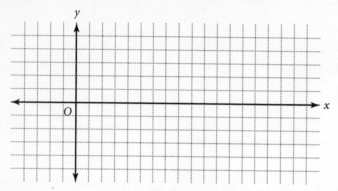

21. Graph one period of $y = \sin\left(\frac{3}{4}x\right) - 2$.

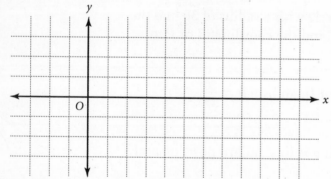

22. Find the phase shift and amplitude of $y = 7.2\sin[4(x - 10°)] - 9$. _____

Evaluate each composite trigonometric function. Give exact answers.

23. $\tan\left[\left(\text{Cos}^{-1}\left(-\frac{1}{2}\right)\right)\right]$

24. $\text{Sin}^{-1}(\cos 25°)$

_____   _____

25. The angle of depression from the top of a building to a street vendor is 34°. If the building is 30 feet high, how far, to the nearest tenth of a foot, from the bottom of the building is the vendor? _____

Alternative Assessment

Working With Right Triangles, Chapter 13, Form A

TASK: Solve problems involving more than one right triangle.

HOW YOU WILL BE SCORED: As you work through the task, your teacher will be looking for the following:

- whether you can use trigonometry to solve right triangles
- whether you can work with 45°-45°-90° and 30°-60°-90° triangles

1. Give an exact value for *x*.

   _____

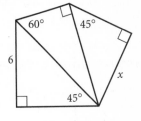

2. Use **△ACD**, **△BCD**, and the fact that the sum of the measures of the angles of a triangle must be 180° to find *θ*.

   _____

3. If *AB* = 50, explain how to find *h*.

   _____

   _____

   _____

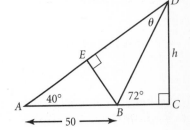

4. Find *h* to the nearest tenth. _____

5. Use the tangent ratio to write an equation using *x* and *h* in **△BCD** and a second equation using *x* and *h* in **△ACD**.

   _____

6. Explain how to combine the two equations into one equation.

   _____

   _____

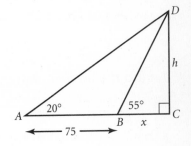

7. Find *h* to the nearest tenth. _____

SELF-ASSESSMENT: In right triangle *ABC*, show that $\frac{a}{b} = \frac{\sin A}{\sin B}$.

Alternative Assessment
Exploring Graphs of Trigonometric Functions, Chapter 13, Form B

TASK: Graph the sine and the cosine functions.

HOW YOU WILL BE SCORED: As you work through the task, your teacher will be looking for the following:

- whether you can identify the period, amplitude, phase shift, and vertical shift of the sine and cosine functions
- how well you can write the sine and cosine functions

Graph each function with its domain in degree measure, and find the period, amplitude, and phase shift.

1. $f(x) = \cos(x - 45°)$ _____

2. $g(x) = 2 \sin(x + 60°)$ _____

3. Find the period, amplitude, and vertical shift for

   $h(x) = 2 + \sin(x - 30°).$ _____

4. Let $f(x) = \cos(x - d)$ and $g(x) = \sin(x - d)$. Describe the effects of d on these functions.

   _____

   _____

Graph each function with its domain in degree measure, and find the domain, range, and period.

5. $f(x) = \cos 2(\theta - 45°)$ _____

6. $g(x) = \sin \frac{1}{2}(\theta + 60°)$ _____

7. Find the domain, range, and period of $h(x) = 5 \sin \frac{1}{3}(\theta - 30°)$.

   _____

8. Write a function in the form $f(x) = a + b \sin c(x + d)$ with a degree measure domain of all real numbers, a range of $-1 \le y \le 1$, and a period of 120°.

   _____

SELF-ASSESSMENT: Compare the graphs of $f(x) = a - b \cos c(x - d)$ and $g(x) = a + b \cos c(x - d)$. How are they alike? How are they different?

Quick Warm-Up: Assessing Prior Knowledge

14.1 The Law of Sines

Solve each of the following:

1. $\dfrac{x}{6} = \dfrac{3}{21}$ _____

2. $\dfrac{51}{90} = \dfrac{30}{x}$ _____

3. $\dfrac{0.7071}{45} = \dfrac{0.7660}{x}$ _____

4. $\dfrac{0.5}{30} = \dfrac{x}{45}$ _____

5. $\dfrac{300}{x} = 0.0152$ _____

Lesson Quiz

14.1 The Law of Sines

1. Find the area of the triangle shown at right to the nearest tenth of a square centimeter.

_____

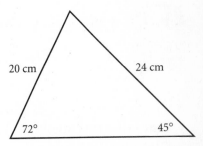

2. Find x and y in the triangle shown at right to the nearest tenth of a meter.

_____

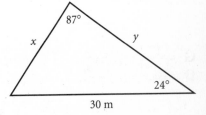

3. Find x in the triangle shown at right to the nearest tenth of a degree.

_____

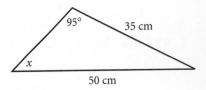

4. In a triangle, $a = 86$, $b = 63$, and $m\angle B = 47°$.

   a. Does the given information determine a triangle? _____

   b. If it does, find all possible values for $m\angle A$ to the nearest tenth of

   a degree. _____

Quick Warm-Up: Assessing Prior Knowledge

14.2 *The Law of Cosines*

In each exercise, find the unknown quantity. Round angles to the nearest degree and lengths to the nearest tenth.

1. $\theta = \sin^{-1} 0.39$ _____

2. $\cos \theta = 0.96$ _____

3. $8^2 + 9^2 - 2(8)(9)\cos \theta = 3^2$ _____

4. In $\triangle ABC$, $a = 27$, $b = 18$, and $m\angle C = 110°$.
   Find the area of the triangle. _____

5. For $\triangle XYZ$, $x = 10$, $y = 12$, and $X = 44°$.
   Solve the triangle. _____

Lesson Quiz

14.2 *The Law of Cosines*

1. Find x in the triangle shown at right to the nearest tenth of a centimeter.

   _____

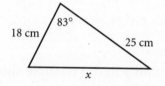

2. Find x in the triangle shown at right to the nearest tenth of a degree.

   _____

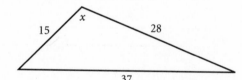

3. Solve $\triangle ABC$. Find b to the nearest tenth of a meter and $m\angle A$ and $m\angle C$ to the nearest tenth of a degree.

   _____

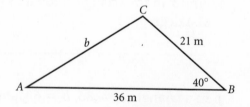

4. A surveyor is measuring the distance across a pond, represented by YZ in the diagram at right. He finds that point X is 150 yards from point Y and 200 yards from point Z. If the measure of the angle formed at point X is 42°, what is the distance across the pond?

   _____

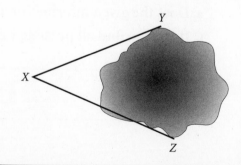

Quick Warm-Up: Assessing Prior Knowledge
14.3 Fundamental Trigonometric Identities

Given the information below, solve for every possible △*ABC*.
Round angle measures to the nearest degree and lengths to the
nearest tenth of a unit.

1. $a = 3, b = 4, c = 5$ _____

2. $A = 45°, B = 30°, c = 10$ _____

3. $B = 120°, a = 12, c = 10$ _____

4. $A = 45°, a = 10, b = 12$ _____

5. $B = 30°, a = 12, b = 4$ _____

Lesson Quiz
14.3 Fundamental Trigonometric Identities

Write each expression in terms of a single trigonometric function.

1. $(\cot \theta)(\sec \theta)$

2. $\dfrac{\sec \theta}{\csc \theta}$

3. $(\csc \theta + 1)(\csc \theta - 1)$

4. $(\tan^2 \theta + 1)(\cos \theta)$

5. $\dfrac{\sin^2 \theta}{1 - \sin^2 \theta}$

6. $\dfrac{\cos^2 \theta + \sin^2 \theta}{(\sec \theta)(\cot \theta)}$

7. $\dfrac{\sec^2 \theta - 1}{\tan \theta}$

8. $\dfrac{\cos \theta}{(\sin \theta)(\cot \theta)}$

Write each expression in terms of tan θ.

9. $\dfrac{(\sec \theta)(\sin \theta)}{\tan \theta + \cot \theta}$

10. $\dfrac{1 - \cos^2 \theta}{\cos^2 \theta}$

11. $\dfrac{\sin \theta}{\cos \theta} + \dfrac{\cos \theta}{\sin \theta}$

12. $\csc^2 \theta - 1$

Mid-Chapter Assessment

Chapter 14 (Lessons 14.1–14.3)

Write the letter that best answers the question or completes the statement.

_____ 1. Find x in the triangle at right.

     a. $x = 41.2$ meters   b. $x = 35.3$ meters

     c. $x = 28.7$ meters   d. $x = 23.4$ meters

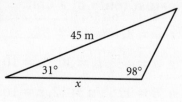

_____ 2. Find x in the triangle at right.

     a. $x = 43.9°$ b. $x = 56.8°$

     c. $x = 62.3°$ d. $x = 73.8°$

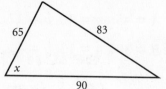

_____ 3. Which of the following is a simpler form of $(\cot \theta)(\cos \theta)(\csc \theta)$?

     a. $\cos^2 \theta$ b. $\sin^2 \theta$ c. $\tan^2 \theta$ d. $\cot^2 \theta$

4. Solve $\triangle ABC$. Find c to the nearest tenth of a foot and
   $m\angle A$ and $m\angle B$ to the nearest tenth of a degree.

   _____

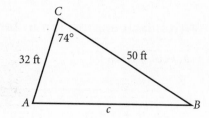

5. In $\triangle ABC$, $a = 54$, $b = 38$, and $m\angle B = 44.7°$. Find all possible

   values for $m\angle A$ to the nearest tenth of a degree. _____

Write each expression in terms of a single trigonometric function.

6. $\dfrac{\cos \theta}{(\tan \theta)(\csc \theta)}$

7. $(1 + \sin \theta)(1 - \sin \theta)(\sec \theta + 1)(\sec \theta - 1)$

_____

8. $\dfrac{\sin \theta - (\sin \theta)(\cos \theta)}{1 - \cos \theta}$

9. $\dfrac{2 \sin \theta}{1 - \cos^2 \theta}$

_____

Quick Warm-Up: Assessing Prior Knowledge
14.4 Sum and Difference Identities

Find the distance between each pairs of points below. Give
approximate values rounded to the nearest tenth.

1. $(4, 1)$ and $(4, 0)$ _____

2. $(3, 2)$ and $(-2, -5)$ _____

3. $(-5, 6)$ and $(5, 1)$ _____

4. $\left(\frac{\sqrt{2}}{2}, \frac{\sqrt{2}}{2}\right)$ and $\left(-\frac{1}{2}, \frac{\sqrt{3}}{2}\right)$ _____

5. $(\cos 30°, \sin 30°)$ and $(\cos 45°, \sin 45°)$ _____

Lesson Quiz
14.4 Sum and Difference Identities

Find the exact value of each expression.

1. $\sin\left(\frac{5\pi}{3} - \frac{\pi}{6}\right)$

2. $\cos\left(\frac{3\pi}{2} + \frac{3\pi}{4}\right)$

_____

_____

3. $\sin(-210°)$

4. $\cos 75°$

_____

_____

Prove each identity.

5. $\sin(\theta - 270°) = \cos\theta$

6. $\cos(\pi + x) = -\cos x$

_____

_____

_____

_____

_____

_____

7. Find the rotation matrix for a rotation of 120° about the origin.
Then find the image of the point $(3, 4)$ after this rotation. Give
coordinates correct to the nearest hundredth.

_____

Quick Warm-Up: Assessing Prior Knowledge
14.5 Double-Angle and Half-Angle Identities

Find the exact value of each expression:

1. $\sin 15°$ _____

2. $\cos 15°$ _____

3. $\sin 255°$ _____

4. $\cos 255°$ _____

5. $\tan (-255°)$ _____

Lesson Quiz
14.5 Double-Angle and Half-Angle Identities

Use the information given to find the exact value of sin 2θ and cos 2θ.

1. $0° \le \theta \le 90°$; $\sin \theta = \frac{4}{5}$

2. $0° \le \theta \le 90°$; $\sin \theta = \frac{2}{\sqrt{5}}$

3. $270° \le \theta \le 360°$; $\cos \theta = \frac{3}{5}$

4. $180° \le \theta \le 270°$; $\cos \theta = -\frac{5}{13}$

Use the information given to find the exact value of $\sin \frac{\theta}{2}$ and $\cos \frac{\theta}{2}$.

5. $270° \le \theta \le 360°$; $\sin \theta = -\frac{12}{13}$

6. $270° \le \theta \le 360°$; $\sin \theta = -\frac{4}{5}$

7. $180° \le \theta \le 360°$; $\cos \theta = \frac{7}{25}$

8. $180° \le \theta \le 360°$; $\cos \theta = -\frac{7}{25}$

Write each expression in terms of a single trigonometric function of θ.

9. $\frac{2 \sin \theta}{\sin(2\theta)}$

10. $\cos(2\theta) + \sin^2 \theta$

Quick Warm-Up: Assessing Prior Knowledge
14.6 Solving Trigonometric Equations

Solve for x.

1. $2x^2 + x - 1 = 0$ _____

2. $x^2 - 2x - 3 = 0$ _____

Solve for $0° \leq \theta° \leq 360°$.

3. $\sin \theta = -1$ _____

4. $\cos \theta = -\dfrac{\sqrt{3}}{2}$ _____

5. $\sin \theta = \dfrac{\sqrt{6} - \sqrt{2}}{4}$ _____

Lesson Quiz
14.6 Solving Trigonometric Equations

Find the exact solutions of each equation for $0° \leq \theta \leq 360°$.

1. $6 \cos \theta + 4 = 1$

_____

2. $5 \sin \theta - \sqrt{2} = 3 \sin \theta$

_____

3. $4 \sin \theta + 1 = 3$

_____

4. $3 \cos \theta + 2 = -\cos^2 \theta$

_____

Find the exact solutions of each equation for $0 \leq x \leq 2\pi$.

5. $\sin^2 x + 3 \sin x - 4 = 0$

_____

6. $3 - 3 \cos x = 2 \sin^2 x$

_____

7. $2 \sin x = -\sqrt{3}$

_____

8. $2 \sin x = 4 \sin x + 2$

_____

Find all solutions of each equation.

9. $5 \cos \theta + 2 = 2 - 3 \cos \theta$

_____

10. $\sin 2\theta = 4 \sin \theta$

_____

11. $3 \sin^2 \theta - \cos^2 \theta = 0$

_____

12. $\cos 2\theta + \sin \theta = 1$

_____

Chapter Assessment

Chapter 14, Form A, page 1

Write the letter that best answers the question or completes the statement.

_____ 1. Find the area of the triangle shown at right.

a. 44.95 square meters

b. 111.26 square meters

c. 120 square meters

d. 222.52 square meters

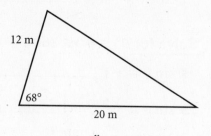

12 m

68°

20 m

_____ 2. Find the value of x in the triangle shown at right.

a. 13.6 meters   b. 24.8 meters

c. 37.1 meters   d. 45.8 meters

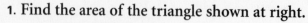

x

33°   54°

25 m

_____ 3. Find the value of x in the triangle shown at right.

a. 106.3 feet   b. 102.4 feet

c. 83.5 feet   d. 61.3 feet

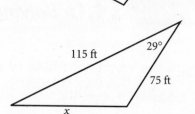

115 ft   29°

75 ft

x

_____ 4. Find the smallest angle in the triangle shown at right.

a. 24.6°   b. 31.2°

c. 40.3°   d. 63.5°

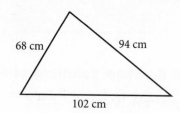

68 cm   94 cm

102 cm

_____ 5. Find the value of x in the triangle shown at right.

a. 50.1°   b. 55.3°

c. 59.7°   d. 64.4°

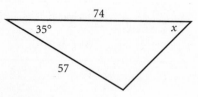

74

35° x

57

_____ 6. In $\triangle ABC$, $b = 42.9$, $c = 39.5$, and m$\angle B = 80°$. Find m$\angle C$.

a. 65.1°   b. 114.9°

c. 65.1° or 114.9°   d. none of these

_____ 7. Which of the following is a simpler form of $\dfrac{(\csc \theta)(\tan \theta)}{(\cot \theta)(\sec \theta)}$?

a. $\cos \theta$ b. $\sin \theta$ c. $\tan \theta$ d. $\sec \theta$

Chapter Assessment

Chapter 14, Form A, page 2

_____ 8. Which of the following is a simpler form of $\dfrac{\sec^2 \theta}{(\sec \theta + 1)(\sec \theta - 1)}$?

     a. $\cot^2 \theta$ b. $\csc^2 \theta$ c. $\cos^2 \theta$ d. $\tan^2 \theta$

_____ 9. Which of the following is a simpler form of $\dfrac{\sin^2 \theta}{1 - \cos \theta} - 1$?

     a. $\sec \theta$ b. $\cos \theta$ c. $\csc \theta$ d. $\sin \theta$

_____ 10. Which of the following is a simpler form of $\cos(\theta + 90°)$?

     a. $\tan \theta$ b. $-\tan \theta$ c. $\sin \theta$ d. $-\sin \theta$

_____ 11. Which of the following is a simpler form of $\sin(3\pi + x)$?

     a. $\cos x$ b. $-\cos x$ c. $\sin x$ d. $-\sin x$

_____ 12. Which of the following is a simpler form of $(\sec^2 \theta)(\sin 2\theta)$?

     a. $2 \sin \theta$ b. $2 \csc \theta$ c. $2 \tan \theta$ d. $2 \cot \theta$

_____ 13. Which of the following is a simpler form of $\sin^2 \theta + \cos^2 \theta + \cos 2\theta$?

     a. $2 \tan^2 \theta$ b. $2 \sin^2 \theta$ c. $2 \csc^2 \theta$ d. $2 \cos^2 \theta$

_____ 14. Find the exact value of $\sin\left(\dfrac{\pi}{6} - \dfrac{2\pi}{3}\right)$.

     a. -1 b. $-\dfrac{\sqrt{3}}{3}$ c. $\dfrac{1}{2}$ d. $\dfrac{\sqrt{3}}{3}$

_____ 15. If $\cos \theta = \dfrac{1}{8}$ and $270° \le \theta \le 360°$, find $\cos\left(\dfrac{\theta}{2}\right)$.

     a. $\dfrac{1}{2}$ b. $\dfrac{3}{4}$ c. $-\dfrac{1}{2}$ d. $-\dfrac{3}{4}$

_____ 16. Solve $7 \sin \theta = 4.7 + 2 \sin \theta$ for $0° \le \theta \le 360°$.

     a. $70°$ and $110°$ b. $70°$ and $290°$ c. $31.5°$ and $148.5°$ d. $31.5°$ and $328.5°$

_____ 17. Solve $8 \cos x + 2\sqrt{3} = 4 \cos x$ for $0 \le x \le 2\pi$.

     a. $\dfrac{\pi}{2}$ and $\dfrac{3\pi}{2}$ b. $\dfrac{5\pi}{6}$ and $\dfrac{7\pi}{6}$ c. $\dfrac{\pi}{2}$ and $\dfrac{3\pi}{2}$ d. $\dfrac{3\pi}{4}$ and $\dfrac{5\pi}{4}$

_____ 18. Which equation would have to be solved in order to solve $3 \sin^2 x + 5 \sin x = 2$?

     a. $\sin x = 3$ and $\sin x = -2$ b. $\sin x = 3$ and $\sin x = -\dfrac{1}{2}$

     c. $\sin x = -3$ and $\sin x = 2$ d. $\sin x = \dfrac{1}{3}$ and $\sin x = -2$

_____ 19. If an isosceles triangle has a base of length 36 and its vertex angle measures 48°, find the perimeter of the triangle.

     a. 75.4   b. 116.9   c. 124.5   d. 192

Chapter Assessment

Chapter 14, Form B, page 1

1. Find x in the triangle at right to the nearest tenth of a foot.

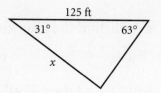

_____

2. Find x in the triangle at right to the nearest tenth of a centimeter.

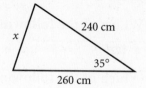

_____

3. Find the area of the triangle at right to the nearest tenth of a square meter.

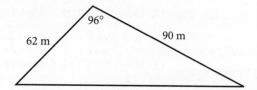

_____

4. Solve $\triangle ABC$. Give the measure of each angle to the nearest tenth of a degree.

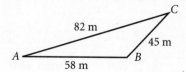

_____

5. Solve $\triangle ABC$. Give c to the nearest tenth of a foot and m$\angle A$ and m$\angle C$ to the nearest tenth of a degree.

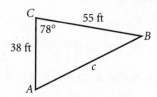

_____

6. In $\triangle ABC$, m$\angle A = 67°$, $a = 20$, and $c = 21.5$. Find all possible values for m$\angle C$ to the nearest tenth of a degree.

_____

7. If $\cos \theta = \frac{7}{8}$ and $270° \leq \theta \leq 360°$, find $\sin\left(\frac{\theta}{2}\right)$. _____

8. If $\sin \theta = -\frac{2}{3}$ and $180° \leq \theta \leq 270°$, find $\cos 2\theta$. _____

9. Find the exact value of $\sin\left(\frac{\pi}{3} - \frac{\pi}{2}\right)$. _____

Chapter Assessment

Chapter 14, Form B, page 2

10. Find the exact value of $\cos\left(\frac{3\pi}{2} + \frac{\pi}{3}\right)$. _____

11. Find the image of $(-2, 6)$ after a rotation of $90°$ about the origin. _____

Prove each identity.

12. $\cos(270° - \theta) = -\sin\theta$

13. $\sin\left(x + \frac{\pi}{2}\right) = \cos x$

Write each expression in terms of a single trigonometric function.

14. $(\sec^2\theta)(\cot\theta)(\sin^2\theta)$

15. $(\sin\theta)(\cot^2\theta + 1)$

16. $\dfrac{\tan^2\theta}{\sec\theta + 1}$

17. $\dfrac{\cos 2\theta + \sin^2\theta}{\sin 2\theta}$

Solve each equation to the nearest tenth of a degree for $0° \le \theta \le 360°$.

18. $6\sin\theta + 7 = 9 - 4\sin\theta$

19. $4\cos^2\theta - 5\cos\theta + 1 = 0$

Solve each equation to the nearest hundredth of a radian for $0 \le x \le 2\pi$.

20. $5(\sin x)(\cot x) + 2 = 6$

21. $5\sin x + 1 = 3\cos^2 x$

Alternative Assessment

Triangle Measurement, Chapter 14, Form A

TASK: Solve a given triangle.

HOW YOU WILL BE SCORED: As you work through the task, your teacher will be looking for the following:

- how well you can use the law of sines to find sides and angles of triangles
- how well you can use the law of cosines to find sides and angles of triangles

A surveying crew needs to find the distances to a point *C* from two points *A* and *B*, but a stream blocks the direct measurement. By adding two stakes, *D* and *E*, the surveyors are able to find the distances between *D* and *A* and between *E* and *B*. With this information, the surveying crew is able to measure the distances between *A* and *B* and between *D* and *B*.

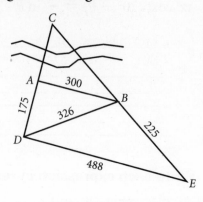

1. Describe the method you would use to find m∠*BAD*. Find m∠*BAD*.

   _____

   _____

2. Describe the method you would use to find m∠*ABD*. Find m∠*ABD*.

   _____

   _____

3. What triangle would you use to find m∠*BDE*? Find m∠*BDE*.

   _____

   _____

4. Find m∠*BAC*, m∠*ABC*, and m∠*ACB*. Use this information to find *AC* and *BC*.

   _____

   _____

SELF-ASSESSMENT: Explain how the law of cosines is related to the Pythagorean Theorem.

_____

Alternative Assessment

Solving Trigonometric Equations, Chapter 14, Form B

TASK: Solve trigonometric equations.

HOW YOU WILL BE SCORED: As you work through the task, your teacher will be looking for the following:

- whether you can solve trigonometric equations algebraically
- how well you can describe the process of solving trigonometric equations
- whether you can solve trigonometric equations by graphing

1. Describe how you can use a Pythagorean identity to solve $2 \tan^2 x + \sec^2 x = 2$ for $0 \leq x \leq 2\pi$. Then find the solutions.

_____

_____

_____

2. Describe how to solve $\sin x + \cos x = 1$ for $0 \leq x \leq 2\pi$ by graphing. Then find the solutions.

_____

_____

_____

Find the exact solutions of each equation for $0 \leq x \leq 2\pi$.

3. $\sin 2x = \cos 2x$

4. $(\sin x)(\cos x) = 0$

_____   _____

5. Describe how the equation $2 \sin^2 x - \sin x - 1 = 0$ is a quadratic equation in the variable $\sin x$. Explain how you could solve this equation for x.

_____

_____

_____

SELF-ASSESSMENT: Explain how you can use graphing to show that the trigonometric Pythagorean identities are always true.

Answers

Chapter 1

Quick Warm-Up 1.1

1–4.

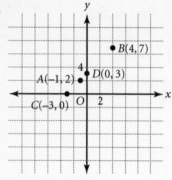

5. c

Lesson Quiz 1.1

1a. $y = 15 + 3x$

b. $33

2.

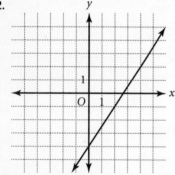

3. linear; $(11, 48)$

Quick Warm-Up 1.2

1. $y = -4x + 3$ **2.** $y = -\frac{1}{2}x + 5$

3. $y = \frac{1}{3}x + \frac{1}{2}$

4.

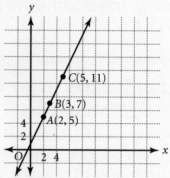

The line crosses the y-axis at $(0, 1)$.

Lesson Quiz 1.2

1. $m = -\frac{8}{7}$

2.

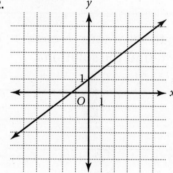

3. $y = -2x + 4$

4.

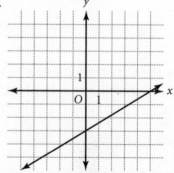

Answers

5.

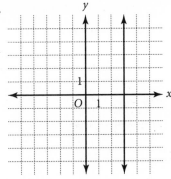

6.

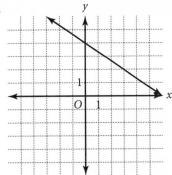

7.

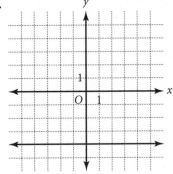

Quick Warm-Up 1.3

1. $m = -3$ 2. slope: -5; y-intercept: 7

3. $y = -x$

Lesson Quiz 1.3

1. $y = 3x - 2$ 2. $y = -\frac{3}{5}x + 8$

3. 80 miles   4. $y = 2x - 6$ 5. $y = \frac{4}{3}x - 2$

8. $x = \frac{40}{3}$ 9. $x = \frac{45}{2}$

10a. $y = 50 + 0.03x$

b. 125 miles

11. 225 hours

Quick Warm-Up 1.4

1. $c = -6.75$ 2. $z = \frac{32}{3}$ 3. $k = -80$

4. $n = -1.25$ 5. $y = -0.4$

Lesson Quiz 1.4

1. $k = -2.5$; $y = -2.5x$

2. 240 minutes

3a. $630

b. Let x represent the area of the floor in square feet and let y represent the cost of laying carpet; $y = 2.25x$; the cost of laying one square foot of carpet

4. $x = 24$ 5. $x = -7$

Quick Warm-Up 1.5

1–4.

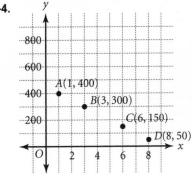

5. negative

Mid-Chapter Assessment—Chapter 1

1. c   2. b   3. d   4. d   5. $y = \frac{3}{5}x - 5$

Answers

Lesson Quiz 1.5

1.

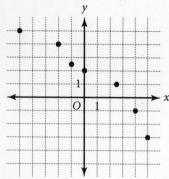

2. negative

3. $y \approx -0.75x + 1.82$

4. $\approx \$1.54$

Quick Warm-Up 1.6

1. $r = 15$ 2. $b = -0.25$ 3. $k = -36$

4. $z = -4$ 5. $m = -15$ 6. $x = -3$

Lesson Quiz 1.6

1. $x = 96$ 2. $x = 4$ 3. $x = 1.8$

4. $x = -\dfrac{17}{14}$ 5. $x = 1.2$

6. $w = \dfrac{A - xh + yh}{h}$ 7. $t = \dfrac{PB}{a} - mh$

Quick Warm-Up 1.7

1–4. $C \ AD \qquad B$

5.
$$-2 \quad -1 \quad 0 \quad 1 \quad 2$$

6.
$$-3 \ -2 \ -1 \ \ 0 \ \ 1 \ \ 2 \ \ 3$$

Lesson Quiz 1.7

1. $x < 1.5$ 2. $x \leq -5$

3. $x > 3$;

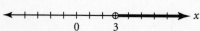

4. at least 95

5. $x > 3 \text{ and } x < 6$;

6. $x \leq -1 \text{ or } x \geq 4$;

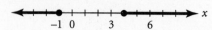

Quick Warm-Up 1.8

1. $m = -4$ 2. $m = 2$ 3. $m = 0$

4. $k > 8$ 5. $k < -12$ 6. $k > -2$

Lesson Quiz 1.8

1. $x = 1 \text{ or } x = -5$;

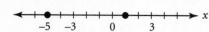

2. $x = 10$

3. $x > 3 \text{ or } x < -2$;

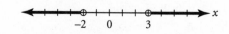

4. $x \geq -1 \text{ and } x \leq 5$;

5a. Let x represent the actual greenhouse temperature. $|x - 72| \leq 2.5$

b. $x \geq 69.5 \text{ and } x \leq 74.5$

Chapter Assessment—Form A—Chapter 1

1. c   2. a   3. d   4. d   5. b

6. d   7. d   8. a   9. a   10. b

11. c   12. c   13. c   14. a   15. c

16. d   17. b   18. a   19. c   20. a

Answers

1. yes; $(19, 63)$

2. $m = -\dfrac{3}{4}$

3.
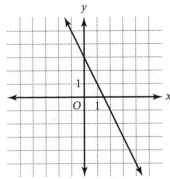

4.
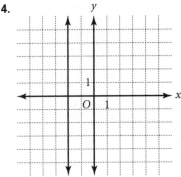

5. $y = -4x + 7$ 6. $y = -\dfrac{3}{2}x + 5$

7. $r \approx 0.86$ 8. $y \approx 0.98x + 2.51$

9. 11 or 12 accidents

10. $x = 14$ 11. $x = 17$

12. $x = 3.75$ or $x = -0.75$

13. $x = -2$ 14. $x \geq \dfrac{8}{3}$ 15. $x > -36$

16. $x \leq -3$ and $x \geq -7$;

17. $x > 3$ or $x < -0.5$;

18. $h = \dfrac{C - mr}{r^2}$ 19. $t = \dfrac{mn(A + B)}{Fd}$

20. $k = 0.25$; $y = 0.25x$

21. 40 gallons

22a. $y = 0.1x + 125$
   b. $2000

23. $|t - 40| \leq 5$

Alternative Assessment—Form A— Chapter 1

1. Answers may vary. Sample answer: Let x be the number of cans recycled and let y be the amount of refund.

2. Answers may vary. Sample answer:

Number of cans	100	200	300
Amount of refund ($)	3.50	7.00	10.50

400	500
14.00	17.50

3. A constant difference in consecutive x-values results in a constant change in y-values in the table, so the data is linearly related.

4. $y = 0.035x$

5. $17.50; 15,000 cans

6. The linear equation is a direct variation with $k = 0.035$, the amount of the refund for one can.

Score Point 4: Distinguished

The student demonstrates a comprehensive understanding of linear relationships. The student uses perceptive, creative, and complex mathematical reasoning and sophisticated, precise, and appropriate mathematical language throughout the task. Theoretical knowledge is apparent and is applied to concrete situations as the student

Answers

successfully demonstrates a comprehensive understanding of core concepts.

Score Point 3: Proficient

The student demonstrates a broad understanding of linear relationships. The student uses perceptive mathematical reasoning and precise and appropriate mathematical language most of the time. Theoretical knowledge is apparent and is applied to concrete situations as the student attempts to draw conclusions based on the investigations.

Score Point 2: Apprentice

The student demonstrates an understanding of linear relationships. The student uses mathematical reasoning and appropriate mathematical language some of the time. The student attempts to apply theoretical knowledge to the task but may not be able to draw conclusions based on the investigations.

Score Point 1: Novice

The student demonstrates a basic understanding of linear relationships. The student uses little mathematical reasoning or appropriate mathematical language. Theoretical knowledge is extremely weak, and many responses are irrelevant or illogical. The student fails to follow directions and has great difficulty in communicating his or her responses.

Score Point 0: Unsatisfactory

The student does not complete the task, and his or her responses just restate the problem.

Form B

1a. 1

b. 1

c. $x = \dfrac{6}{5}$

d. $a > 0 \text{ and } a < 2$

2. Any real number; the graph of $y = |3x + 5|$ is always above the graph of $y = -2$.

3. No solution; the graph of $y = |7x - 2|$ is never below the graph of $y = -6$.

4a. $3x + 6 \geq 9 \text{ or } 3x + 6 \leq -9$

b. $x \geq 1 \text{ or } x \leq -5$

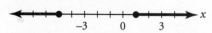

5a. At least 245 milliliters and no more than 255 milliliters

b. $|x - 250| \leq 5$

c. $x \leq 255 \text{ and } x \geq 245$

Score Point 4: Distinguished

The student demonstrates a comprehensive understanding of absolute-value equations and inequalities. The student uses perceptive, creative, and complex mathematical reasoning and sophisticated, precise, and appropriate mathematical language throughout the task. Theoretical knowledge is apparent and is applied to concrete situations as the student successfully demonstrates a comprehensive understanding of core concepts.

Score Point 3: Proficient

The student demonstrates a broad understanding of absolute-value equations and inequalities. The student uses perceptive mathematical reasoning and precise and

Answers

appropriate mathematical language most of the time. Theoretical knowledge is apparent and is applied to concrete situations as the student attempts to draw conclusions based on the investigations.

Score Point 2: Apprentice

The student demonstrates an understanding of absolute-value equations and inequalities. The student uses mathematical reasoning and appropriate mathematical language some of the time. The student attempts to apply theoretical knowledge to the task but may not be able to draw conclusions based on the investigations.

Score Point 1: Novice

The student demonstrates a basic understanding of absolute-value equations and inequalities. The student uses little mathematical reasoning or appropriate mathematical language. Theoretical knowledge is extremely weak, and many responses are irrelevant or illogical. The student fails to follow directions and has great difficulty in communicating his or her responses.

Score Point 0: Unsatisfactory

The student does not complete the task, and his or her responses just restate the problem.

Chapter 2

Quick Warm-Up 2.1

1. $-\dfrac{2}{15}$ 2. $-2\dfrac{2}{3}$ 3. -1 4. 9

5. 625 6. 5

Lesson Quiz 2.1

1. irrational and real

2. integer, rational, and real

3. rational and real

4a. Commutative Property of Addition

b. Associative Property of Addition

c. Inverse Property for Addition

d. Identity Property for Addition

5. $A = 0.015n + n$
   $= 0.015n + 1n$ Identity Property for Multiplication
   $= n(0.015 + 1)$
   $= n(1.015)$ Distributive Property
   $= 1.015n$ Commutative Property of Multiplication

6. $\dfrac{5}{3}$ 7. -25

Quick Warm-Up 2.2

1. 27 2. 49 3. 288 4. 24 5. 2 6. $\dfrac{16}{25}$

Lesson Quiz 2.2

1. 5.92 feet per second squared

2. $\dfrac{20y^5}{x^2}$ 3. $\dfrac{27a^{12}}{-8b^9}$

4a. 5

b. 32

5. 1.94 square meters

Quick Warm-Up 2.3

1. -7 2. 3 3. 16 4. -1.44

5. -8 6. 0.001

Answers

Lesson Quiz 2.3

1. Yes; for each x in the table, there is exactly one value of y.

2. No; there are many vertical lines that intersect the graph at more than one point.

3. domain: $x \leq 2$; range: $y \leq 3$

4. $f(5) = 8$; $f(2) = \frac{17}{4}$

Quick Warm-Up 2.4

1. $2x + 3$ 2. $x + 10$ 3. $x^2 - x - 6$

4. $-5x$ 5. $9x^2 - 3x$

Lesson Quiz 2.4

1. $(f + g)(x) = x^2 + x + 9$

2. $(g - f)(x) = x^2 - x + 1$

3. $\left(\frac{g}{f}\right)(x) = \frac{x^2 + 5}{x + 4}, x \neq -4$

4. $(fg)(x) = x^3 + 4x^2 + 5x + 20$

5. $(g \circ f)(x) = x^2 + 8x + 21$

6. $(f \circ g)(x) = x^2 + 9$

7. $P(x) = x - 10$; $C(x) = 1.05x$;
$(C \circ P)(x) = 1.05(x - 10)$;
$(P \circ C)(x) = 1.05x - 10$;
The function $(C \circ P)(x)$ gives the total amount that you will pay because you must pay sales tax on the cost of the CD player after the coupon is used.

Mid-Chapter Assessment—Chapter 2

1. c   2. a   3. d   4. c   5. 5   6. 10

7. $\frac{-48x^7}{y^2}$ 8. $\frac{16a^{12}}{529b^8}$ 9. $-4 \leq x \leq 5$

10. Yes; no vertical line intersects the graph at more than one point.

11. $(f + g)(x) = x^2 + x + 4$

12. $\left(\frac{g}{f}\right)(x) = \frac{x^2 + 7}{x - 3}, x \neq 3$

13. $(g \circ f)(x) = x^2 - 6x + 16$

Quick Warm-Up 2.5

1. $y = -0.25x$ 2. $y = 0.5x - 1.5$

3. $y = 5x - 3$ 4. $y = -3x - 1$

5. $(f \circ g)(x) = (g \circ f)(x) = x$

Lesson Quiz 2.5

1. $B = \frac{3}{2}(A + 24) - 18$, or $\frac{3}{2}A - 18$

2. $\{(5, 3), (7, 5), (2, 7), (0, 9)\}$; the relation is a function; the inverse is a function.

3. $\{(2, 7), (4, 8), (2, 9), (6, 10)\}$; the relation is a function; the inverse is not a function.

4. $y = 4x - 3$ 5. $y = \pm\sqrt{x - 4} + 5$

6. $f(g(x)) = \frac{(5x + 7) - 7}{5} = x$;

$g(f(x)) = 5\left(\frac{x - 7}{5}\right) + 7 = x$

Quick Warm-Up 2.6

1. 3   2. -4 3. 0   4. -7 5. 25.1   6. 0.7

Lesson Quiz 2.6

1.

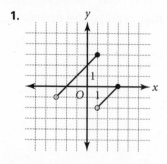

2. 6   3. 4   4. -8

Answers

5.

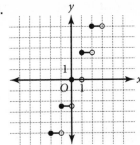

6.

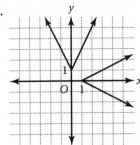

Quick Warm-Up 2.7

1. 64 2. -2 3. 28 4. 196

5. -4 6. 4 7. -13 8. -49

Lesson Quiz 2.7

1. horizontal translation 6 units to the right

2. vertical translation 2 units down

3. vertical stretch by a factor of 4

4. vertical compression by a factor of $\frac{2}{3}$

5. horizontal compression by a factor of $\frac{1}{3}$

6. horizontal stretch by a factor of 5

7. reflection across the x-axis

8. reflection across the y-axis

9. reflection across the x-axis, vertical stretch by a factor of 3, and horizontal translation 7 units to the left

10. reflection across the y-axis, horizontal compression by a factor of $\frac{1}{2}$, and vertical translation 4 units up

Chapter Assessment—Form A— Chapter 2

1. c 2. d 3. c 4. a 5. b 6. b 7. d

8. a 9. c 10. b 11. c 12. c 13. d

14. a 15. a 16. b 17. d 18. c 19. b

Form B

1. real, rational, and integer

2. real and irrational

3. real and rational

4. 8 5. 10 6. $16x^{16}$ 7. $\dfrac{a^{16}}{4}$

8. Yes; no vertical line intersects the graph at more than one point.

9. domain: $x \geq -2$; range: $y \geq 0$

10. No; there are horizontal lines that intersect the graph at more than one point.

11. domain: $x \geq 0$; range: $y \geq -2$

12. $f(-3) = -252$ 13. $g(-3) = 10$

14. $(f + g)(x) = 3x - 5$

15. $(fg)(x) = 2x^2 - 11x - 6$

16. $(f \circ g)(x) = 2x - 11$

17. $\left(\dfrac{f}{g}\right)(x) = \dfrac{2x + 1}{x - 6}, x \neq 6$

18. $f^{-1}(x) = 4(x - 10)$

19.

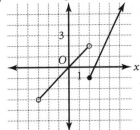

Answers

20. horizontal compression by a factor of $\frac{1}{2}$ and vertical stretch by a factor of $\frac{3}{2}$

21. $g(x) = -\left[\frac{1}{3}\right]x$

22a. Commutative Property of Addition

  b. Associative Property of Addition

  c. Distributive Property

  d. Inverse Property for Addition

  e. Identity Property for Addition

23a. $M(n) = 200 + 1.50n$

  b. $n(M) = \frac{M - 200}{1.50}$

  c. 400 square feet

24a. $c(n) = 5 + 0.50\lceil n \rceil$

  b. $7

Alternative Assessment—Form A—Chapter 2

1. Any real number may represent a. Any real numbers may represent m and n.

2. The equation $a^m a^n = a^{mn}$ is false. The true equation is $a^m a^n = a^{m+n}$.
$\frac{a^n}{a^m} = a^{n-m}$ is true.

3. $\frac{1}{3xy}$; $(ax^m y^n)^{-1} = \frac{1}{ax^m y^n}$, where a, x, and y are any real numbers except 0, and m and n are integers

4. 1; $(x^m y^n)^0 = 1$, where x and y are any real numbers, and m and n are integers

5. Answers may vary. Sample response:
$(1 + 2)^{-1} \neq -1 + \frac{1}{2}$

6. Answers may vary. Sample response:
$1 + 2^{-1} \neq \frac{1}{3}$

7. Answers may vary. Sample response:
$1^{-1} + 2^{-1} = 1 + \frac{1}{2}$

8. Answers may vary. Sample response:
$(1 + 2)^{-1} = \frac{1}{3}$

9. Exercises 7 and 8 are true.

10. For all real numbers a, $(1 + a)^{-1} = \frac{1}{1 + a}$.

Score Point 4: Distinguished

The student demonstrates a comprehensive understanding of the properties of exponents. The student uses perceptive, creative, and complex mathematical reasoning and sophisticated, precise, and appropriate mathematical language throughout the task. Theoretical knowledge is apparent and is applied to concrete situations as the student successfully demonstrates a comprehensive understanding of core concepts.

Score Point 3: Proficient

The student demonstrates a broad understanding of the properties of exponents. The student uses perceptive mathematical reasoning and precise and appropriate mathematical language most of the time. Theoretical knowledge is apparent and is applied to concrete situations as the student attempts to draw conclusions based on the investigations.

Score Point 2: Apprentice

The student demonstrates an understanding of the properties of exponents. The student uses mathematical reasoning and appropriate mathematical language some of the time. The student attempts to apply theoretical knowledge to the task but may not be able to draw conclusions based on the investigations.

Answers

Score Point 1: Novice

The student demonstrates a basic understanding of the properties of exponents. The student uses little mathematical reasoning or appropriate mathematical language. Theoretical knowledge is extremely weak, and many responses are irrelevant or illogical. The student fails to follow directions and has great difficulty in communicating his or her responses.

Score Point 0: Unsatisfactory

The student does not complete the task, and his or her responses just restate the problem.

Form B

1. Taxi fare

2. Sample answer: The company charges for an entire mile if a person rides for any part of the mile, so the fare steps up by $0.75 when a new mile starts.

3. Sample answer: The function is a rounding-up function. A person pays for the entire mile if the person rides any part of a mile.

4. $f(m) = 0.75\lceil m \rceil$

5. vertical compression by a factor of 0.75

Score Point 4: Distinguished

The student demonstrates a comprehensive understanding of the applications of step functions. The student uses perceptive, creative, and complex mathematical reasoning and sophisticated, precise, and appropriate mathematical language throughout the task. Theoretical knowledge is apparent and is applied to concrete situations as the student successfully demonstrates a comprehensive understanding of core concepts.

Score Point 3: Proficient

The student demonstrates a broad understanding of the applications of step functions. The student uses perceptive mathematical reasoning and precise and appropriate mathematical language most of the time. Theoretical knowledge is apparent and is applied to concrete situations as the student attempts to draw conclusions based on the investigations.

Score Point 2: Apprentice

The student demonstrates an understanding of the applications of step functions. The student uses mathematical reasoning and appropriate mathematical language some of the time. The student attempts to apply theoretical knowledge to the task but may not be able to draw conclusions based on the investigations.

Score Point 1: Novice

The student demonstrates a basic understanding of the applications of step functions. The student uses little mathematical reasoning or appropriate mathematical language. Theoretical knowledge is extremely weak, and many

Answers

responses are irrelevant or illogical. The student fails to follow directions and has great difficulty in communicating his or her responses.

Score Point 0: Unsatisfactory

The student does not complete the task, and his or her responses just restate the problem.

Chapter 3

Quick Warm-Up 3.1

1. $y = x - 9$ 2. $y = \frac{2}{5}x$, or $y = 0.4x$

3. $y = -\frac{4}{7}x + 2$ 4. $y = 15x - 30$

5. $y = 3x - 3.24$

Lesson Quiz 3.1

1. inconsistent; none

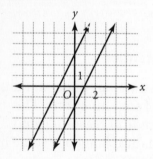

2. consistent and independent; $(4, 2)$

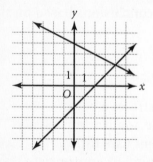

3. $(-1, 7)$ 4. $(2, 3, -1)$

Quick Warm-Up 3.2

1. $15y$ 2. $11x$ 3. $-4x + 5y$

4. $-x + 4y$ 5. $17x - 20y$

Lesson Quiz 3.2

1. $(5, 2)$ 2. $(-3, 6)$

3a. Let x be the price of a hamburger and y be the price of a drink.
$$\begin{cases} 7x + 4y = 20 \\ 9x + 5y = 25.50 \end{cases}$$

b. A hamburger costs $2 and a drink costs $1.50.

4. dependent   5. inconsistent

6. inconsistent   7. dependent

Quick Warm-Up 3.3

1. $c = -3$;

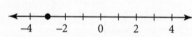

2. $r \leq 2$;

3. $m > -1$;

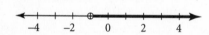

Lesson Quiz 3.3

1.

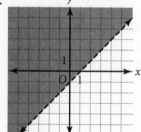

Answers

2.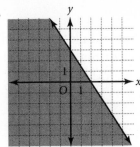

3.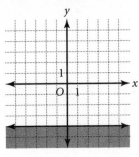

4.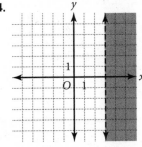

Mid-Chapter Assessment—Chapter 3

1. d   **2.** b   **3.** a   **4.** $(2, -5)$ **5.** $(-3, 6)$

6.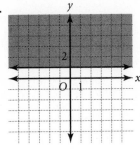

7.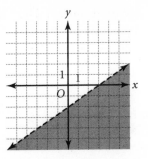

8. Let x be the amount of 10% solution and let y be the amount of 60% solution.
$$\begin{cases} x + y = 200 \\ 0.10x + 0.60y = 0.45(200) \end{cases}$$
60 milliliters of the 10% solution and 140 milliliters of the 60% solution

9. Let x be the number of minutes on the treadmill and y be the number of minutes on the exercise bike;
$12x + 9y \geq 500$

Quick Warm-Up 3.4

1.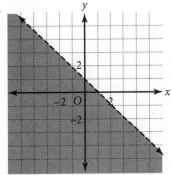

2.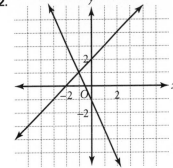

Answers

Lesson Quiz 3.4

1.

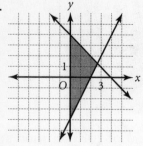

2.

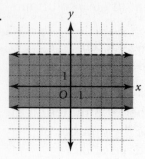

3. $\begin{cases} x > -2 \\ y \ge 0 \\ y \le -\dfrac{3}{4}x + 3 \end{cases}$

Quick Warm-Up 3.5

1. $(5, 2)$

2.

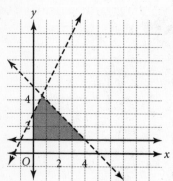

Lesson Quiz 3.5

1a. Let x be the number of oak tables and let y be the number of mahogany tables
$\begin{cases} x + y \le 50 \\ x \ge 10 \\ 15 \le y \le 25 \end{cases}$

b. $P = 250x + 175y$

2a.

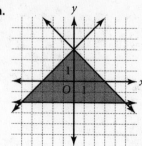

$(0, 3), (5, -2), (-5, -2)$

b. maximum: 250 at $(5, -2)$;
minimum: -550 at $(-5, -2)$

Quick Warm-Up 3.6

1. $-5, 7$ **2.** $-1, 1$ **3.** $3, -5$ **4.** $7, -11$

5. $11, -17$

Lesson Quiz 3.6

1.

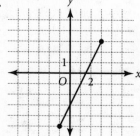

2. $y = \dfrac{1}{4}x + 2$ **3.** $y = -2x - 3$

4a. 261 feet

b. Yes; after 8 seconds, the rocket has traveled horizontally 160 feet, reaching the edge of the pond, and is still 5 feet above the pond.

Answers

Chapter Assessment—Form A—Chapter 3

1. b   **2.** c   **3.** c   **4.** d   **5.** c   **6.** d

7. a   **8.** b   **9.** b   **10.** d   **11.** c

Form B

1a. inconsistent

  b. 0

2. $(-2, 5)$ **3.** $(3, -6)$ **4.** $(2, -3, 1)$

5.

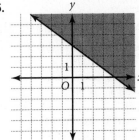

6.

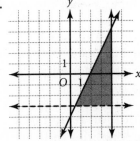

7a. Let x be the number of cars cleaned and y be the number of cars polished.
$$\begin{cases} x \geq 0 \\ y \geq 0 \\ 1.5x + 2y \leq 120 \\ 2.25x + 4.50y \leq 160 \end{cases}$$

  b. $P = 7.75x + 8.50y$

8. 5100 at $(5, 8)$

9a.

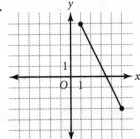

  b. $y = -2x + 7$

10. Let x be the number of passengers that paid the lower fare and y be the number of passengers that paid the higher fare.
$$\begin{cases} x + y = 120 \\ 150x + 200y = 22{,}550 \end{cases}$$
29 passengers paid the lower fare.

11. 1.2 liters of 40% juice and 0.8 liters of 90% juice

12a. 116 feet

  b. ≈ 235.7 feet

Alternative Assessment Form A—Chapter 3

1. Answers may vary. Sample answer: Let x be the number of adventure games and y be the number of sports games;
$15x + 10y \leq 120$

2. $x \leq -\frac{2}{3}y + 8$; $y \leq -\frac{3}{2}x + 12$

3. x and y can be only whole numbers.

4.

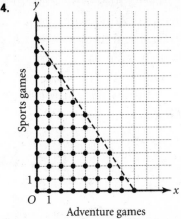

Answers

5. $130

6.

Adventure	8	6	4	2	0
Sports	0	3	6	9	12

Score Point 4: Distinguished

The student demonstrates a comprehensive understanding of solving linear inequalities. The student uses perceptive, creative, and complex mathematical reasoning and sophisticated, precise, and appropriate mathematical language throughout the task. Theoretical knowledge is apparent and is applied to concrete situations as the student successfully demonstrates a comprehensive understanding of core concepts.

Score Point 3: Proficient

The student demonstrates a broad understanding of solving linear inequalities. The student uses perceptive mathematical reasoning and precise and appropriate mathematical language most of the time. Theoretical knowledge is apparent and is applied to concrete situations as the student attempts to draw conclusions based on the investigations.

Score Point 2: Apprentice

The student demonstrates an understanding of solving linear inequalities. The student uses mathematical reasoning and appropriate mathematical language some of the time. The student attempts to apply theoretical knowledge to the task but may not always be able to draw conclusions based on the investigations.

Score Point 1: Novice

The student demonstrates a basic understanding of solving linear inequalities. The student uses little mathematical reasoning or appropriate mathematical language. Theoretical knowledge is extremely weak, and many responses are irrelevant or illogical. The student fails to follow directions and has great difficulty in communicating his or her responses.

Score Point 0: Unsatisfactory

The student does not complete the task, and his or her responses just restate the problem.

Form B

1. The region is polygonal in shape.

2. Bounded; the solutions do not extend beyond the boundary lines of the region.

3. Points may vary. Substitute the x- and y-values of each point into each inequality. If the point makes the inequality true, it is a solution to the system.

4. All points in the solution region of a system of linear inequalities indicate the feasible region.

5. $A(3, 2)$, $B(6, 2)$, $C(9, 3)$, and $D(3, 9)$. The coordinates represent the maximum or minimum values of P that are feasible.

6. The maximum value of the objective function is 63 and occurs at $C(9, 3)$.

Score Point 4: Distinguished

The students demonstrates a comprehensive understanding of solving systems of linear inequalities. The student uses perceptive, creative, and complex mathematical reasoning and sophisticated, precise, and

Answers

appropriate mathematical language throughout the task. Theoretical knowledge is apparent and is applied to concrete situations as the student successfully demonstrates a comprehensive understanding of core concepts.

Score Point 3: Proficient

The student demonstrates a broad understanding of solving systems of linear inequalities. The student uses perceptive mathematical reasoning and precise and appropriate mathematical language most of the time. Theoretical knowledge is apparent and is applied to concrete situations as the student attempts to draw conclusions based on the investigations.

Score Point 2: Apprentice

The student demonstrates an understanding of solving systems of linear inequalities. The student uses mathematical reasoning and appropriate mathematical language some of the time. The student attempts to apply theoretical knowledge to the task but may not be able to draw conclusions based on the investigations.

Score Point 1: Novice

The student demonstrates a basic understanding of solving systems of linear inequalities. The student uses little mathematical reasoning or appropriate mathematical language. Theoretical knowledge is extremely weak, and many responses are irrelevant or illogical. The student fails to follow directions and has great difficulty in communicating his or her responses.

Score Point 0: Unsatisfactory

The student does not complete the task, and his or her responses just restate the problem.

Chapter 4

Quick Warm-Up 4.1

1. -3.7 2. 8.3 3. -13.3 4. -5.2

5. $x = 10.5$ 6. $y = -5.75$

Lesson Quiz 4.1

1.
$$\begin{array}{c} \\ \text{First} \\ \text{Second} \\ \text{Third} \end{array} \begin{array}{ccc} \text{Central} & \text{North} & \text{South} \\ \left[\begin{array}{ccc} 7 & 5 & 3 \\ 3 & 5 & 7 \\ 4 & 6 & 5 \end{array}\right] \end{array};$$
the number of third-place finishes for Central

2. $x = 6; y = -7$

3. $\begin{bmatrix} -5 & 5 \\ 9 & 6 \end{bmatrix}$ 4. $\begin{bmatrix} 6 & 2 \\ -14 & 1 \end{bmatrix}$

5. $\begin{bmatrix} -20 & 25 \\ 5 & 0 \end{bmatrix}$

6.
$$\begin{array}{c} \\ \\ \end{array} \begin{array}{cccc} A & B & C & D \\ \left[\begin{array}{cccc} -1 & -4 & 1 & 4 \\ 4 & 1 & -4 & -1 \end{array}\right] \end{array}$$

Quick Warm-Up 4.2

1. 2×4 2. 3×2 3. 0 4. -2 5. 1

Lesson Quiz 4.2

1. $\begin{bmatrix} 22 & 7 \\ 10 & 2 \end{bmatrix}$

2. not possible

Answers

3. $\begin{bmatrix} 1 & 12 \\ 2 & 10 \\ 3 & 12 \end{bmatrix}$

4a. $\begin{array}{ccc} & \text{1st} & \text{2nd} & \text{3rd} \end{array}$
$N = \begin{bmatrix} 5 & 3 & 1 \end{bmatrix}$

b. $NT = \begin{bmatrix} 48 & 46 & 41 \end{bmatrix}$

c. The values in the matrix represent the total number of points earned by each team; Central won the meet.

5a. $\begin{array}{c} \\ A \\ B \\ C \end{array} \begin{array}{ccc} A & B & C \\ \begin{bmatrix} 0 & 2 & 1 \\ 2 & 1 & 1 \\ 1 & 1 & 0 \end{bmatrix} \end{array}$

b. $\begin{array}{c} \\ A \\ B \\ C \end{array} \begin{array}{ccc} A & B & C \\ \begin{bmatrix} 5 & 3 & 2 \\ 3 & 6 & 3 \\ 2 & 3 & 2 \end{bmatrix} \end{array}$

Quick Warm-Up 4.3

1. $-\dfrac{1}{3}$ 2. 0.4   3. -7 4. $\dfrac{5}{6}$ 5. 1   6. 1

Lesson Quiz 4.3

1. $\begin{bmatrix} 3 & 2 \\ 7 & 5 \end{bmatrix}\begin{bmatrix} 5 & -2 \\ -7 & 3 \end{bmatrix} =$
$\begin{bmatrix} 5 & -2 \\ -7 & 3 \end{bmatrix}\begin{bmatrix} 3 & 2 \\ 7 & 5 \end{bmatrix} = \begin{bmatrix} 1 & 0 \\ 0 & 1 \end{bmatrix}$

2. $\begin{bmatrix} -4 & 3 \\ -2.5 & 2 \end{bmatrix}$

3. $\begin{bmatrix} 0.05 & -0.05 & 0.4 \\ 0.15 & 0.1 & -0.3 \\ -0.4 & -0.1 & 0.8 \end{bmatrix}$

4. -2; the matrix has an inverse.

5. 0; the matrix has no inverse.

6. $x = 2$

Mid-Chapter Assessment—Chapter 4

1. c   2. d   3. c

4. $\begin{bmatrix} -10 & 14 \\ -3 & -5 \end{bmatrix}$

5. not possible

6. $\begin{bmatrix} 12 & 23 & -9 \\ 0 & 16 & 6 \end{bmatrix}$

7. not possible

8. $\begin{bmatrix} 13 & -18 \\ 6 & 1 \end{bmatrix}$

9. $\begin{bmatrix} 0.5 & -2.5 \\ 0 & 1 \end{bmatrix}$

10. $x = -2$ 11. $x = 4$

12a. $\begin{array}{c} \\ \text{Saturday} \\ \text{Sunday} \end{array} \begin{array}{ccc} S & M & L \\ \begin{bmatrix} 65 & 120 & 45 \\ 95 & 150 & 80 \end{bmatrix} \end{array}$;

$\begin{array}{c} S \\ M \\ L \end{array} \begin{bmatrix} 0.50 \\ 0.75 \\ 1.25 \end{bmatrix}$

b. $\begin{bmatrix} 178.75 \\ 260 \end{bmatrix}$; The matrix represents income from yogurt sales on Saturday and Sunday.

Quick Warm-Up 4.4

1. $\begin{bmatrix} -6 & 43 \\ -54 & -117 \end{bmatrix}$ 2. $\begin{bmatrix} 16 & -14 \\ -2 & -4 \end{bmatrix}$

Lesson Quiz 4.4

1. Let x be the amount invested at 15% and y be the amount invested at 7%.

$\begin{cases} x + y = 25{,}000 \\ 0.15x + 0.07y = 3000 \end{cases}$

He should invest \$15,625 at 15% and \$9375 at 7%.

Answers

2. $\begin{bmatrix} -3 & 1 \\ 5 & -1 \end{bmatrix} \begin{bmatrix} x \\ y \end{bmatrix} = \begin{bmatrix} -8 \\ 4 \end{bmatrix}$

3. $\begin{bmatrix} 0 & 2 & -3 \\ 3 & 5 & -4 \\ 5 & -2 & 0 \end{bmatrix} \begin{bmatrix} x \\ y \\ z \end{bmatrix} = \begin{bmatrix} 12 \\ 9 \\ 0 \end{bmatrix}$

4. $(7, -3)$ 5. $(-5, 8, -3)$

Quick Warm-Up 4.5

1. $\begin{bmatrix} 1 & 7 \\ -3 & 2 \end{bmatrix} \begin{bmatrix} x \\ y \end{bmatrix} = \begin{bmatrix} 5 \\ 8 \end{bmatrix}$; $x = -2$ and $y = 1$

2. $\begin{bmatrix} 3 & -6 \\ -4 & 8 \end{bmatrix} \begin{bmatrix} x \\ y \end{bmatrix} = \begin{bmatrix} -3 \\ -4 \end{bmatrix}$; no solution

Lesson Quiz 4.5

1. $\begin{bmatrix} 7 & 1 & \vdots & 6 \\ -4 & 1 & \vdots & 0 \end{bmatrix}$

2. $\begin{bmatrix} 2 & 5 & 0 & \vdots & 9 \\ 1 & 6 & 1 & \vdots & 0 \\ 5 & 0 & 0 & \vdots & 8 \end{bmatrix}$

3. $\begin{bmatrix} 1 & 0 & 0 & \vdots & 1 \\ 0 & 1 & 0 & \vdots & 1 \\ 0 & 0 & 1 & \vdots & -3 \end{bmatrix}$

4. $\begin{bmatrix} 1 & 0 & 1 & \vdots & 0 \\ 0 & 1 & 2 & \vdots & 0 \\ 0 & 0 & 0 & \vdots & 1 \end{bmatrix}$; inconsistent

5. $\begin{bmatrix} 1 & 0 & 3 & \vdots & -4 \\ 0 & 1 & -1 & \vdots & 2 \\ 0 & 0 & 0 & \vdots & 0 \end{bmatrix}$;
$(-3z - 4, z + 2, z)$; dependent

Chapter Assessment—Form A— Chapter 4

1. d   2. b   3. c   4. c   5. d   6. a   7. b
8. d   9. a   10. d   11. d   12. a   13. b

Form B

1. $\begin{bmatrix} 23 & 8 \\ 27 & 16 \end{bmatrix}$

2. not possible

3. $\begin{bmatrix} 7 & 9 \\ 21 & 18 \\ 12 & 26 \end{bmatrix}$

4. $\begin{bmatrix} 2 & -1 \\ -4.5 & 2.5 \end{bmatrix}$

5. $x = -3$ 6. $x = 2$

7a. 0

b. B^{-1} does not exist.

8a. $\begin{bmatrix} 2 & 3 & 1 \\ 3 & 1 & -4 \\ -4 & -1 & 3 \end{bmatrix} \begin{bmatrix} x \\ y \\ z \end{bmatrix} = \begin{bmatrix} 12 \\ -5 \\ 6 \end{bmatrix}$

b. $(-2, 5, 1)$

9. $(3, 4)$

10. $\begin{bmatrix} 2 & 3 & 4 & \vdots & 1 \\ 2 & 1 & 3 & \vdots & -1 \\ 0 & -1 & -9 & \vdots & 8 \end{bmatrix}$

11a. $\begin{bmatrix} 1 & 0 & -2 & \vdots & 2 \\ -2 & 2 & 6 & \vdots & 2 \\ 0 & 3 & 3 & \vdots & 9 \end{bmatrix}$

b. $\begin{bmatrix} 1 & 0 & -2 & \vdots & 2 \\ 0 & 1 & 1 & \vdots & 3 \\ 0 & 0 & 0 & \vdots & 0 \end{bmatrix}$

c. consistent and dependent;
$(2z + 2, 3 - z, z)$

12. $\begin{array}{c} \\ A \\ B \\ C \end{array} \overset{\begin{array}{ccc} A & B & C \end{array}}{\begin{bmatrix} 0 & 2 & 1 \\ 2 & 0 & 1 \\ 1 & 1 & 1 \end{bmatrix}}$

Answers

13a. Let x represent the measure of the largest angle, y represent the measure of the second largest angle, and z represent the measure of the smallest angle.

$$\begin{cases} x + y + z = 180 \\ x = 6z \\ x = 2(y + z) \end{cases}$$

b. (120, 40, 20); The largest angle measures 120°, the second largest angle measures 40°, and the smallest angle measures 20°.

14. 75 pounds of peanuts and 25 pounds of cashews

Alternative Assessment—Form A—Chapter 4

1a. 4 square units

b. $S = \begin{array}{cccc} A & B & C & D \\ \left[\begin{array}{cccc} 2 & 2 & 0 & 0 \\ 0 & 2 & 2 & 0 \end{array}\right] \end{array}$

2a. $S' = \begin{array}{cccc} A' & B' & C' & D' \\ \left[\begin{array}{cccc} 2 & 2 & 0 & 0 \\ 0 & 6 & 6 & 0 \end{array}\right] \end{array}$

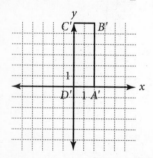

b. vertical stretch by a factor of 3

c. 12 square units; determinant of $T_1 = 3$; the area of the transformed figure is equal to the area of the original figure times the determinant of the transformation matrix.

d. $T_1^{-1} = \begin{bmatrix} 1 & 0 \\ 0 & \frac{1}{3} \end{bmatrix}$; vertical compression by a factor of $\frac{1}{3}$

3a. horizontal stretch by a factor of 2 and vertical stretch by a factor of 3; horizontal compression by a factor of $\frac{1}{2}$ and vertical compression by a factor of $\frac{1}{3}$

b. determinant of $T_2 = 6$; area = 24 square units

Score Point 4: Distinguished

The student demonstrates a comprehensive understanding of matrices and transformations. The student uses perceptive, creative, and complex mathematical reasoning and sophisticated, precise, and appropriate mathematical language throughout the task. Theoretical knowledge is apparent and is applied to concrete situations as the student successfully demonstrates a comprehensive understanding of core concepts.

Score Point 3: Proficient

The student demonstrates a broad understanding of matrices and transformations. The student uses perceptive mathematical reasoning and precise and appropriate mathematical language most of the time. Theoretical knowledge is apparent and is applied to concrete situations as the student attempts to draw conclusions based on the investigations.

Score Point 2: Apprentice

The student demonstrates an understanding of matrices and transformations. The student uses mathematical reasoning and appropriate mathematical language some of the time. The student attempts to apply theoretical knowledge to the task but may not be able to draw conclusions based on the investigations.

Answers

Score Point 1: Novice

The student demonstrates a basic understanding of matrices and transformations. The student uses little mathematical reasoning or appropriate mathematical language. Theoretical knowledge is extremely weak, and many responses are irrelevant or illogical. The student fails to follow directions and has great difficulty in communicating his or her responses.

Score Point 0: Unsatisfactory

The student does not complete the task, and his or her responses just restate the problem.

Form B

1. $A = 100t + 800$; $A = 60t + 1200$

2. $\begin{bmatrix} -100 & 1 \\ -60 & 1 \end{bmatrix} \begin{bmatrix} t \\ A \end{bmatrix} = \begin{bmatrix} 800 \\ 1200 \end{bmatrix}$

3. $t = 100$ and $A = \$1800$

4. After 10 years, Brett will owe $1800 under either option.

5. The intersection represents the time when Brett will owe the same amount of money under either option; first option; both options are equal; second option

Score Point 4: Distinguished

The student demonstrates a comprehensive understanding of applying matrix algebra to a real-world problem. The student uses perceptive, creative, and complex mathematical reasoning and sophisticated, precise, and appropriate mathematical language throughout the task. Theoretical knowledge is apparent and is applied to concrete situations as the student successfully demonstrates a comprehensive understanding of core concepts.

Score Point 3: Proficient

The student demonstrates a broad understanding of applying matrix algebra to a real-world problem. The student uses perceptive mathematical reasoning and precise and appropriate mathematical language most of the time. Theoretical knowledge is apparent and is applied to concrete situations as the student attempts to draw conclusions based on the investigations.

Score Point 2: Apprentice

The student demonstrates an understanding of applying matrix algebra to a real-world problem. The student uses mathematical reasoning and appropriate mathematical language some of the time. The student attempts to apply theoretical knowledge to the task but may not be able to draw conclusions based on the investigations.

Score Point 1: Novice

The student demonstrates a basic understanding of applying matrix algebra to a real-world problem. The student uses little mathematical reasoning or appropriate mathematical language. Theoretical knowledge is extremely weak, and many responses are irrelevant or illogical. The student fails to follow directions and has great difficulty in communicating his or her responses.

Score Point 0: Unsatisfactory

The student does not complete the task, and his or her responses just restate the problem.

Answers

Chapter 5

Quick Warm-Up 5.1

1. $x^2 - 1$ 2. $x^2 + 11x + 18$

3. $4x^2 + 13x - 35$ 4. $15x^2 + 7x - 4$

5. $2x^2 + 9x + 9$

Lesson Quiz 5.1

1. $f(x) = 4x^2 - 19x - 5$;
   $a = 4, b = -19, c = -5$

2. $f(x) = x^2 + 10x + 15$;
   $a = 1, b = 10, c = 15$

3. The parabola opens down. The y-coordinate of the vertex is the maximum value of the function.

4. The parabola opens up. The y-coordinate of the vertex is the minimum value of the function.

5.

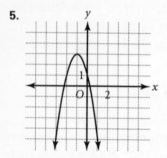

The vertex is at $(-1, 3)$.

Quick Warm-Up 5.2

1. 9   2. -12 3. $1, -1$ 4. 15   5. 44

6. $4\sqrt{11}$

Lesson Quiz 5.2

1. $x = \pm\sqrt{31} \approx \pm 5.57$

2. $x = 4 \text{ or } x = -14$

3. $x = \pm 7$ 4. 10.82 units

5. 15 units   6. 8   7. 6   8. 10

9. 7.62 meters

Quick Warm-Up 5.3

1. 1, 2, 5, 10

2. 1, 2, 3, 4, 6, 8, 12, 16, 24, 48

3. 1, 7   4. 2   5. 6   6. 1

Lesson Quiz 5.3

1. $5bx(3 + 5x)$ 2. $(a + 2)(2b + 3)$

3. $(x + 3)(x - 9)$ 4. $3x(y + 3)(y + 6)$

5. $(2x - 3)(x + 4)$ 6. $(2x - 5)^2$

7. $(x + 7)(x - 7)$ 8. $(4a + 9)(4a - 9)$

9. $x = 5 \text{ or } x = -8$ 10. $x = \frac{1}{4} \text{ or } x = -1$

11. $0, 9$ 12. $x = 10$

Quick Warm-Up 5.4

1. $(x + 7)^2$ 2. $(x - 11)^2$

3. $(x + 4)(x - 16)$ 4. $d = 10 \text{ and } d = -10$

5. $z = 1$ 6. $t = -4$

Lesson 5.4

1. $x^2 - 18x + 81$; $(x - 9)^2$

2. $x^2 + 9x + \frac{81}{4}$; $\left(x + \frac{9}{2}\right)^2$

3. $x = 4 \text{ or } x = -8$

4. $x \approx 5.4 \text{ or } x \approx -0.4$

5. $x = 0.8 \text{ or } x = -2$

6. $g(x) = (x - 3)^2 + 4$; horizontal translation 3 units to the right and vertical translation 4 units up; vertex: $(3, 4)$; axis: $x = 3$

Answers

Mid-Chapter Assessment—Chapter 5

1. b   2. d   3. c

4. $x = 12 \text{ or } x = 2$

5. $x \approx \pm 3.87$

6. $(x + 5)(x - 9)$

7. $(7x + 10)(7x - 10)$

8. $(5x - 4)(x + 3)$

9. $x = 6 \text{ or } x = 7$

10. $x \approx 6.5 \text{ or } x \approx -1.5$

11a. The graph opens up.

  b. $f(x) = (x + 2)^2 - 6$; axis: $x = -2$

Quick Warm-Up 5.5

1. $x = -4 \text{ or } x = -9$ 2. $x = -6$

3. $x = -3 \text{ or } x = 7$ 4. $x = -4 \text{ or } x = \frac{3}{2}$

5. $x = 2 \pm \sqrt{11}$; $x \approx 5.3 \text{ or } x \approx -1.3$

Lesson Quiz 5.5

1. $x = \frac{9 \pm \sqrt{21}}{10}$; $x \approx 1.4 \text{ or } x \approx 0.4$

2. $x = 6 \text{ or } x = -9$

3. axis: $x = 0.75$; vertex: $(0.75, -15.125)$; x-intercepts: $(3.5, 0)$, $(-2, 0)$

4. axis: $x = -4$; vertex: $(-4, 1)$; no x-intercepts

5. after $t = 0.25$ second and after $t = 1.25$ seconds

Quick Warm-Up 5.6

1. $x = -7 \text{ or } x = -5$ 2. $x = 9$

3. $x = \frac{-4 \pm \sqrt{52}}{2}$ 4. $x = \frac{5 \pm \sqrt{97}}{4}$

Lesson Quiz 5.6

1. discriminant $= 0$; 1 real solution

2. discriminant $= 260$; 2 real solutions

3. discriminant $= -4$; no real solutions

4. $x = 2 \pm 3i$ 5. $-11 + 19i$

6. $23 + (-2i)$ 7. $-\frac{18}{25} + \frac{26}{25}i$

8a, c.

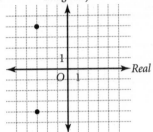

  b. $|-3 + 4i| = 5$

Quick Warm-Up 5.7

1. $\begin{cases} 2x + 2y = 16 \\ x - 3y = -4 \end{cases}$ 2. $\begin{bmatrix} 1 & 1 \\ 2 & 0 \end{bmatrix}\begin{bmatrix} x \\ y \end{bmatrix} = \begin{bmatrix} 6 \\ 4 \end{bmatrix}$

3. $\begin{bmatrix} -1 & -0.5 \\ -2 & -1.5 \end{bmatrix}$ 4. $x = 4, y = 9$

Lesson Quiz 5.7

1. $f(x) = 3x^2 - 8x + 2$

2a. The second differences are a constant 4.

  b. $y = 2x^2 + 5x - 9$

  c. $y = 339$

3a. $M \approx -0.011v^2 + 1.300v - 0.019$

  b. ≈ 38 miles

Quick Warm-Up 5.8

1. $p \geq -2 \text{ and } p \leq 4$

Answers

2. $z < -3$ or $z > 1$

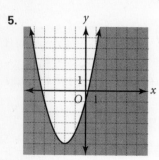

3. $t \geq 2$ or $t < -2$

Lesson Quiz 5.8

1. $x \geq -4$ and $x \leq 1$

2. $x < -3$ or $x > 5$

3. no solution

4. all real numbers except 4

5.

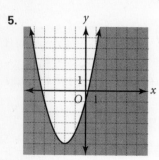

Chapter Assessment—Form A— Chapter 5

1. c **2.** d **3.** d **4.** d **5.** a

6. d **7.** b **8.** a **9.** c **10.** d

11. a **12.** b **13.** a **14.** c **15.** d

16. c **17.** b **18.** d **19.** b **20.** a

Form B

1. $x = \pm 15$

2. 72 centimeters

3. vertex: $(6, 12)$;
axis of symmetry: $x = 6$

4. vertex: $(-3, -8)$;
axis of symmetry: $x = -3$

5. no x-intercepts

6. $(1.25, 0)$ and $(-3, 0)$

7. $16 + 30i$

8. $-\dfrac{7}{25} + \dfrac{23}{50}i$

9. $3 + 8i$

10. $(12x + 5)(12x - 5)$

11. $(x + 5)(x - 8)$

12. $(3x - 1)(x - 5)$

13. $x = -2$ or $x = -6$

14. $f(x) = (x - 3)^2 + 7$

15. discriminant $= -152$; no real solutions

16. $x = -\dfrac{3}{5} \pm \dfrac{6}{5}i$

17. $x = \dfrac{7 \pm \sqrt{5}}{2}$; $x \approx 4.62$ or $x \approx 2.38$

18. $y = -2x^2 + 7x + 3$

19a, c.

b. $\sqrt{29} \approx 5.4$

20. $x > -9$ and $x < 4$

Answers

21.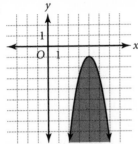

22. Output is maximized when there are 20 workers. Maximum output per worker is 56.

Alternative Assessment—Form A—Chapter 5

1. vertex: $(2, 1)$; axis of symmetry: $x = 2$
   x-intercepts: $(1, 0)$, $(3, 0)$;
   Answers may vary. Sample answer:
   Solve the equation $-(x - 2)^2 + 1 = 0$ or expand and factor $-(x - 2)^2 + 1$ into $-(x + 3)(x + 1)$. Then set the product equal to 0 and use the Zero-Product Property.

2. horizontal translation 2 units to the right and vertical translation 1 unit up

3. The value of f for any value of x is twice as big as the value of g for the same value of x. So the graph of f rises faster and appears narrower than the graph of g.

4. f is increasing when $x > -1$ and g is decreasing when $x > -1$. f is decreasing when $x < -1$ and g is increasing when $x < -1$. The negative coefficient of x^2 in g causes the y-coordinates of g to be the opposite of those for f for the same value of x. The parabola opens down instead of up.

5. Answers may vary. Sample answer:
   $f(x) = 9x^2$

Score Point 4: Distinguished

The student demonstrates a comprehensive understanding of the graphs of quadratic functions. The student uses perceptive, creative, and complex mathematical reasoning and sophisticated, precise, and appropriate mathematical language throughout the task. Theoretical knowledge is apparent and is applied to concrete situations as the student successfully demonstrates a comprehensive understanding of core concepts.

Score Point 3: Proficient

The student demonstrates a broad understanding of the graphs of quadratic functions. The student uses perceptive mathematical reasoning and precise and appropriate mathematical language most of the time. Theoretical knowledge is apparent and is applied to concrete situations as the student attempts to draw conclusions based on the investigations.

Score Point 2: Apprentice

The student demonstrates an understanding of the graphs of quadratic functions. The student uses mathematical reasoning and appropriate mathematical language some of the time. The student attempts to apply theoretical knowledge to the task but may not be able to draw conclusions based on the investigations.

Score Point 1: Novice

The student demonstrates a basic understanding of the graphs of quadratic functions. The student uses little mathematical reasoning or appropriate mathematical language. Theoretical knowledge is extremely weak, and many

Answers

responses are irrelevant or illogical. The student fails to follow directions and has great difficulty in communicating his or her responses.

Score Point 0: Unsatisfactory

The student does not complete the task, and his or her responses just restate the problem.

Form B

1. Answers may vary. Sample answer: The number of pages that can be held does not vary directly as the size of the staple, so a linear model does not fit. A quadratic model can be found for any set of three points.

2. $f(x) = -320x^2 + 520x - 80$

3. ≈ 70 sheets

4. The maximum size of a staple is about $\frac{13}{16}$ of an inch. That staple will hold about 131 sheets of paper.

5. any staple greater than 0 inches and less than or equal to $\frac{13}{16}$ of an inch

Score Point 4: Distinguished

The student demonstrates a comprehensive understanding of finding a quadratic model for data. The student uses perceptive, creative, and complex mathematical reasoning and sophisticated, precise, and appropriate mathematical language throughout the task. Theoretical knowledge is apparent and is applied to concrete situations as the student successfully demonstrates a comprehensive understanding of core concepts.

Score Point 3: Proficient

The student demonstrates a broad understanding of finding a quadratic model for data. The student uses perceptive mathematical reasoning and precise and appropriate mathematical language most of the time. Theoretical knowledge is apparent and is applied to concrete situations as the student attempts to draw conclusions based on the investigations.

Score Point 2: Apprentice

The student demonstrates an understanding of finding a quadratic model for data. The student uses mathematical reasoning and appropriate mathematical language some of the time. The student attempts to apply theoretical knowledge to the task but may not be able to draw conclusions based on the investigations.

Score Point 1: Novice

The student demonstrates a basic understanding of finding a quadratic model for data. The student uses little mathematical reasoning or appropriate mathematical language. Theoretical knowledge is extremely weak, and many responses are irrelevant or illogical. The student fails to follow directions and has great difficulty in communicating his or her responses.

Score Point 0: Unsatisfactory

The student does not complete the task, and his or her responses just restate the problem.

Answers

Chapter 6

Quick Warm-Up 6.1

1. 0.08   2. 0.024   3. 0.001   4. 729

5. 5184   6. 192

Lesson Quiz 6.1

1. 0.91   2. 1.0025

3a. 2000 bacteria

b. The population triples every hour.

c. 486,000 bacteria

4a. $17,500(1.045)^n$

b. 20,900 people

5a. $9500(0.80)^n$

b. $3100

Quick Warm-Up 6.2

1. 81   2. 1   3. 16   4. $\frac{1}{16}$ 5. 32

6. 25   7. $\frac{1}{25}$ 8. $\frac{1}{25}$

Lesson Quiz 6.2

1. exponential growth; $(0, 5)$

2. exponential decay; $(0, 10)$

3. exponential decay; $(0, 1)$

4. compounded annually: $1999.00;
   compounded quarterly: $2039.89

5. 6% compounded monthly

6. 4.37% effective yield

7. 28.14% per year

Quick Warm-Up 6.3

1. $f^{-1}(x) = x - 10$ 2. $g^{-1}(x) = \frac{x}{3}$

3. $h^{-1}(x) = \frac{1}{5}x - \frac{3}{5}$ 4. $j^{-1}(x) = 4x - 8$

Lesson Quiz 6.3

1. $\log_5 625 = 4$ 2. $\log_9 3 = \frac{1}{2}$ 3. $4^{-3} = \frac{1}{64}$

4. $2^6 = 64$ 5. $x \approx 3.67$ 6. $x = -2$

7. $x = 0$ 8. $x = 6$ 9. $x = 4$ 10. $x = 7$

11. $10^{-8.5}$ moles / liter

Quick Warm-Up 6.4

1. z^7 2. t^{12} 3. c^3 4. $\frac{m^3}{n^3}$ 5. a^6b^6

6. r^8s^4

Lesson Quiz 6.4

1. $\log_4(abc)$ 2. $\log_6 36 = 2$

3. $\log_5 m - \log_5 n - \log_5 p$

4. $\log_3 27 + \log_3 a + \log_3 b$
   $= 3 + \log_3 a + \log_3 b$

5. 8   6. 24   7. 32   8. 18   9. $x = 5$

10. $x = 3$

Mid-Chapter Assessment—Chapter 6

1. b   2. d   3. a   4. $7^4 = 2401$

5. $\log_5 \frac{1}{125} = -3$ 6. 14   7. 17

8. $\log_5 125 = 3$ 9. $\log_9\left(\frac{a^6}{b^9c^3}\right)$

10. $x \approx 5.66$ 11. $x = 32$

12. $x = \frac{1}{2}$ 13. $x = \frac{3}{4}$

14. compounded quarterly: $3364.52;
    compounded monthly: $3375.40

15. 7.18%

16a. $48,500(0.975)^n$

b. 39,600

Answers

Quick Warm-Up 6.5

1. $x \approx 1.51$ 2. $x \approx 0.25$ 3. $x \approx -2.30$

4. $v = 0.001$ 5. $v = 7$ 6. $v = \frac{1}{2}$

Lesson Quiz 6.5

1. about 75 decibels

2. $x \approx 2.41$ 3. $x \approx -1.66$ 4. $x \approx -2.70$

5. $x \approx 38.58$ 6. 1.96   7. 0.66

Quick Warm-Up 6.6

1. 1   2. -1 3. undefined   4. 0

5. $1480.24   6. $1488.86

Lesson Quiz 6.6

1. 66.686   2. 0.082   3. 6.477

4. -2.590 5. 9.5   6. $2a$

7. compounded monthly: $985.05;
   compounded continuously: $986.94

8. about 7.53 years

9. about 4000 years old

Quick Warm-Up 6.7

1. $x = 1000$ 2. $x \approx 3.00$ 3. $x = 1$

4. $x \approx 5.00$ 5. $x = -1$ 6. $x \approx 0.90$

7. $x = 0$ 8. $x \approx 2.08$

Lesson Quiz 6.7

1. $E \approx 1.58 \times 10^{23}$ ergs

2. $x = 4$ 3. $x \approx 0.71$

4. about 11 years

5. loss of 9.27 billion

Chapter Assessment—Form A—Chapter 6

1. c   2. d   3. b   4. c   5. b

6. d   7. d   8. a   9. c   10. b

11. a   12. c   13. b   14. d   15. c

16. a   17. b   18. d   19. c

Form B

1. $\log_4 1024 = 5$ 2. 2.2   3. 7.2

4. 15   5. $\log_7(9x^3y^2w)$

6. $\log_a\left(\dfrac{n^3}{m^6}\right)$

7. compounded quarterly: $7706.01;
   compounded monthly: $7775.24

8a. $774.21

  b. about 15.05 years

9. $x \approx 3.93$ 10. $x \approx 2.60$ 11. $x = 729$

12. $x = 625$ 13. $x = 2.5$ 14. $x = 530$

15. $x \approx 126.49$ 16. $x = 5$ 17. 1.24

18. 0.992   19. $(0, -3)$

20a. $C(n) = 430(1.15)^n$

  b. 6 years

  c. about $1315

21a. $F(n) = 3000(0.91)^n$

  b. about 2261 fish

  c. about 7.3 months

22a. $A(4) \approx 43.2$ milligrams

  b. about 10.96 hours

23. 5.24%

Answers

Alternative Assessment—Form A—Chapter 6

1.

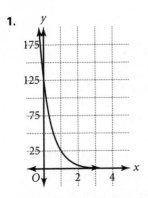

2. domain: all real numbers;
   range: all positive real numbers

3. The variable, x, is in the exponent, and the base is a positive number not equal to 1.

4. Because f is in the form $f(x) = ab^x$ and b is between 0 and 1, f is a decay function.

5. The graph of g is the graph of f reflected across the y-axis.

6.

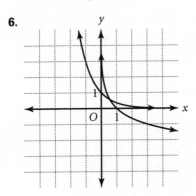

f and g are inverses of one another.

Score Point 4: Distinguished

The student demonstrates a comprehensive understanding of exponential and logarithmic functions. The student uses perceptive, creative, and complex mathematical reasoning and sophisticated, precise, and appropriate mathematical language throughout the task. Theoretical knowledge is apparent and is applied to concrete situations as the student successfully demonstrates a comprehensive understanding of core concepts.

Score Point 3: Proficient

The student demonstrates a broad understanding of exponential and logarithmic functions. The student uses perceptive mathematical reasoning and precise and appropriate mathematical language most of the time. Theoretical knowledge is apparent and is applied to concrete situations as the student attempts to draw conclusions based on the investigations.

Score Point 2: Apprentice

The student demonstrates an understanding of exponential and logarithmic functions. The student uses mathematical reasoning and appropriate mathematical language some of the time. The student attempts to apply theoretical knowledge to the task but may not be able to draw conclusions based on the investigations.

Answers

Score Point 1: Novice

The student demonstrates a basic understanding of exponential and logarithmic functions. The student uses little mathematical reasoning or appropriate mathematical language. Theoretical knowledge is extremely weak, and many responses are irrelevant or illogical. The student fails to follow directions and has great difficulty in communicating his or her responses.

Score Point 0: Unsatisfactory

The student does not complete the task, and his or her responses just restate the problem.

Form B

1. Answers may vary. Sample answer: Graph $y = \log(x + 9) - \log x - 1$. Then use the root or zero feature to find the solutions, or use the trace feature to find where $y = 0$; $x = 1$

2. $x = 4$; check the solution by substituting 4 for x in the original equation.

3. $x = 2$ 4. $x = 3$ 5. $x = 2$

6. Answers may vary. Sample answer: The graph shows no solution. Solving algebraically gives $x = -5$. Because the function $f(x) = \log x$ is not defined for negative numbers, $x = -5$ cannot be a solution, so the equation has no solution.

Score Point 4: Distinguished

The student demonstrates a comprehensive understanding of exponential and logarithmic equations. The student uses perceptive, creative, and complex mathematical reasoning and sophisticated, precise, and appropriate mathematical language throughout the task. Theoretical knowledge is apparent and is applied to concrete situations as the student successfully demonstrates a comprehensive understanding of core concepts.

Score Point 3: Proficient

The student demonstrates a broad understanding of exponential and logarithmic equations. The student uses perceptive mathematical reasoning and precise and appropriate mathematical language most of the time. Theoretical knowledge is apparent and is applied to concrete situations as the student attempts to draw conclusions based on the investigations.

Score Point 2: Apprentice

The student demonstrates an understanding of exponential and logarithmic equations. The student uses mathematical reasoning and appropriate mathematical language some of the time. The student attempts to apply theoretical knowledge to the task but may not be able to draw conclusions based on the investigations.

Score Point 1: Novice

The student demonstrates a basic understanding of exponential and logarithmic equations. The student uses little mathematical reasoning or appropriate mathematical language. Theoretical knowledge is extremely weak, and many responses are irrelevant or illogical. The student fails to follow directions and has great difficulty in communicating his or her responses.

Answers

Chapter 7

Quick Warm-Up 7.1

1. 3   2. -1 3. 8   4. 15   5. $-x + 3$

6. $x^2 - 5x - 1$ 7. $7x$ 8. $3x + 8$

9. $-3x + 3$ 10. $-2x^2$

Lesson Quiz 7.1

1. quintic binomial

2. quartic trinomial

3a. $f(2) = 31$

b. $f(-3) = -19$

4. $-2x^4 + 7x^3 + 3x^2 - 15x + 4$

5. $-2x^2 - 11x + 13$

6. The graph is S-shaped with 2 turns.

7. The graph is W-shaped with 3 turns.

Quick Warm-Up 7.2

1. maximum; $(1, 7)$

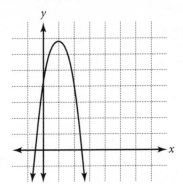

Lesson Quiz 7.2

1.

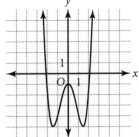

local minima at $(-1.4, -5)$ and $(1.4, -5)$; local maximum at $(0, 1)$; the graph is increasing when $-1.4 < x < 0$ and $x > 1.4$; the graph is decreasing when $x < -1.4$ and $0 < x < 1.4$.

2. The graph falls on the left and on the right.

3. The graph falls on the left and rises on the right.

4. $f(x) = 0.5x^3 - 3x^2 + 2x - 5$

Quick Warm-Up 7.3

1. $3x(2x - 5)$ 2. $(x + 7)(x - 4)$

3. $(x + 8)(x - 8)$ 4. $4(x - 1)^2$

5. $(3x + 2)(2x - 3)$

6. $(4x^2 + 1)(2x + 1)(2x - 1)$

Lesson Quiz 7.3

1. $f(x) = x^3 + 2x^2 - 26x + 8$

2. $3x(x + 2)(x - 5)$

3. $(x + 7)(x^2 - 7x + 49)$

4a. $x + 3$ is not a factor.

b. $x - 4$ is a factor.

5. $x + 4$

6. $(x - 2)(x - 3)(x + 4)$

Answers

Mid-Chapter Assessment—Chapter 7

1. c   **2.** a   **3.** d

4. The graph rises on the left and on the right.

5. $(3x - 2)(9x^2 + 6x + 4)$

6.

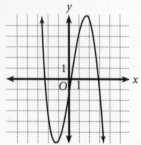

local minimum at $(-1.1, -6.1)$; local maximum at $(1.8, 6.2)$

7. $f(x) = 3x^4 - 5x^3 - 2x^2 - 6$

8. $2x^2 + 3x - 3$

9. $x^2 - 5$

Quick Warm-Up 7.4

1. $x = -2 \text{ or } x = 7$ **2.** $x = 0 \text{ or } x = -9$

3. $x = -11 \text{ or } x = 11$ **4.** $x = -2 \text{ or } x = 8$

5. $x(2x - 7)(x + 1)$ **6.** $x^2 - 4x + 3$

Lesson Quiz 7.4

1. $-2, 0, \text{ and } 7$ **2.** $-4, 0, \text{ and } 4$

3a. $(x - 2)(x + 1)(x + 3)$

 b. $-3, -1, \text{ and } 2$

4. $-5 \text{ and } 2$

5. $\pm 3 \text{ and } \pm \sqrt{3}$

Quick Warm-Up 7.5

1. $1, 3, 7, 21$

2. $1, 2, 3, 4, 5, 6, 10, 12, 15, 20, 30, 60$

3. $x = 2 \pm \sqrt{2}$ **4.** $x = 1 \text{ or } x = -\dfrac{5}{2}$

5. yes   **6.** no

Lesson Quiz 7.5

1. a. $\pm 1, \pm 3, \pm 5, \pm 9, \pm 15, \pm 45, \pm \dfrac{1}{3}, \pm \dfrac{5}{3}$

   b. $x = 3$

2. $-4, \dfrac{-5 + \sqrt{13}}{2}, \text{ and } \dfrac{-5 - \sqrt{13}}{2}$

3. $2, 1 + 2i, \text{ and } 1 - 2i$

4. $P(x) = 2(x - 5)^2(x + 2);$
$P(x) = 2x^3 - 16x^2 + 10x + 100$

5. $P(x) = 3(x - 4)(x^2 - 4x + 29)$
$P(x) = 3x^3 - 24x^2 + 135x - 348$

Chapter Assessment—Form A—Chapter 7

1. c   **2.** d   **3.** d   **4.** a   **5.** a   **6.** c   **7.** b

8. c   **9.** d   **10.** a   **11.** c   **12.** c   **13.** b

14. d   **15.** a   **16.** c

Form B

1. quintic trinomial

2. $f(-4) = -360$

3. $-6x^4 - 11x^3 + 12x^2 - 3x - 6$

4. $x^3 - 12x - 16$

5. $3x(x + 2)(x - 4)$

6. $(x + y)(x^2 - xy + y^2)$

7. $(x + 5)(x + 1)(x - 4)$

8. $(5x - 3)(25x^2 + 15x + 9)$

Answers

9.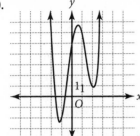

local minima at $(-1.2, -2.4)$ and $(2.1, 0.9)$; local maximum at $(0.6, 6.9)$

10. The graph falls on the left and on the right.

11. The graph rises on the left and falls on the right.

12. $P(4) = -5$

13. $f(x) = 2x^3 - 3x^2 - 4.5x + 8$

14. $x = 3$

15. $x^2 + 6x + 8$

16. $x^3 + 2x^2 - 5x - 3$

17. $5x^2 - 2x + 4$

18. $3x - 6$

19. $3, 5 + i$, and $5 - i$

20. ± 3 and $\pm\sqrt{2}$

21. $\pm 1, \pm 2, \pm 4, \pm\frac{1}{5}, \pm\frac{2}{5}, \pm\frac{4}{5}$

22. $-\frac{4}{5}, -3$, and 1

23. $P(x) = -5(x + 2)(x - 4)$
    $= -5x^2 + 10x + 40$

24. $P(x) = 3(x - 3)^2(x^2 - 6x + 25)$

Alternative Assessment—Form A—Chapter 7

1. The zeros of f are 0 (multiplicity of 2) and -2. The degree of f is 3. The zeros of g are 0 (multiplicity of 2) and -2. The degree of g is 3.

2. f is increasing when $x < -\frac{4}{3}$ or $x > 0$;

   f is decreasing when $-\frac{4}{3} < x < 0$;

   $\left(-\frac{4}{3}, \frac{32}{27}\right)$ and $(0, 0)$

   g is increasing when $-\frac{4}{3} < x < 0$;

   g is decreasing when $x < -\frac{4}{3}$ or $x > 0$;

   $\left(-\frac{4}{3}, -\frac{32}{27}\right)$ and $(0, 0)$

3. Changing the sign of the leading coefficient reflects the graph across the x-axis.

4. $f(x) = (x - 1)(x + 1)(x + 2)(x - 3)$

5. At a turning point, the graph reaches a local maximum or a local minimum and changes from increasing to decreasing or from decreasing to increasing; none of the zeros of f are turning points.

6. At a crossing point, the graph crosses the x-axis, and the value of the function changes from positive to negative or from negative to positive; f has 4 crossing points.

Score Point 4: Distinguished

The student demonstrates a comprehensive understanding of polynomial function behavior. The student uses perceptive, creative, and complex mathematical reasoning and sophisticated, precise, and appropriate mathematical language throughout the task. Theoretical knowledge is apparent and is applied to concrete

Answers

situations as the student successfully demonstrates a comprehensive understanding of core concepts.

Score Point 3: Proficient

The student demonstrates a broad understanding of polynomial function behavior. The student uses perceptive mathematical reasoning and precise and appropriate mathematical language most of the time. Theoretical knowledge is apparent and is applied to concrete situations as the student attempts to draw conclusions based on the investigations.

Score Point 2: Apprentice

The student demonstrates an understanding of polynomial function behavior. The student uses mathematical reasoning and appropriate mathematical language some of the time. The student attempts to apply theoretical knowledge to the task but may not be able to draw conclusions based on the investigations.

Score Point 1: Novice

The student demonstrates a basic understanding of polynomial function behavior. The student uses little mathematical reasoning or appropriate mathematical language. Theoretical knowledge is extremely weak, and many responses are irrelevant or illogical. The student fails to follow directions and has great difficulty in communicating his or her responses.

Score Point 0: Unsatisfactory

The student does not complete the task, and his or her responses just restate the problem.

Form B

1. No; the number of linear factors is one more than the degree of the function.

2. Answers may vary. Sample answers: If $f(-2) = 0$, then $x + 2$ is a factor of $f(x)$ by the Remainder Theorem. Use long division or synthetic division to find whether $x + 2$ divides evenly into $f(x)$. Graph $f(x)$ to see if the graph crosses the x-axis at -2.

3. $f(x) = (x - 5)(x + 4)$

4. $f(x) = x(9x - 4)(9x + 4)$

5. Answers may vary. Sample answer: The real number r is a zero of the polynomial function $P(x)$ if and only if $x - r$ is a factor of $P(x)$.

6. f has one real zero and two complex zeros; the zeros of f are 3, i, and $-i$;

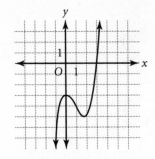

$$f(x) = (x - 3)(x - i)(x + i)$$

Score Point 4: Distinguished

The student demonstrates a comprehensive understanding of the factored form of a polynomial. The student uses perceptive, creative, and complex mathematical reasoning and sophisticated, precise, and appropriate mathematical language throughout the task. Theoretical knowledge is apparent and is applied to concrete situations as the student successfully demonstrates a comprehensive understanding of core concepts.

Answers

Score Point 3: Proficient

The student demonstrates a broad understanding of the factored form of a polynomial. The student uses perceptive mathematical reasoning and precise and appropriate mathematical language most of the time. Theoretical knowledge is apparent and is applied to concrete situations as the student attempts to draw conclusions based on the investigations.

Score Point 2: Apprentice

The student demonstrates an understanding of the factored form of a polynomial. The student uses mathematical reasoning and appropriate mathematical language some of the time. The student attempts to apply theoretical knowledge to the task but may not be able to draw conclusions based on the investigations.

Score Point 1: Novice

The student demonstrates a basic understanding of the factored form of a polynomial. The student uses little mathematical reasoning or appropriate mathematical language. Theoretical knowledge is extremely weak, and many responses are irrelevant or illogical. The student fails to follow directions and has great difficulty in communicating his or her responses.

Score Point 0: Unsatisfactory

The student does not complete the task, and his or her responses just restate the problem.

Chapter 8

Quick Warm-Up 8.1

1. $k = -2; y = -2x$

2. $k = -0.5; y = -0.5x$

3. $k = 12.5; y = 12.5x$ 4. $a = -48$

5. $b = -3$

Lesson Quiz 8.1

1a. $k = 2000; y = \dfrac{2000}{x}$

b. $y = 50$

2a. $k = 0.5; y = 0.5xz$

b. $y = 180$

3a. $k = 1.5; y = \dfrac{1.5xz}{w}$

b. $y = 90$

4. 120 revolutions per minute

Quick Warm-Up 8.2

1. $x = -5$ 2. $x = 0$ 3. $x = -\dfrac{2}{5}$

4. $x = 0 \ or \ x = 5$ 5. $x = 7 \ or \ x = -2$

6. $x = 0 \ or \ x = -9 \ or \ x = 6$ 7. $x = 1$

Lesson Quiz 8.2

1a. all real numbers except 2 and -5

b. $x = 2; x = -5$

2. $y = 0$

3. $y = -\dfrac{1}{2}$

Answers

4.

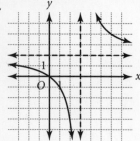

$x = 3, y = 2$

5. $x = 5$

Quick Warm-Up 8.3

1. $\frac{2}{7}$ **2.** $\frac{2}{5}$ **3.** $\frac{16}{15}$, or $1\frac{1}{15}$ **4.** 3

5. $(x + 9)(x - 9)$ **6.** $(x - 18)(x + 2)$

Lesson Quiz 8.3

1. $\frac{x + 7}{x + 2}$ **2.** $6x^3$ **3.** $\frac{1}{x^2(x + 2)}$ **4.** $\frac{x}{x - 2}$

5. $\frac{24}{5}$ **6.** $\frac{x - 1}{x}$

7. $(x + 4)(x + 3)$, or $x^2 + 7x + 12$

8. $\frac{x + 5y}{x + 2y}$ **9.** -1 **10.** $5x^2$

Quick Warm-Up 8.4

1. $-\frac{1}{2}$ **2.** $-\frac{5}{9}$ **3.** $\frac{2}{x}$ **4.** $\frac{1}{n}$ **5.** $\frac{a + b}{ab}$

6. $\frac{2x}{y}$

Lesson Quiz 8.4

1. $\frac{7x - 10}{3x + 5}$ **2.** 3 **3.** $\frac{5x + 6}{x(x + 3)}$

4. $\frac{6x + 23}{(x + 2)(x + 3)}$ **5.** $\frac{x(11x + 16)}{(x + 5)(2x - 3)}$

6. $\frac{x(5x + 1)}{(x - 1)(x + 1)}$ **7.** $\frac{-x^2 - x - 1}{x^2 - 5x + 6}$

8. $\frac{-x}{x + y}$ **9.** $\frac{1 - x + y}{x - 2y}$ **10.** $\frac{xyz}{yz + xz + xy}$

Mid-Chapter Assessment—Chapter 8

1. a   **2.** c   **3.** b   **4.** d

5.

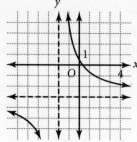

$y = -3, x = -2$

6. $y = 450$

7. all real numbers except 3 and -6

8. $\frac{x(x + 4)}{x + 2}$ **9.** $\frac{5x^2 + 3x - 6}{x^3 - 4x}$

Quick Warm-Up 8.5

1. $c > -0.75$ **2.** $r \le -7.5$

3. $x = -9 \ or \ x = 4$ **4.** $x = -1 \ or \ x = \frac{4}{3}$

5. $m = 9.6$ **6.** $g = 24$ **7.** $a = 1.2$

8. $x = 4.5$

Lesson Quiz 8.5

1. $T(x) = \frac{48}{x} + \frac{192}{2x}$

2. $x = 2.6$ **3.** $x = 4$ **4.** $2 < x < 4$

5. $-2 < x < \frac{2}{3} \ or \ x > 2$

6. $x = \frac{19}{3}$ **7.** $x = \frac{15}{13}$ **8.** $x > -2$

9. $-2 < x < -1 \ or \ 3 < x < 9$

Quick Warm-Up 8.6

1. 5 units up   **2.** 5 units to the left

3. vertical stretch by 5

4. vertical stretch by 5; reflection across the x-axis

Answers

5. horizontal compression by $\frac{1}{5}$

6. horizontal stretch by 5

Lesson Quiz 8.6

1. all real numbers greater than or equal to -2

2. vertical stretch by a factor of 3, vertical translation 2 units down, horizontal translation 4 units to the right

3. horizontal compression by a factor of $\frac{1}{2}$, horizontal translation 3 units to the left, vertical translation 5 units up

4. $y = \pm\sqrt{x-3}$

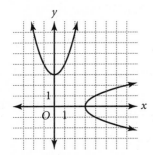

5. -8 6. -17

Quick Warm-Up 8.7

1. 6   2. -25 3. a^3b^5 4. m^6n^3

5. $\frac{s^2}{r^3}$ 6. $\frac{1}{c^6d^2}$ 7. $6x^2 + x - 2$

Lesson Quiz 8.7

1. $9x^2y^4|z|\sqrt{y}$ 2. $-5x^3y^2z\sqrt[3]{y^2z}$

3. $10x^3y\sqrt{x}$ 4. $8x^2y\sqrt[3]{y}$

5. $6 + 5\sqrt{5}$ 6. $85 + 13\sqrt{7}$

7. $\frac{3\sqrt{5}}{5}$ 8. $-4 - 2\sqrt{6}$

Quick Warm-Up 8.8

1. $a = -4$ 2. $t = 4.5$ 3. $y = 0$ or $y = -4$

4. $m = -3$ or $m = 5$ 5. $x = 1 \pm 2\sqrt{2}$

6. $x = -2$

Lesson Quiz 8.8

1. $x = 48$ 2. $x = 3$ 3. $x = 5$

4. $x = 3$ or $x = -1$ 5. $x = -\frac{5}{6}$

6. $x = 5$ 7. $x \geq 7$

8. $x < -6$ or $0.76 < x < 5.24$ 9. $x > 4$

10. $x > 0$ 11. $x \geq 5$ 12. $x \geq -5$

Chapter Assessment—Form A— Chapter 8

1. d   2. c   3. b   4. d   5. d

6. a   7. b   8. b   9. c   10. b

11. d   12. a   13. c   14. b   15. a

16. a   17. a   18. d   19. b

Form B

1. $k = 360;\ y = 40$

2. $y = \frac{1}{4};\ x = \pm\frac{3}{2}$

3.

4. $-9 - 3\sqrt{5}$ 5. $3x^2y^5\sqrt[3]{x^2}$

6. $\frac{x+5}{x^2}$ 7. $\frac{9x^2 - 4x - 5}{6x^2 + 7x + 2}$

8. $\frac{1}{x+4}$ 9. $2|x^3y|\sqrt{2}$

Answers

10. vertical stretch by a factor of 5, vertical translation 4 units down, reflection across the y-axis, horizontal compression by a factor of $\frac{1}{3}$, horizontal translation 2 units to the left

11. all real numbers except 7 and -4

12. all real numbers greater than or equal to $\frac{1}{2}$

13. -110 14. $\dfrac{20 + 5\sqrt{10}}{6}$ 15. $x = 0.9$

16. $x = 2.5$ 17. $x = 2$ or $x = -6$ 18. $x = 6$

19. $x = 9$ or $x = -2$ 20. $x = 2$

21. $x < 2$ or $x > 6$ 22. $-9 < x < 3$

23. $y = \dfrac{-3 \pm \sqrt{9 + 4x}}{2}$ 24. 300

25. Sample answer: $y = \dfrac{2x + 3}{x + 2}$

Alternative Assessment—Form A—Chapter 8

1. The degree of the numerator is less than that of the denominator, so the horizontal asymptote is $y = 0$. Because $x + 2$ is a factor of the denominator and not a factor of the numerator, $x = -2$ is a vertical asymptote.

2.

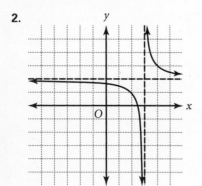

The graphs of $f(x)$ and $g(x)$ are the same. The graph of $g(x)$ is the graph of $h(x) = \frac{1}{x}$ translated 2 units up and 3 units to the right. The asymptotes of $h(x)$ are $y = 0$

and $x = 0$, so the asymptotes of $g(x)$ are at $y = 2$ and $x = 3$. Since the graphs of $f(x)$ and $g(x)$ are the same, they have the same asymptotes.

3.

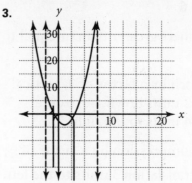

4. The zeros of p are 3 and -1. The vertical asymptotes of q are the zeros of p. The domain of q is all real numbers except 3 and 1.

Score Point 4: Distinguished

The student demonstrates a comprehensive understanding of reciprocals of polynomial functions. The student uses perceptive, creative, and complex mathematical reasoning and sophisticated, precise, and appropriate mathematical language throughout the task. Theoretical knowledge is apparent and is applied to concrete situations as the student successfully demonstrates a comprehensive understanding of core concepts.

Score Point 3: Proficient

The student demonstrates a broad understanding of reciprocals of polynomial functions. The student uses perceptive mathematical reasoning and precise and appropriate mathematical language most of the time. Theoretical knowledge is apparent and is applied to concrete situations as the student attempts to draw conclusions based on the investigations.

Answers

Score Point 2: Apprentice

The student demonstrates an understanding of reciprocals of polynomial functions. The student uses mathematical reasoning and appropriate mathematical language some of the time. The student attempts to apply theoretical knowledge to the task but may not be able to draw conclusions based on the investigations.

Score Point 1: Novice

The student demonstrates a basic understanding of reciprocals of polynomial functions. The student uses little mathematical reasoning or appropriate mathematical language. Theoretical knowledge is extremely weak, and many responses are irrelevant or illogical. The student fails to follow directions and has great difficulty in communicating his or her responses.

Score Point 0: Unsatisfactory

The student does not complete the task, and his or her responses just restate the problem.

Form B

1. Graph $y = \frac{x-3}{x}$ and $y = \frac{x-4}{x-2}$. Use the trace or intersect feature of a graphics calculator to find any points of intersection; $x = 6$

2. Multiply both sides of the equation by x^2 to change the rational equation into a polynomial equation; $x = 1$ or $x = -\frac{1}{5}$; Extraneous roots may occur when both sides of an equation are multiplied by a variable.

3. The algebraic method yields the solution $x = 1$, which is extraneous. Graphing shows that no solution exists.

4. The domain for both f and g is all real numbers except 0.

5. $h(x) = 1$; the domain of $h(x)$ is all real numbers except 0 because the domain of the sum function is restricted by the domains of the functions that are added.

Score Point 4: Distinguished

The student demonstrates a comprehensive understanding of solving rational equations. The student uses perceptive, creative, and complex mathematical reasoning and sophisticated, precise, and appropriate mathematical language throughout the task. Theoretical knowledge is apparent and is applied to concrete situations as the student successfully demonstrates a comprehensive understanding of core concepts.

Score Point 3: Proficient

The student demonstrates a broad understanding of solving rational equations. The student uses perceptive mathematical reasoning and precise and appropriate mathematical language most of the time. Theoretical knowledge is apparent and is applied to concrete situations as the student attempts to draw conclusions based on the investigations.

Score Point 2: Apprentice

The student demonstrates an understanding of solving rational equations. The student uses mathematical reasoning and appropriate mathematical language some of the time. The student attempts to apply theoretical knowledge to the task but may not be able to draw conclusions based on the investigations.

Answers

Score Point 1: Novice

The student demonstrates a basic understanding of solving rational equations. The student uses little mathematical reasoning or appropriate mathematical language. Theoretical knowledge is extremely weak, and many responses are irrelevant or illogical. The student fails to follow directions and has great difficulty in communicating his or her responses.

Score Point 0: Unsatisfactory

The student does not complete the task, and his or her responses just restate the problem.

Chapter 9

Quick Warm-Up 9.1

1. $y = -3x + 7$ 2. $y = -2x - 5$

3. $y = x - 4$ 4. $x = \pm 4$ 5. $x = \pm\sqrt{7}$

6. $x = \pm\sqrt{15}$ 7. $b \approx 6.93$ 8. $r \approx 13.93$

Lesson Quiz 9.1

1.

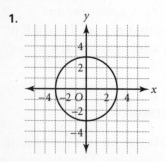

2. $PQ = 13$; $M = (9, 9.5)$

3. $PQ = \sqrt{116} \approx 10.77$; $M = (-6, 2)$

4. $Q(10, 13)$

5. center: $(8, 4)$; radius: 5; circumference: 10π, or ≈ 31.42

Quick Warm-Up 9.2

1. $x = 0$; $(0, 0)$; down; maximum

2. $x = 2$; $(2, -4)$; up; minimum

3. $x = -1$; $(-1, 7)$; down; maximum

Lesson Quiz 9.2

1.

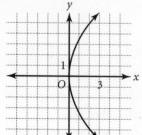

focus: $(3, 0)$; directrix: $x = -3$

2. $x - 2 = -\frac{1}{8}y^2$

3. $y + 3 = \frac{1}{16}(x - 2)^2$

4.

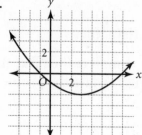

vertex: $(3, -2)$; focus: $(3, 0)$; directrix: $y = -4$

Quick Warm-Up 9.3

1. 15   2. $\sqrt{13}$ 3. $x = 6$ or $x = -2$

4. $x = -3 \pm 2\sqrt{2}$

Answers

5.

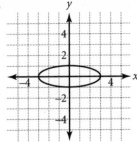

ellipse

6.

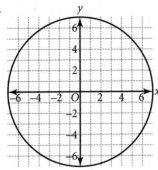

circle

Lesson Quiz 9.3

1. $x^2 + y^2 = 36$

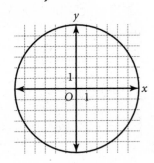

2. $(x + 1)^2 + (y - 2)^2 = 16$

3. $(x - 4)^2 + (y + 3)^2 = 49$;
   radius: 7; center: $(4, -3)$

Mid-Chapter Assessment—Chapter 9

1. a   2. c   3. d   4. d

5.

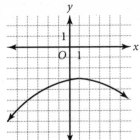

vertex: $(1, -3)$; focus: $(1, -6)$;
directrix: $y = 0$

6.

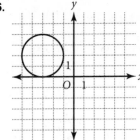

center: $(-3, 2)$; radius: 2

7. $x - 6 = \frac{1}{20}(y - 2)^2$

8. $(x - 10)^2 + (y - 11)^2 = 100$

Quick Warm-Up 9.4

1. $x^2 + y^2 = 81$ 2. $x^2 + (y - 5)^2 = 1$

3. $(x + 8)^2 + (y + 1)^2 = 16$

4. $(x + 4)^2 + (y - 2)^2 = 25$

5. $(x + 1)^2 + (y - 3)^2 = 16$; center: $(-1, 3)$;
   radius: 4

Lesson Quiz 9.4

1. center: $(0, 0)$; vertices: $(7, 0)$ and $(-7, 0)$;
   co-vertices: $(0, 3)$ and $(0, -3)$

2. center: $(-2, 5)$; vertices: $(-2, 0)$ and
   $(-2, 10)$; co-vertices: $(-6, 5)$ and $(2, 5)$

3. $\frac{x^2}{169} + \frac{y^2}{25} = 1$

Answers

4. $\dfrac{(x+4)^2}{4} + \dfrac{(y-1)^2}{16} = 1$

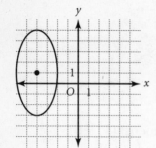

5. $\dfrac{(x+1)^2}{4} + \dfrac{y^2}{9} = 1$; center: $(-1, 0)$;
foci: $(-1, \sqrt{5})$ and $(-1, -\sqrt{5})$

Quick Warm-Up 9.5

1.

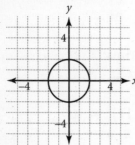

circle

2.

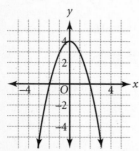

parabola

3.

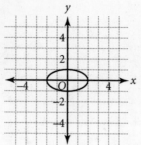

ellipse

4. $\dfrac{(x+2)^2}{9} + \dfrac{(y-3)^2}{4} = 1$; center: $(-2, 3)$;
vertices: $(-5, 3)$ and $(1, 3)$;
co-vertices: $(-2, 1)$ and $(-2, 5)$;
foci: $(-2 - \sqrt{5}, 3)$ and $(-2 + \sqrt{5}, 3)$

Lesson Quiz 9.5

1. vertices: $(0, 5)$ and $(0, -5)$;
asymptotes: $y = \pm\dfrac{5}{8}x$

2. vertices: $(3, 0)$ and $(-3, 0)$;
asymptotes: $y = \pm\dfrac{7}{3}x$

3. $\dfrac{x^2}{49} - \dfrac{y^2}{81} = 1$

4. $\dfrac{(y-6)^2}{4} - \dfrac{(x-2)^2}{12} = 1$

5.

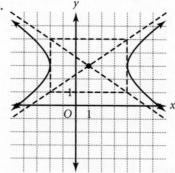

center: $(1, 3)$; vertices: $(4, 3)$ and $(-2, 3)$

Quick Warm-Up 9.6

1. $(1, 5)$ 2. $(0, -3)$ 3. no solution

4. $(-23, 39)$ 5. $(-2, -1)$

Answers

Lesson Quiz 9.6

1. $(4, 8)$, $(-4, -8)$ 2. $(0, 2)$

3. $(3, 0)$, $(-3, 0)$

4. $(2, 4)$, $(2, -4)$, $(-2, 4)$, $(-2, -4)$

5. ellipse with center $(-2, 3)$, vertices $(2, 3)$ and $(-6, 3)$, and co-vertices $(-2, 0)$ and $(-2, 6)$; $\dfrac{(x + 2)^2}{16} + \dfrac{(y - 3)^2}{9} = 1$

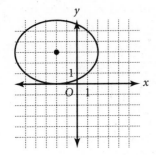

Chapter Assessment Form A—Chapter 9

1. c   2. d   3. a   4. c   5. a

6. b   7. d   8. b   9. c   10. a

11. d   12. d   13. c   14. d

Form B

1. $PQ = 17$; $M(5, -0.5)$

2. $Q(10, -27)$

3.

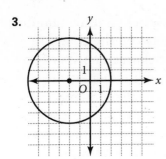

radius: 4; center: $(-2, 0)$

4.

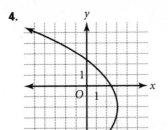

vertex: $(3, -2)$; focus: $(1, -2)$; directrix: $x = 5$

5.

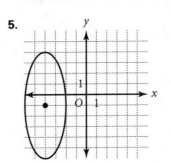

center: $(-4, -1)$; vertices: $(-4, 4)$ and $(-4, -6)$; co-vertices: $(-6, -1)$ and $(-2, -1)$

6. $(3, 4)$, $(3, -4)$, $(-3, 4)$, $(-3, -4)$

7. $(1, 3)$, $(-1, 3)$

8.

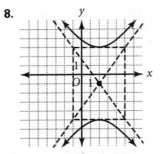

center: $(2, -1)$; vertices: $(2, 3)$ and $(2, -5)$

9. $(x + 2)^2 + (y - 13)^2 = 100$

10. $y - 3 = \dfrac{1}{20}(x - 6)^2$

11. $\dfrac{(x - 5)^2}{64} + \dfrac{(y + 7)^2}{28} = 1$

12. $\dfrac{(x - 2)^2}{25} + \dfrac{(y - 4)^2}{49} = 1$

Answers

13. $\dfrac{(x-8)^2}{16} - \dfrac{y^2}{20} = 1$

14. $\dfrac{(y+5)^2}{16} - \dfrac{(x-3)^2}{81} = 1$

15. $y = \pm \dfrac{10}{7}x$

16. $(x-5)^2 + (y+3)^2 = 16$

17. $\dfrac{(x+4)^2}{9} + \dfrac{(y+2)^2}{1} = 1$

18. $(3, 4)$ and $(-4, -3)$

19. $(x+3)^2 + (y+1)^2 = 16$

Alternative Assessment—Form A— Chapter 9

1. Answers may vary. Write the equation in standard form by completing the square: $y - 2 = \dfrac{1}{8}(x - 3)^2$. The parabola opens upward because $\dfrac{1}{8}$ is greater than 0, and the distance from the focus to the vertex is $8 \div 4 = 2$. The vertex is $(3, 2)$, the focus is $(3, 4)$, and the directrix is $y = 0$.

2. Answers may vary. Write the equation in standard form by completing the square twice: $(x - 3)^2 + (y - 1)^2 = 4$. Graph the circle with center $(3, 1)$ and radius $= 2$.

3. The equation in standard form is $\dfrac{x^2}{12} + \dfrac{y^2}{16} = 1$. The center is $(0, 0)$, the vertices are at $(0, 4)$ and $(0, -4)$, and the foci are at $(0, 2)$ and $(0, -2)$. If the larger denominator is under the numerator with x, then the major axis is horizontal. If the larger denominator is under the numerator with y, then the major axis is vertical. In this case, the major axis is vertical.

4. $\dfrac{x^2}{25} + \dfrac{y^2}{9} = 1$

Score Point 4: Distinguished

The student demonstrates a comprehensive understanding of the relationship between the equation of a conic section and the characteristics of its graph. The student uses perceptive, creative, and complex mathematical reasoning and sophisticated, precise, and appropriate mathematical language throughout the task. Theoretical knowledge is apparent and is applied to concrete situations as the student successfully demonstrates a comprehensive understanding of core concepts.

Score Point 3: Proficient

The student demonstrates a broad understanding of the relationship between the equation of a conic section and the characteristics of its graph. The student uses perceptive mathematical reasoning and precise and appropriate mathematical language most of the time. Theoretical knowledge is apparent and is applied to concrete situations as the student attempts to draw conclusions based on the investigations.

Score Point 2: Apprentice

The student demonstrates an understanding of the relationship between the equation of a conic section and the characteristics of its graph. The student uses mathematical reasoning and appropriate mathematical language some of the time. The student attempts to apply theoretical knowledge to the task but may not be able to draw conclusions based on the investigations.

Answers

Score Point 1: Novice

The student demonstrates a basic understanding of the relationship between the equation of a conic section and the characteristics of its graph. The student uses little mathematical reasoning or appropriate mathematical language. Theoretical knowledge is extremely weak, and many responses are irrelevant or illogical. The student fails to follow directions and has great difficulty in communicating his or her responses.

Score Point 0: Unsatisfactory

The student does not complete the task, and his or her responses just restate the problem.

Form B

1. Answers may vary. Sample answer:

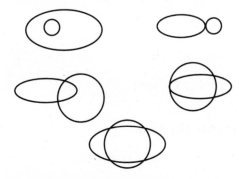

A circle and an ellipse can intersect in 0, 1, 2, 3, or 4 points.

2. Answers may vary. Sample answer:

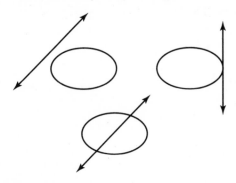

The graphs of a first-degree equation and a second-degree equation can intersect in 0, 1, or 2 points.

3. Answers may vary. Solve each equation for y. Graph $y_1 = \sqrt{16 + x^2}$, $y_2 = -\sqrt{16 + x^2}$, $y_3 = \sqrt{34 - x^2}$, and $y_4 = -\sqrt{34 - x^2}$. Then trace or use an intersect command on a calculator to find the points where the graphs intersect. The solutions are $(3, 5)$, $(3, -5)$, $(-3, 5)$, and $(-3, -5)$.

4. $\left(2\sqrt{2}, \sqrt{2}\right)$ and $\left(-2\sqrt{2}, -\sqrt{2}\right)$

Score Point 4: Distinguished

The student demonstrates a comprehensive understanding of solving nonlinear systems of equations. The student uses perceptive, creative, and complex mathematical reasoning and sophisticated, precise, and appropriate mathematical language throughout the task. Theoretical knowledge is apparent and is applied to concrete situations as the student successfully demonstrates a comprehensive understanding of core concepts.

Score Point 3: Proficient

The student demonstrates a broad understanding of solving nonlinear systems of equations. The student uses perceptive mathematical reasoning and precise and appropriate mathematical language most of the time. Theoretical knowledge is apparent and is applied to concrete situations as the student attempts to draw conclusions based on the investigations.

Answers

Score Point 2: Apprentice

The student demonstrates an understanding of solving nonlinear systems of equations. The student uses mathematical reasoning and appropriate mathematical language some of the time. The student attempts to apply theoretical knowledge to the task but may not be able to draw conclusions based on the investigations.

Score Point 1: Novice

The student demonstrates a basic understanding of solving nonlinear systems of equations. The student uses little mathematical reasoning or appropriate mathematical language. Theoretical knowledge is extremely weak, and many responses are irrelevant or illogical. The student fails to follow directions and has great difficulty in communicating his or her responses.

Score Point 0: Unsatisfactory

The student does not complete the task, and his or her responses just restate the problem.

Chapter 10

Quick Warm-Up 10.1

1. 15.7%   2. 1012.2%   3. 40%   4. 34%

5. 66.5%   6. 42.9%

7. 25π cm^2, or $\approx$78.5 cm^2

8. 9π in^2, or $\approx$28.3 in^2

Lesson Quiz 10.1

1. $\frac{7}{25}$, or 28%   2. $\frac{1}{4}$, or 25%   3. 150

4. 480   5. 60

Quick Warm-Up 10.2

1. 26,000   2. 50,625   3. 17,576,000

4. 2,025,000

Lesson Quiz 10.2

1. 126   2. 3024   3. 840   4. 720

5. 116,280   6. 665,280   7. 2520

8. 60   9. 120

Quick Warm-Up 10.3

1. 720   2. 2880   3. 6720   4. 126

5. 210   6. 7200   7. 40,320   8. 5040

Lesson Quiz 10.3

1. 1   2. 3003   3. 2.75   4. 6435

5a. 6840

  b. 1140

6. 997,920

7. $\approx$0.34866, or about 35%

Quick Warm-Up 10.4

1. $\frac{35}{150} \approx 23.3\%$ 2. $\frac{60}{150} = 40\%$

3. 140   4. 220

Lesson Quiz 10.4

1a. $\frac{3}{4}$, or 75%

  b. $\frac{19}{40}$, or 47.5%

2. $\frac{8}{25}$, or 32%

Answers

Mid-Chapter Assessment—Chapter 10

1. c   2. a   3. d   4. c

5. ≈0.1989, or about 20%

6. 35   7. 1320   8. 317,520

9. $\frac{11}{25}$, or 44%

Quick Warm-Up 10.5

1. $\frac{6}{20}$, or 30%   2. $\frac{0}{20}$, or 0%   3. $\frac{3}{4}$, or 75%

4. $\frac{20}{20}$, or 100%   5. $\frac{9}{20}$, or 45%

Lesson Quiz 10.5

1. 0.4

2. $\frac{1}{12}$, or about 8.3%

3. $\frac{1}{16}$, or 6.25%

4a. ≈0.0527, or about 5%

b. 0.34375, or about 34%

5. Answers may vary. Sample answer:
No; $P(A$ does not work$) = 0.06$,
$P(B$ does not work$) = 0.08$, and
$P(A$ and B do not work$) = 0.02$. Since
$P(A) \times P(B) \neq P(A$ and $B)$, the networks
do not operate independently.

Quick Warm-Up 10.6

1. $\frac{6}{36} \approx 17\%$ 2. $\frac{5}{36} \approx 14\%$ 3. $\frac{11}{36} \approx 31\%$

4. $\frac{15}{36} \approx 42\%$ 5. $\frac{25}{36} \approx 69\%$ 6. $\frac{36}{36} = 100\%$

Lesson Quiz 10.6

1. 0.25, or 25%   2. $\frac{1}{2}$, or 50%

3. $\frac{2}{5}$, or 40%   4. $\frac{21}{50}$, or 42%

5. $\frac{2}{3}$, or about 66.7%

Quick Warm-Up 10.7

1. $\frac{1}{2} = 50\%$ 2. $\frac{1}{2} = 50\%$ 3. $\frac{11}{20}$, or 55%

4. $\frac{9}{20}$, or 45%   5. 500   6. 550

Lesson Quiz 10.7

1.

Number	Probability	Random numbers
0	0.01	01
1	0.07	02–08
2	0.12	09–20
3	0.18	21–38
4	0.19	39–57
5	0.17	58–74
6	0.13	75–87
7	0.08	88–95
8	0.05	96–100

2. Answers will vary.

3. Answers will vary.

Chapter Assessment—Form A—Chapter 10

1. c   2. c   3. a   4. c   5. b   6. b
7. d   8. b   9. d   10. c   11. d   12. c
13. d   14. a   15. d   16. a   17. c

Form B

1. 1   2. 3,268,760   3. 1,816,214,400

4. 672   5. 5,586,853,480   6. 302,400

7. 336   8. 9900   9. ≈0.2146, or 21%

10a. 0

b. 0.7

c. 0.5

Answers

11a. 0.3

 b. 0.5

 c. 0.8

12. ≈ 0.2384, or about 24%

13a. 120

 b. $\dfrac{1}{120}$

14a. $\dfrac{31}{40}$, or 77.5%

 b. $\dfrac{5}{8}$, or 62.5%

 c. $\dfrac{3}{5}$, or 60%

15. $\dfrac{27}{1000}$, or 2.7%

16a. $\dfrac{1}{3}$, or about 33.3%

 b. Answers may vary. Sample answer:
 $P(B) = 0.45$ and $P(B|A) \approx 0.33$;
 Because $P(B) \neq P(B|A)$, A and B are
 not independent events.

Alternative Assessment—Form A—Chapter 10

1a. Permutation; the jobs are different, so
 the order in which the applicants are
 selected matters; $_{12}P_2 = 132$ ways to fill
 the two positions

 b. Combination; the jobs are the same, so
 the order in which the applicants are
 selected does not matter; $_{12}C_2 = 66$
 ways to fill the two positions

2a. Permutation; the trophies are different,
 so the order in which they are awarded
 matters; $_{10}P_3 = 720$ ways to award the
 trophies

 b. Combination; the trophies are the same,
 so the order in which they are awarded
 does not matter; $_{10}C_3 = 120$ ways to
 award the trophies

3a. Combination; the order in which the
 members of a committee are chosen
 does not matter; $_8C_2 = 28$ ways to form
 the committee

 b. Permutation; the positions are different,
 so the order in which they are filled
 matters; $_8P_2 = 56$ ways to fill the
 positions

Score Point 4: Distinguished

The student demonstrates a comprehensive
understanding of the difference between a
combination and a permutation. The
student uses perceptive, creative, and
complex mathematical reasoning and
sophisticated, precise, and appropriate
mathematical language throughout the task.
Theoretical knowledge is apparent and is
applied to concrete situations as the student
successfully demonstrates a comprehensive
understanding of core concepts.

Score Point 3: Proficient

The student demonstrates a broad
understanding of the difference between a
combination and a permutation. The
student uses perceptive mathematical
reasoning and precise and appropriate
mathematical language most of the time.
Theoretical knowledge is apparent and is
applied to concrete situations as the student
attempts to draw conclusions based on the
investigations.

Answers

Score Point 2: Apprentice

The student demonstrates an understanding of the difference between a combination and a permutation. The student uses mathematical reasoning and appropriate mathematical language some of the time. The student attempts to apply theoretical knowledge to the task but may not be able to draw conclusions based on the investigations.

Score Point 1: Novice

The student demonstrates a basic understanding of the difference between a combination and a permutation. The student uses little mathematical reasoning or appropriate mathematical language. Theoretical knowledge is extremely weak, and many responses are irrelevant or illogical. The student fails to follow directions and has great difficulty in communicating his or her responses.

Score Point 0: Unsatisfactory

The student does not complete the task, and his or her responses just restate the problem.

Form B

1.

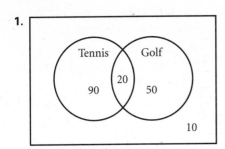

2. $P(T \text{ and } G) = \frac{2}{17}$

3. No; $P(T \text{ and } G) = \frac{2}{17}$ and

$$P(T) \times P(G) = \frac{11}{17} \times \frac{7}{17} = \frac{77}{289}$$

Since $P(T \text{ and } G) \neq P(T) \times P(G)$, the events are not independent.

4. No; there are people who signed up for both tennis lessons and golf lessons.

5. $P(T \text{ or } G) = \frac{16}{17}$; the complement of this event is not signing up for either tennis or golf; $P(\text{not } T \text{ and not } G) = \frac{1}{17}$

Score Point 4: Distinguished

The student demonstrates a comprehensive understanding of conditional probability. The student uses perceptive, creative, and complex mathematical reasoning and sophisticated, precise, and appropriate mathematical language throughout the task. Theoretical knowledge is apparent and is applied to concrete situations as the student successfully demonstrates a comprehensive understanding of core concepts.

Score Point 3: Proficient

The student demonstrates a broad understanding of conditional probability. The student uses perceptive mathematical reasoning and precise and appropriate mathematical language most of the time. Theoretical knowledge is apparent and is applied to concrete situations as the student attempts to draw conclusions based on the investigations.

Score Point 2: Apprentice

The student demonstrates an understanding of conditional probability. The student uses mathematical reasoning and appropriate mathematical language some of the time. The student attempts to apply theoretical knowledge to the task but may not be able to draw conclusions based on the investigations.

Answers

Score Point 1: Novice

The student demonstrates a basic understanding of conditional probability. The student uses little mathematical reasoning or appropriate mathematical language. Theoretical knowledge is extremely weak, and many responses are irrelevant or illogical. The student fails to follow directions and has great difficulty in communicating his or her responses.

Score Point 0: Unsatisfactory

The student does not complete the task, and his or her responses just restate the problem.

Chapter 11

Quick Warm-Up 11.1

1. $-5, -9, -13$ 2. $13, 18, 23$

3. $25, 31, 38$ 4. $486, 1458, 4374$

5. $3, 1.5, 0.75$ 6. $36, 49, 81$

Lesson Quiz 11.1

1. $20, 15, 10, 5$

2. $5, 12, 19, 26$

3a. $-20, -27, -34$

b. $\begin{cases} t_1 = 15 \\ t_1 = t_{n-1} - 7 \end{cases}$, where $n \geq 2$

4. $-5 + (-10) + (-15) + (-20) = -50$

5. $12 + 12 + 12 + 12 + 12 + 12 = 72$

6. $3 + 8 + 13 + 18 + 23 = 65$

7. 776 8. 90 9. 245

Quick Warm-Up 11.2

1. $3, 6, 9, 12, 15$ 2. $-1, 5, 11, 17, 23$

3. $-8, -17, -26, -35, -44$

4. $2, -6, 18, -54, 162$ 5. $9, 5, 1, -3, -7$

6. $-1, 2, 11, 38, 119$

Lesson Quiz 11.2

1. arithmetic; $d = \frac{1}{6}$

2. not arithmetic

3. $a_n = 20 + (n - 1)(-8)$

4. $a_n = -12 + (n - 1)(9)$

5. $t_{12} = 181$ 6. $3200

7. $t_{10} = 71$ 8. $13, 19, 25, 31, 37$

Quick Warm-Up 11.3

1. 24 2. 33 3. 60 4. 45 5. 36 6. 30

Lesson Quiz 11.3

1. $S_{30} = 8040$ 2. $S_{40} = 6400$ 3. 975

4. 275 5. -2730 6. 1300 7. 1300 seats

8. $116.25

Quick Warm-Up 11.4

1. 28 2. -19 3. 55 4. -31

5. $-2, 11, 24$ 6. $-6, -13, -20$

Lesson Quiz 11.4

1. geometric; $r = -3$

2. geometric; $r = 0.75$

3. $t_n = 6(-4)^{n-1}$ 4. $t_n = 16(1.5)^{n-1}$

5. $t_{10} = 65,536$ 6. $311.04

7. $t_9 = 20,480$ 8. $80, 100$

Answers

Mid-Chapter Assessment—Chapter 11

1. c   2. b   3. c

4. $t_n = 3(8)^{n-1}$

5. $t_n = 16.5 + (n-1)(8.6)$

6. 702   7. 2292   8. 220

9. $t_{12} = 0.25$ or -0.25

10. 54.5, 67, 79.5, 92, 104.5, 117, 129.5

11. $S_{100} = 28,700$

12a. $35,800

b. $728,000

13. $53,146.83

Quick Warm-Up 11.5

1. 48   2. 60   3. 14   4. 76   5. 234

6. -1150

Lesson Quiz 11.5

1. 4674.6   2. 255.2   3. 43,690.5

4. -524.7 5. $13,444.03

6. 1. Show that the statement is true for
$n = 1: 2(1) - 1 = 1^2$

2. Assume that $1 + 3 + \cdots + (2k - 1) = k^2$ and show $1 + 3 + \cdots + (2k - 1) + [2(k + 1) - 1] = (k + 1)^2$.
$1 + 3 + \cdots + (2k - 1) + [2(k + 1) - 1] = k^2 + [2(k + 1) - 1] = k^2 + 2k + 2 - 1 = k^2 + 2k + 1 = (k + 1)^2$

Quick Warm-Up 11.6

1. 20   2. $\frac{63}{32}$ 3. -25 4. 43,692   5. ≈ 0.4

Lesson Quiz 11.6

1. 12.5   2. 100   3. 18

4. No sum exists.

5. 12   6. $\frac{41}{90}$ 7. $\frac{25}{99}$ 8. 350 feet

Quick Warm-Up 11.7

1. 330   2. 11   3. 1   4. 1   5. 21   6. 21

7. 8   8a. $\frac{1}{8}$ b. $\frac{3}{8}$ c. $\frac{3}{8}$ d. $\frac{1}{8}$

Lesson Quiz 11.7

1. 19

2a. 1001

b. 11th

3. 1024

4a. 126

b. 0.25

c. 0.41

d. 0.09

5a. 0.31

b. 0.34

Quick Warm-Up 11.8

1. $x^2 - 10x + 25$ 2. $x^2 + 2xy + y^2$

3. $16m^2 + 24mn + 9n^2$

4. $a^3 + a^2 - 2a + 12$

5. $r^3 + 6r^2 + 12r + 8$ 6. 28   7. 1   8. 4

Lesson Quiz 11.8

1. 22

2. $c^5 + 5c^4d + 10c^3d^2 + 10c^2d^3 + 5cd^4 + d^5$

3. $x^4 - 12x^3y + 54x^2y^2 - 108xy^3 + 81y^4$

Answers

4. $84x^6y^3$

5. $5940x^9$

6a. 0.25

b. 0.35

c. 0.14

Chapter Assessment—Form A—Chapter 11

1. b   2. d   3. b   4. c   5. a   6. c

7. a   8. b   9. c   10. d   11. d   12. c

13. a   14. b   15. d   16. c   17. b   18. b

19. d   20. a   21. d   22. d

Form B

1. -21

2. $t_n = \frac{1}{2} + (n-1)\left(\frac{3}{8}\right)$

3. $t_n = 500(0.2^{n-1})$

4. $-26{,}745.47$ 5. $18{,}530$ 6. 40 7. 924

8. $1{,}310{,}720$ 9. -5590 10. $\frac{72}{99}$

11a. $12{,}376$

b. 12th

c. $131{,}072$

12. $r^7 - 7r^6t + 21r^5t^2 - 35r^4t^3 + 35r^3t^4 - 21r^2t^5 + 7rt^6 - t^7$

13. $81x^4 + 216x^3y + 216x^2y^2 + 96xy^3 + 16y^4$

14. $1125x^8$

15a. 220

b. ≈ 0.54

16a. $\$4587.52$

b. $\$6000$

17. $\$32{,}930.08$

18a. 4 miles

b. 108.5 miles

19a. about 917 people

b. about 211,564 people

20a. 0.17

b. 0.46

21. 1. Show that the statement is true for $n = 1: 4(1) - 1 = 1[2(1) + 1]$

2. Assume that $3 + 7 + 11 + \cdots + (4k - 1) = k(2k + 1)$ and show that $3 + 7 + 11 + \cdots + (4k - 1) + [4(k + 1) - 1] = (k + 1)[2(k +1) + 1]$.
$3 + 7 + 11 + \cdots + (4k - 1) + [4(k + 1) - 1] = k(2k + 1) + [4(k + 1) - 1]$
$= 2k^2 + 5k + 3$
$= (k + 1)(2k + 3)$
$= (k + 1)[2(k + 1) + 1]$

Alternative Assessment—Form A—Chapter 11

1. Answers may vary. Sample answer: $1, 6, 11, 16, \ldots; a_n = 1 + 5(n - 1); d = 5$

2. Answers may vary. Sample answer: $2, 10, 50, 250, \ldots; g_n = 2 \cdot 5^{n-1}; r = 5$

3. Answers may vary. Sample answer: $1, 4, 9, 16, \ldots; t_n = n^2$

4. The linear function f generates an arithmetic sequence. The slope of the linear function, 3, is the common difference of the arithmetic sequence.

5. The exponential function g generates a geometric sequence. The base of the exponential function, $\frac{1}{3}$, is the common ratio of the geometric sequence.

Answers

Score Point 4: Distinguished

The student demonstrates a comprehensive understanding of arithmetic and geometric sequences. The student uses perceptive, creative, and complex mathematical reasoning and sophisticated, precise, and appropriate mathematical language throughout the task. Theoretical knowledge is apparent and is applied to concrete situations as the student successfully demonstrates a comprehensive understanding of core concepts.

Score Point 3: Proficient

The student demonstrates a broad understanding of arithmetic and geometric sequences. The student uses perceptive mathematical reasoning and precise and appropriate mathematical language most of the time. Theoretical knowledge is apparent and is applied to concrete situations as the student attempts to draw conclusions based on the investigations.

Score Point 2: Apprentice

The student demonstrates an understanding of arithmetic and geometric sequences. The student uses mathematical reasoning and appropriate mathematical language some of the time. The student attempts to apply theoretical knowledge to the task but may not be able to draw conclusions based on the investigations.

Score Point 1: Novice

The student demonstrates a basic understanding of arithmetic and geometric sequences. The student uses little mathematical reasoning or appropriate mathematical language. Theoretical knowledge is extremely weak, and many responses are irrelevant or illogical. The student fails to follow directions and has great difficulty in communicating his or her responses.

Score Point 0: Unsatisfactory

The student does not complete the task, and his or her responses just restate the problem.

Form B

1. 1; $a + b$; $a^2 + 2ab + b^2$; $a^3 + 3a^2b + 3ab^2 + b^3$

2. The number of terms in the expanded form of the binomial is one more than the exponent of the binomial.

3. The exponents of a start at the exponent of the binomial and decrease by one from term to term down to 0. The exponents of b start at 0 and increase by one from term to term up to the exponent of the binomial.

4.
```
        1
      1   1
    1   2   1
  1   3   3   1
```
The numbers in row n of Pascal's triangle are the coefficients of the terms in the expansion of $(a + b)^n$.

Answers

Answers may vary. Sample answer: Start with a^6. Write all the terms using powers of a and b, decreasing the power of a by 1 and increasing the powers of b by 1 from term to term. Write b^6. Finally, use the terms in the 6th row of Pascal's triangle as the coefficients.

5a. RRR

 b. RRW; RWR; WRR

 c. RWW; WRW; WWR

 d. WWW

 The frequencies are the terms of the 3rd row of Pascal's triangle.

Score Point 4: Distinguished

The student demonstrates a comprehensive understanding of the Binomial Theorem. The student uses perceptive, creative, and complex mathematical reasoning and sophisticated, precise, and appropriate mathematical language throughout the task. Theoretical knowledge is apparent and is applied to concrete situations as the student successfully demonstrates a comprehensive understanding of core concepts.

Score Point 3: Proficient

The student demonstrates a broad understanding of the Binomial Theorem. The student uses perceptive mathematical reasoning and precise and appropriate mathematical language most of the time. Theoretical knowledge is apparent and is applied to concrete situations as the student attempts to draw conclusions based on the investigations.

Score Point 2: Apprentice

The student demonstrates an understanding of the Binomial Theorem. The student uses mathematical reasoning and appropriate mathematical language some of the time. The student attempts to apply theoretical knowledge to the task but may not be able to draw conclusions based on the investigations.

Score Point 1: Novice

The student demonstrates a basic understanding of the Binomial Theorem. The student uses little mathematical reasoning or appropriate mathematical language. Theoretical knowledge is extremely weak, and many responses are irrelevant or illogical. The student fails to follow directions and has great difficulty in communicating his or her responses.

Score Point 0: Unsatisfactory

The student does not complete the task, and his or her responses just restate the problem.

Chapter 12

Quick Warm-Up 12.1

 1. 13   2. 17.5   3. 42   4. 104   5. 2.75

 6. 3.65   7. 0.8, 1.5, 2.6, 3.7, 3.9, 6.4

Lesson Quiz 12.1

 1. mean: 24.1; median: 21; mode: 18

 2. mean: 2.5 children; median: 2 children; mode: 2 children

 3. about 12.4 hours   4. 10   5. 0.25

Answers

Quick Warm-Up 12.2

1. ≈19.1   **2.** 20   **3.** 22

4.

Number	Frequency
1–5	0
6–10	1
11–15	0
16–20	6
21–25	5

5. ≈19.25

Lesson Quiz 12.2

1.

Stem	Leaf	$8|1 = 81$
8	1 5	
7	0 1 3 4 5 7	
6	0 2 5 5 5 7 8 9	
5	3 6 9	
4	7	

2.

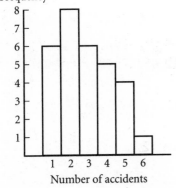

3.

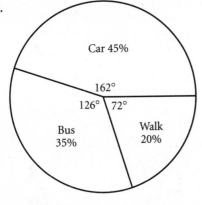

Quick Warm-Up 12.3

1. mean: 5; median: 4.5; no mode

2. mean: 8.25; median: 8.25; modes: 8.2, 8.3

3. mean: 12; median: 12; no mode

4. mean: 1.6; median: 1.6; mode: 1.6

Lesson Quiz 12.3

1a. $Q_1 = 2$; $Q_2 = 5$; $Q_3 = 7$; range: 14; interquartile range: 5

b.

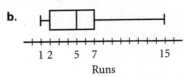

c. 15

2a. math: 30 minutes; English: 40 minutes

b. 75%

c. time studying for math tests

Mid-Chapter Assessment—Chapter 12

1. b   **2.** d   **3.** c

4a.

Stem	Leaf	$8|0 = 80$
8	0	
7	0 1 2 4 6	
6	1 2 3 3 4 5 6 7 7 8	
5	8 9	

b. mean: 67 inches; median: 67 inches; mode: 67 inches

Answers

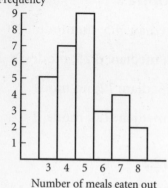

5a. Frequency
Number of meals eaten out

b. 30%

6a. $Q_1 = 37$ CDs; $Q_2 = 56$ CDs;
$Q_3 = 64$ CDs; range: 50 CDs;
interquartile range: 27 CDs

b.

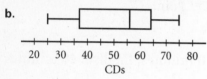

CDs

Quick Warm-Up 12.4

1. ≈ 40.8 2. 41.5 3. 37 and 45 4. 31

5. 37 6. 41.5 7. 45 8. 8

Lesson Quiz 12.4

1. Answers may vary. Sample answer:
   The standard deviation will be greater in
   Chicago, where temperatures vary a great
   deal in March, than in an equatorial city,
   where the temperatures will be fairly
   consistent year round.

2. range: 34; mean deviation: 8

3. $\sigma^2 = 767.56$; $\sigma = 27.70$

4. 7.6

5. range: 3; mean: 55.67; median: 56;
   standard deviation: 0.94

Quick Warm-Up 12.5

1. 210 2. 8 3. 1 4. $\frac{1}{16}$, or 6.25%

5. $\frac{15}{16}$, or 93.75% 6. $\frac{5}{16}$, or 31.25%

7. $\frac{2}{16}$, or 12.5%

Lesson Quiz 12.5

1. 0.234

2a. 0.250

b. 0.526

3a. 0.279

b. 0.174

4a. 0.283

b. 0.558

Quick Warm-Up 12.6

1. 2.1 2. 2.05 3. none 4. 1.85, 2.05, 2.45

5. 1.5 6. 0.35 7. 0.195 8. ≈ 0.442

Lesson Quiz 12.6

1a. 0.9591

b. 0.0202

c. 0.7328

2a. 0.0548

b. about 110 VCRs

3a. 0.1056

b. 0.5467

Chapter Assessment—Form A—Chapter 12

1. b 2. d 3. c 4. a 5. c 6. a

7. d 8. a 9. d 10. a 11. b 12. c

13. b 14. b 15. d

Answers

Form B

1a.

Stem	Leaf	$3\vert 0 = 30$
3	0 1 2 3 5	
2	0 1 3 3 3 5 5 7 8	
1	1 4 6 7 7 9	

b. mean: 23.5 students; median: 23 students; mode: 23 students

2a. Frequency

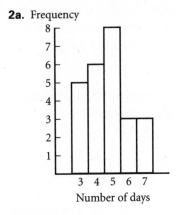

Number of days

b. 56%

3a. $Q_1 = 42$ people; $Q_2 = 56$ people; $Q_3 = 66$ people; IQR = 24 people

b.

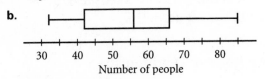

Number of people

4. range: 4.2 inches;
variance: 2.00 square inches;
standard deviation: 1.42 inches;
mean deviation: 1.24 inches

5.

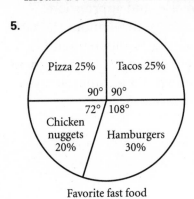

Pizza 25%   Tacos 25%
90°   90°
72° 108°
Chicken nuggets 20%   Hamburgers 30%

Favorite fast food

6. 0.7486   **7.** 0.9901   **8.** 0.049

9. 0.061   **10.** 0.986

11a. $z = 1.25$

b. 0.8944

12a. 0.9332

b. 0.9104

Alternative Assessment—Form A—Chapter 12

1. Chris: mean: 21 points;
median: 20 points
Pat: mean: 21 points;
median: 20 points
No

2. Chris: $Q_1 = 17$ points, $Q_3 = 24$ points, range: 17 points, IQR = 7 points;
Pat: $Q_1 = 14$ points, $Q_3 = 29$ points, range: 31 points, IQR = 15 points

3.

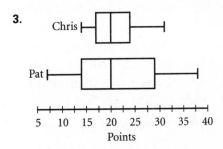

Points

4. Answers will vary. Sample answer: I would rather have Chris on my team because Chris seems to be a more consistent player. While Pat might score a lot of points in some games, Pat might also score very few points in others. I would be able to count on Chris to have a good game.

Score Point 4: Distinguished

The student demonstrates a comprehensive understanding of statistical measures. The student uses perceptive, creative, and

Answers

complex mathematical reasoning and sophisticated, precise, and appropriate mathematical language throughout the task. Theoretical knowledge is apparent and is applied to concrete situations as the student successfully demonstrates a comprehensive understanding of core concepts.

Score Point 3: Proficient

The student demonstrates a broad understanding of statistical measures. The student uses perceptive mathematical reasoning and precise and appropriate mathematical language most of the time. Theoretical knowledge is apparent and is applied to concrete situations as the student attempts to draw conclusions based on the investigations.

Score Point 2: Apprentice

The student demonstrates an understanding of statistical measures. The student uses mathematical reasoning and appropriate mathematical language some of the time. The student attempts to apply theoretical knowledge to the task but may not be able to draw conclusions based on the investigations.

Score Point 1: Novice

The student demonstrates a basic understanding of statistical measures. The student uses little mathematical reasoning or appropriate mathematical language. Theoretical knowledge is extremely weak, and many responses are irrelevant or illogical. The student fails to follow directions and has great difficulty in communicating his or her responses.

Score Point 0: Unsatisfactory

The student does not complete the task, and his or her responses just restate the problem.

Form B

1. The experiment is binomial. There are a fixed number of independent trials, each trial results in two possible outcomes, and the probability of success on each trial is the same; $P(\text{exactly 3 odd}) = 0.216$, or 21.6%.

2. The experiment is not binomial because there are more than two possible outcomes for each trial.

3. The experiment is not binomial because the two trials are not independent.

4. The experiment is binomial. There are a fixed number of independent trials, each trial results in two possible outcomes, and the probability of success on each trial is the same; $P(\text{exactly 1 win}) \approx 0.087$, or about 8.7%.

Score Point 4: Distinguished

The student demonstrates a comprehensive understanding of binomial experiments. The student uses perceptive, creative, and complex mathematical reasoning and sophisticated, precise, and appropriate mathematical language throughout the task. Theoretical knowledge is apparent and is applied to concrete situations as the student successfully demonstrates a comprehensive understanding of core concepts.

Answers

Score Point 3: Proficient

The student demonstrates a broad understanding of binomial experiments. The student uses perceptive mathematical reasoning and precise and appropriate mathematical language most of the time. Theoretical knowledge is apparent and is applied to concrete situations as the student attempts to draw conclusions based on the investigations.

Score Point 2: Apprentice

The student demonstrates an understanding of binomial experiments. The student uses mathematical reasoning and appropriate mathematical language some of the time. The student attempts to apply theoretical knowledge to the task, but may not be able to draw conclusions based on the investigations.

Score Point 1: Novice

The student demonstrates a basic understanding of binomial experiments. The student uses litle mathematical reasoning or appropriate mathematical language. Theoretical knowledge is extremely weak, and many responses are irrelevant or illogical. The student fails to follow directions and has great difficulty in communicating his or her responses.

Score Point 0: Unsatisfactory

The student does not complete the task, and his or her responses just restate the problem.

Chapter 13

Quick Warm-Up 13.1

1. ≈ 0.5417 2. ≈ 1.8462 3. $m = 2.4$

4. $y = 5.6$ 5. $a \approx 5.9$

Lesson Quiz 13.1

1. $\sin \theta = \frac{8}{17} \approx 0.4706$; $\cos \theta = \frac{15}{17} \approx 0.8824$;

$\tan \theta = \frac{8}{15} \approx 0.5333$; $\csc \theta = \frac{17}{8} = 2.1250$;

$\sec \theta = \frac{17}{15} \approx 1.3333$; $\cot \theta = \frac{15}{8} = 1.8750$

2. $x \approx 12.87$; $y \approx 16.12$

3. $m\angle A \approx 59°$; $m\angle B \approx 31°$; $AB \approx 23.3$

Quick Warm-Up 13.2

1. $\frac{21}{29} \approx 0.7241$ 2. $\frac{20}{29} \approx 0.6897$

3. $\frac{21}{20} \approx 1.0500$ 4. $\frac{29}{21} \approx 1.3810$

5. $\frac{29}{20} \approx 1.4500$ 6. $\frac{20}{21} \approx 0.9524$

Lesson Quiz 13.2

1. $-235°$ 2. $145°$ 3. $55°$ 4. $80°$ 5. $12°$

6. $\sin \theta = \frac{3\sqrt{34}}{34}$; $\cos \theta = -\frac{5\sqrt{34}}{34}$;

$\tan \theta = -\frac{3}{5}$; $\csc \theta = \frac{\sqrt{34}}{3}$; $\sec \theta = -\frac{\sqrt{34}}{5}$;

$\cot \theta = -\frac{5}{3}$

7. $\sin \theta = -\frac{12}{13}$; $\tan \theta = -\frac{12}{5}$

8. sample answer: $472°, 832°, -248°, -608°$

Quick Warm-Up 13.3

1. $17°$ 2. $17°$ 3. $80°$ 4. $49°$

5. $-\frac{2\sqrt{5}}{5}$ 6. $\frac{\sqrt{5}}{5}$ 7. -2 8. $-\frac{\sqrt{5}}{2}$

Answers

9. $\sqrt{5}$ 10. $-\dfrac{1}{2}$

Lesson Quiz 13.3

1. $\sin 750° = \dfrac{1}{2}$; $\cos 750° = \dfrac{\sqrt{3}}{2}$

2. $\sin(-945°) = \dfrac{\sqrt{2}}{2}$; $\cos(-945°) = -\dfrac{\sqrt{2}}{2}$

3. $\sin(-1260°) = 0$; $\cos(-1260°) = -1$

4. $\sin 1140° = \dfrac{\sqrt{3}}{2}$; $\cos 1140° = \dfrac{1}{2}$

5. $r = 16$; $P(-8, -8\sqrt{3})$

6. $P\left(-\dfrac{7\sqrt{2}}{2}, \dfrac{7\sqrt{2}}{2}\right)$

Mid-Chapter Assessment—Chapter 13

1. c   2. b   3. d

4. $BC \approx 14.8$; $AB \approx 17.9$; $m\angle B = 34°$

5. $RT \approx 13.3$; $m\angle R \approx 28°$; $m\angle S \approx 62°$

6. 85°   7. 70°   8. 35°

9. $\sin \theta = -\dfrac{24}{25}$; $\cos \theta = \dfrac{7}{25}$; $\tan \theta = -\dfrac{24}{7}$;

   $\csc \theta = -\dfrac{25}{24}$; $\sec \theta = \dfrac{25}{7}$; $\cot \theta = -\dfrac{7}{24}$

10. $\sin 1305° = -\dfrac{\sqrt{2}}{2}$; $\tan 1305° = 1$

Quick Warm-Up 13.4

1. $\dfrac{\sqrt{3}}{2}$ 2. $-\dfrac{\sqrt{2}}{2}$ 3. $-\dfrac{\sqrt{3}}{3}$ 4. $-\dfrac{1}{2}$ 5. 1

6. -1 7. 0   8. undefined   9. 2   10. $\dfrac{1}{4}$

11. $\dfrac{1}{6}$ 12. $\dfrac{3}{2}$

Lesson Quiz 13.4

1. $\dfrac{3\pi}{4}$ radians   2. $\dfrac{5\pi}{2}$ radians

3. 120.0°   4. 143.2°   5. -0.3508

6. -0.5774 7. 32 meters   8. 15.7 meters

9. 0.24 radians   10. 4 meters

Quick Warm-Up 13.5

1. horizontal translation 2 units to the right

2. vertical translation 2 units down

3. vertical stretch by a factor of 3, reflection across the x-axis

4. reflection across the y-axis

5. horizontal compression by a factor of $\dfrac{1}{6}$, horizontal translation $\dfrac{1}{6}$ unit to the left

Lesson Quiz 13.5

1.

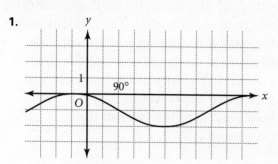

2.

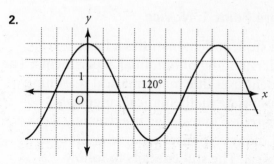

3. phase shift: 20°; vertical translation: 6; amplitude: 2.5; period: 120°

Quick Warm-Up 13.6

1. $f^{-1}(x) = x + 4$ 2. $g^{-1}(x) = \dfrac{x}{-5}$

3. $h^{-1}(x) = 0.5x - 3$ 4. $j^{-1}(x) = \log_3 x$

5. $k^{-1}(x) = e^x$

Answers

Lesson Quiz 13.6

1. 48.59°   2. 82.41°   3. 1.84

4. 1.05   5. $\frac{1}{2}$ 6. -1

7. ≈ -0.4636 radians, or $\approx -26.5651°$

8. $\frac{3}{4}$ radians, or 135°   9. 36.9°

Chapter Assessment—Form A— Chapter 13

1. d   2. b   3. d   4. b   5. a   6. c

7. d   8. a   9. b   10. c   11. d   12. c

13. c   14. b   15. b   16. a   17. d

Form B

1. $x \approx 64.3; y \approx 71.0$

2. $\theta \approx 36.9°$ 3. 74°   4. 75°

5. 85°   6. -3.0777 7. 0.0698

8. -0.0831 9. $P(19.3, -23.0)$

10. $\tan \theta = -\frac{20}{21}; \sec \theta = -\frac{29}{21}$

11. $\csc \theta = \frac{13}{5}; \cot \theta = -\frac{12}{5}$

12. $\sin 1650° = -\frac{1}{2}; \cos 1650° = -\frac{\sqrt{3}}{2}$

13. $-110°$ 14. $\frac{4\pi}{3}$ radians   15. $\frac{7\pi}{4}$ radians

16. 630°   17. 149°   18. 1.25 radians

19. 87.3 meters

20.

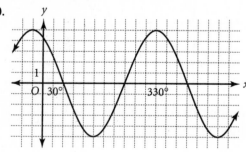

21.

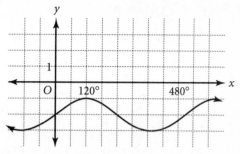

22. phase shift: 10°; amplitude: 7.2

23. $-\sqrt{3}$ 24. 65°   25. 44.5 feet

Alternative Assessment—Form A— Chapter 13

1. $x = 3\sqrt{3}$

2. $\theta = 32°$

3. Answers may vary. Sample answer:
Use AB and $\sin 40°$ to find EB. Use EB and $\sin 32°$ to find BD. Use BD and $\sin 72°$ to find h.

4. $h \approx 57.7$

5. $\tan 55° = \frac{h}{x}; \tan 20° = \frac{h}{x + 75}$

6. Answers may vary. Sample answer:
Solve both equations for either x or h and use the substitution method.

7. $h \approx 36.6$

Score Point 4: Distinguished

The student demonstrates a comprehensive understanding of right triangles. The student uses perceptive, creative, and complex mathematical reasoning and sophisticated, precise, and appropriate mathematical language throughout the task. Theoretical knowledge is apparent and is applied to concrete situations as the student successfully demonstrates a comprehensive understanding of core concepts.

Answers

Score Point 3: Proficient

The student demonstrates a broad understanding of right triangles. The student uses perceptive mathematical reasoning and precise and appropriate mathematical language most of the time. Theoretical knowledge is apparent and is applied to concrete situations as the student attempts to draw conclusions based on the investigations.

Score Point 2: Apprentice

The student demonstrates an understanding of right triangles. The student uses mathematical reasoning and appropriate mathematical language some of the time. The student attempts to apply theoretical knowledge to the task but may not be able to draw conclusions based on the investigations.

Score Point 1: Novice

The student demonstrates a basic understanding of right triangles. The student uses little mathematical reasoning or appropriate mathematical language. Theoretical knowledge is extremely weak, and many responses are irrelevant or illogical. The student fails to follow directions and has great difficulty in communicating his or her responses.

Score Point 0: Unsatisfactory

The student does not complete the task, and his or her responses just restate the problem.

Form B

1.
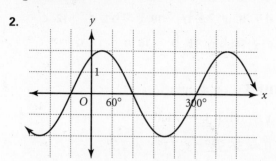

period: 360°; amplitude: 1; phase shift: 45°

2.
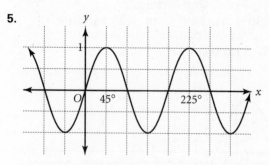

period: 360°; amplitude: 2; phase shift: −60°

3. period: 360°; amplitude: 1; vertical shift: 2

4. The graphs of $f(x) = \cos x$ and $g(x) = \sin x$ are shifted d units to the right if $d > 0$ or $|d|$ units to the left if $d < 0$.

5.

domain: all real numbers; range: $-1 \leq y \leq 1$; period: 180°

Answers

6.

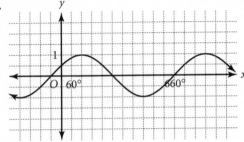

domain: all real numbers;
range: $-1 \le y \le 1$; period: 720°

7. domain: all real numbers;
range: $-5 \le y \le 5$; period: 1080°

8. $f(x) = \sin 3x$

Score Point 4: Distinguished

The student demonstrates a comprehensive understanding of the graphs of trigonometric functions. The student uses perceptive, creative, and complex mathematical reasoning and sophisticated, precise, and appropriate mathematical language throughout the task. Theoretical knowledge is apparent and is applied to concrete situations as the student successfully demonstrates a comprehensive understanding of core concepts.

Score Point 3: Proficient

The student demonstrates a broad understanding of the graphs of trigonometric functions. The student uses perceptive mathematical reasoning and precise and appropriate mathematical language most of the time. Theoretical knowledge is apparent and is applied to concrete situations as the student attempts to draw conclusions based on the investigations.

Score Point 2: Apprentice

The student demonstrates an understanding of the graphs of trigonometric functions. The student uses mathematical reasoning and appropriate mathematical language some of the time. The student attempts to apply theoretical knowledge to the task but may not be able to draw conclusions based on the investigations.

Score Point 1: Novice

The student demonstrates a basic understanding of the graphs of trigonometric functions. The student uses little mathematical reasoning or appropriate mathematical language. Theoretical knowledge is extremely weak, and many responses are irrelevant or illogical. The student fails to follow directions and has great difficulty in communicating his or her responses.

Score Point 0: Unsatisfactory

The student does not complete the task, and his or her responses just restate the problem.

Chapter 14

Quick Warm-Up 14.1

1. $x \approx 0.857$ **2.** $x \approx 52.94$ **3.** $x \approx 48.75$

4. $x = 0.75$ **5.** $x \approx 19{,}736.84$

Lesson Quiz 14.1

1. 213.8 square centimeters

2. $x \approx 12.2$ meters; $y \approx 28.0$ meters

3. $x \approx 44.2°$

4a. yes

b. $m\angle A \approx 86.7°$ or $m\angle A \approx 93.3°$

Answers

Quick Warm-Up 14.2

1. $\theta \approx 23°$ or $\theta \approx 157°$ 2. $\theta \approx 16°$ or $\theta \approx 344°$

3. $\theta \approx 19°$ or $\theta \approx 341°$ 4. ≈ 228.3

5. $Y \approx 56°, Z \approx 80°, z \approx 14.2$ or $Y \approx 124°$, $Z \approx 12°, z \approx 3$

Lesson Quiz 14.2

1. $x \approx 29.0$ centimeters

2. $x \approx 115.4°$

3. $b = 24.1$ meters; $m\angle A \approx 34.1°$; $m\angle C \approx 105.9°$

4. 133.8 yards

Quick Warm-Up 14.3

1. $A \approx 37°, B \approx 53°, C = 90°$

2. $C = 105°, a \approx 7.3, b \approx 5.2$

3. $A \approx 33°, C \approx 27°, b \approx 19.1$

4. two possible triangles: $B \approx 58°, C \approx 77°$, $c \approx 13.8$; or $B \approx 122°, C \approx 13°, c \approx 3.2$

5. no possible triangles

Lesson Quiz 14.3

1. $\csc \theta$ 2. $\tan \theta$ 3. $\cot^2 \theta$

4. $\sec \theta$ 5. $\tan^2 \theta$ 6. $\sin \theta$

7. $\tan \theta$ 8. 1   9. $\dfrac{\tan^2 \theta}{\tan^2 \theta + 1}$ 10. $\tan^2 \theta$

11. $\tan \theta + \dfrac{1}{\tan \theta}$ 12. $\dfrac{1}{\tan^2 \theta}$

Mid-Chapter Assessment—Chapter 14

1. b   2. c   3. d

4. $c \approx 51.4$ feet; $m\angle A \approx 69.2°$; $m\angle B \approx 36.8°$

5. $m\angle A \approx 88.3°$ or $m\angle A \approx 91.7°$

6. $\cos^2 \theta$ 7. $\sin^2 \theta$ 8. $\sin \theta$ 9. $2 \csc \theta$

Quick Warm-Up 14.4

1. 1   2. ≈ 8.6 3. ≈ 11.2 4. ≈ 1.2

5. ≈ 0.26

Lesson Quiz 14.4

1. -1 2. $\dfrac{\sqrt{2}}{2}$ 3. $\dfrac{1}{2}$ 4. $\dfrac{\sqrt{6} - \sqrt{2}}{4}$

5. $\sin (\theta - 270°) = (\sin \theta)(\cos 270°) - (\cos \theta)(\sin 270°) = (\sin \theta)(0) - (\cos \theta)(-1) = \cos \theta$

6. $\cos (\pi + x) = (\cos \pi)(\cos x) - (\sin \pi)(\sin x) = (-1)(\cos x) - (0)(\sin x) = -\cos x$

7. $\begin{bmatrix} -\dfrac{1}{2} & -\dfrac{\sqrt{3}}{2} \\ \dfrac{\sqrt{3}}{2} & -\dfrac{1}{2} \end{bmatrix}$; $(-4.96, 0.60)$

Quick Warm-Up 14.5

1. $\dfrac{\sqrt{6} - \sqrt{2}}{4}$ 2. $\dfrac{\sqrt{6} + \sqrt{2}}{4}$ 3. $-\dfrac{\sqrt{6} + \sqrt{2}}{4}$

4. $\dfrac{\sqrt{2} - \sqrt{6}}{4}$ 5. $-2 - \sqrt{3}$

Lesson Quiz 14.5

1. $\sin 2\theta = -\dfrac{24}{25}$; $\cos 2\theta = -\dfrac{7}{25}$

2. $\sin 2\theta = \dfrac{4}{5}$; $\cos 2\theta = -\dfrac{3}{5}$

3. $\sin 2\theta = -\dfrac{24}{25}$; $\cos 2\theta = -\dfrac{7}{25}$

4. $\sin 2\theta = \dfrac{120}{13}$; $\cos 2\theta = -\dfrac{119}{169}$

5. $\sin \dfrac{\theta}{2} = \dfrac{2\sqrt{26}}{13}$; $\cos \dfrac{\theta}{2} = -\dfrac{3\sqrt{13}}{13}$

6. $\sin \dfrac{\theta}{2} = \dfrac{\sqrt{5}}{5}$; $\cos \dfrac{\theta}{2} = -\dfrac{2\sqrt{5}}{5}$

7. $\sin \dfrac{\theta}{2} = \dfrac{3}{5}$; $\cos \dfrac{\theta}{2} = -\dfrac{4}{5}$

Answers

8. $\sin\frac{\theta}{2} = \frac{4}{5}$; $\cos\frac{\theta}{2} = -\frac{3}{5}$

9. $\frac{1}{\cos\theta} = \sec\theta$ 10. $\cos^2\theta$

Quick Warm-Up 14.6

1. $x = -1$ or $x = \frac{1}{2}$ 2. $x = -1$ or $x = 3$

3. $270°$ 4. $150°$ or $210°$ 5. $15°$ or $165°$

Lesson Quiz 14.6

1. $120°$ and $240°$ 2. $45°$ and $135°$

3. $30°$ and $150°$ 4. $180°$ 5. $\frac{\pi}{2}$

6. $0, 2\pi, \frac{\pi}{3}, \frac{5\pi}{3}$ 7. $\frac{4\pi}{3}$ and $\frac{5\pi}{3}$ 8. $\frac{3\pi}{2}$

9. $90° + n(360°)$, $270° + n(360°)$

10. $n(180°)$

11. $30° + n(360°)$, $150° + n(360°)$

12. $n(180°)$, $30° + n(360°)$, $150° + n(360°)$

Chapter Assessment—Form A— Chapter 14

1. b   2. d   3. d   4. c   5. a   6. a

7. c   8. b   9. b   10. d   11. d   12. c

13. d   14. a   15. d   16. a   17. b   18. d

19. c

Form B

1. 111.6 feet

2. 151.6 centimeters

3. 2774.7 square meters

4. $m\angle A \approx 32.0°$; $m\angle B \approx 104.8°$; $m\angle C \approx 43.2°$

5. $c \approx 60.0$ feet; $m\angle A \approx 63.7°$; $m\angle B \approx 38.3°$

6. $m\angle C \approx 81.7°$ or $m\angle C \approx 98.3°$

7. $-\frac{1}{4}$ 8. $\frac{1}{9}$ 9. $-\frac{1}{2}$ 10. $\frac{\sqrt{3}}{2}$

11. $(-6, -2)$

12. $\cos(270° - \theta) = (\cos 270°)(\cos\theta) + (\sin 270°)(\sin\theta) = (0)(\cos\theta) + (-1)(\sin\theta) = -\sin\theta$

13. $\sin\left(x + \frac{\pi}{2}\right) = (\sin x)\left(\cos\frac{\pi}{2}\right) + (\cos x)\left(\sin\frac{\pi}{2}\right) = (\sin x)(0) + (\cos x)(1) = \cos x$

14. $\tan\theta$ 15. $\frac{1}{\sin\theta} = \csc\theta$ 16. $\sec\theta - 1$

17. $\frac{\cot\theta}{2}$ 18. $11.5°$ and $168.5°$

19. $75.5°$, $284.5°$, $0°$, and $360°$

20. 0.64 and 5.64   21. 0.34 and 2.80

Alternative Assessment—Form A— Chapter 14

1. Use the three sides of $\triangle ABD$ and the law of cosines; $m\angle BAD = 82.15°$.

2. Use the three sides of $\triangle ABD$ and the law of cosines; or use DB, another side of $\triangle ABD$, $m\angle BAD$ from Exercise 1, and the law of sines; $m\angle ABD = 32.13°$.

3. Use $\triangle BDE$ because all three sides are known; $m\angle BDE = 22.58°$.

4. $m\angle BAC = 97.85°$; $m\angle ABC = 24.24°$; $m\angle ACB = 57.91°$; $AC = 145.38$; $BC = 350.78$

Answers

Score Point 4: Distinguished

The student demonstrates a comprehensive understanding of solving a triangle. The student uses perceptive, creative, and complex mathematical reasoning and sophisticated, precise, and appropriate mathematical language throughout the task. Theoretical knowledge is apparent and is applied to concrete situations as the student successfully demonstrates a comprehensive understanding of core concepts.

Score Point 3: Proficient

The student demonstrates a broad understanding of solving a triangle. The student uses perceptive mathematical reasoning and precise and appropriate mathematical language most of the time. Theoretical knowledge is apparent and is applied to concrete situations as the student attempts to draw conclusions based on the investigations.

Score Point 2: Apprentice

The student demonstrates an understanding of solving a triangle. He or she uses mathematical reasoning and appropriate mathematical language some of the time. The student attempts to apply theoretical knowledge to the task but may not be able to draw conclusions based on the investigations.

Score Point 1: Novice

The student demonstrates a basic understanding of solving a triangle. The student uses little mathematical reasoning or appropriate mathematical language. Theoretical knowledge is extremely weak, and many responses are irrelevant or illogical. The student fails to follow directions and has great difficulty in communicating his or her responses.

Score Point 0: Unsatisfactory

The student does not complete the task, and his or her responses just restate the problem.

Form B

1. Replace $\sec^2 x$ with $1 + \tan^2 x$; $\frac{\pi}{6}, \frac{5\pi}{6}, \frac{7\pi}{6}$, and $\frac{11\pi}{6}$

2. Answers may vary. Sample answer: Graph $y = \sin x + \cos x - 1$ and find where the graph intersects the x-axis; 0 and $\frac{\pi}{2}$

3. $\frac{\pi}{8}, \frac{5\pi}{8}, \frac{9\pi}{8}$, and $\frac{13\pi}{8}$

4. $0, \frac{\pi}{2}, \pi$, and $\frac{3\pi}{2}$

5. Answers may vary. Sample answer: Use the quadratic formula with $a = 2$, $b = -1$, and $c = -1$ to find $\sin x$. Then use inverse sine to find x; $\frac{\pi}{2}, \frac{7\pi}{6}$, and $\frac{11\pi}{6}$

Answers

Score Point 4: Distinguished

The student demonstrates a comprehensive understanding of solving trigonometric equations. The student uses perceptive, creative, and complex mathematical reasoning and sophisticated, precise, and appropriate mathematical language throughout the task. Theoretical knowledge is apparent and is applied to concrete situations as the student successfully demonstrates a comprehensive understanding of core concepts.

Score Point 3: Proficient

The student demonstrates a broad understanding of solving trigonometric equations. The student uses perceptive mathematical reasoning and precise and appropriate mathematical language most of the time. Theoretical knowledge is apparent and is applied to concrete situations as the student attempts to draw conclusions based on the investigations.

Score Point 2: Apprentice

The student demonstrates an understanding of solving trigonometric equations. The student uses mathematical reasoning and appropriate mathematical language some of the time. The student attempts to apply theoretical knowledge to the task but may not be able to draw conclusions based on the investigations.

Score Point 1: Novice

The student demonstrates a basic understanding of solving trigonometric equations. The student uses little mathematical reasoning or appropriate mathematical language. Theoretical knowledge is extremely weak, and many responses are irrelevant or illogical. The student fails to follow directions and has great difficulty in communicating his or her responses.

Score Point 0: Unsatisfactory

The student does not complete the task, and his or her responses just restate the problem.